ORGANOCHLORINE INSECTICIDES:

Persistent Organic Pollutants

Edited by

F. MORIARTY

Monks Wood Experimental Station,
Institute of Terrestrial Ecology, Abbots Ripton, Huntingdon, England

1975

ACADEMIC PRESS
London · New York · San Francisco
A Subsidiary of Harcourt Brace Jovanovich Publishers

ACADEMIC PRESS INC. (LONDON) LTD
24–28 Oval Road,
London NW1

U.S. Edition published by
ACADEMIC PRESS INC.
111 Fifth Avenue,
New York, New York 10003

Library of Congress Catalog Card Number: 74-18528

ISBN: 0-12-506750-X

Text set in 11/12 pt. Monotype Baskerville, printed by letterpress,
and bound in Great Britain at The Pitman Press, Bath

Contributors

J. P. DEMPSTER, *Monks Wood Experimental Station, Institute of Terrestrial Ecology, Abbots Ripton, Huntingdon PE17 2LS, England*

A. V. HOLDEN, *Department of Agriculture and Fisheries for Scotland, Freshwater Fisheries Laboratory, Faskally, Pitlochry, Perthshire PH16 5LB, Scotland*

D. J. JEFFERIES, *Monks Wood Experimental Station, Institute of Terrestrial Ecology, Abbots Ripton, Huntingdon PE17 2LS, England*

W. M. MANSELL, *Eliot College, The University of Kent, Canterbury, Kent CT2 7NS, England*

F. MORIARTY, *Monks Wood Experimental Station, Institute of Terrestrial Ecology, Abbots Ripton, Huntingdon PE17 2LS, England*

P. A. VICTOR, *Ministry of the Environment, 135 St. Clair Avenue West, Suite 100, Toronto, Ontario M4V 1P5, Canada*

C. H. WALKER, *Department of Physiology and Biochemistry, The University, Whiteknights, Reading RG6 2AJ, England*

Preface

In essence there are four questions that need to be asked and answered about pollution: how much is present, what effects do these amounts have, what do we want to do about it, and how do we do it? Our knowledge is, at present, fragmentary and in many instances scanty. However, we now know enough about some of the persistent organic compounds, especially the organochlorine insecticides, to delineate some ideas that should be relevant to pollutants in general and should help to answer three of these questions.

The first three chapters centre on the amounts of residues present: how to monitor them, the relationship between exposure and size of residues found in animals, and why different animals may acquire different residues from similar exposures. The next two chapters discuss the effects of residues on animals: single individuals, and populations. The final chapter discusses some of the economic and legal constraints that exist, or could be imposed, for the control of pesticide use.

This book does not consider, except by implication, what we want to do about pollution. The answers to this question require value judgements, which are not the prerogative of pollution experts alone.

Contents

3. Variations in the Intake and Elimination of Pollutants
C. H. WALKER

4. The Role of the Thyroid in the Production of Sublethal Effects by Organochlorine Insecticides and Polychlorinated Biphenyls
D. J. JEFFERIES

5. Effects of Organochlorine Insecticides on Animal Populations
J. P. DEMPSTER

1. Monitoring Persistent Organic Pollutants

A. V. HOLDEN

Freshwater Fisheries Laboratory, Pitlochry, Scotland

I. INTRODUCTION

Modern chemical technology has produced many organic compounds which are relatively resistant to physical or metabolic degradation. Some, such as the insecticide DDT, have been produced and used in the environment because of their chemical stability and toxic properties, while others, such as the polychlorinated biphenyls used in industry, had entered the environment for a long time before they were detected by the sophisticated methods of modern chemical analysis. Yet others, of which there are probably hundreds, are known to be manufactured and used in large quantities and believed to be stable, but have not so far been detected in the environment because of the lack of suitable analytical methods.

Some of these chemicals are known to interfere with various life-processes and the fear that they may in some way endanger plant and animal communities has encouraged a demand for systems of monitoring which can measure pollutant levels and detect changes in those levels. Thus, it is hoped that any undesirable concentration of a pollutant can be recognized and appropriate action taken, before any detrimental effects occur. This chapter is concerned with the purposes of monitoring, the types of sample required, the design of appropriate monitoring programmes, the accuracy attainable in estimating levels of environmental contamination, and the practical problems involved in establishing monitoring systems. Most of the chapter refers to experience with organochlorine pollutants but the general principles are applicable to most types of pollutant which can be detected and measured in biological material.

II. PURPOSES OF MONITORING

The Inter-Governmental Working Group on Monitoring or Surveillance (U.N., 1971) defined monitoring as 'a system of continual observation, measurement and evaluation for defined purposes'. This definition includes not only the acquisition of physical, chemical and biological information but also the assessment of this information. An alternative definition, which excludes assessment as a component of monitoring (SCOPE, 1973) is 'the process of repetitive observing, for defined purposes, of one or more elements or indicators of the environment according to pre-arranged schedules in space and time, and using comparable methodologies for environmental sensing and data collection'. Monitoring for pollutants thus involves repetitive sampling of material obtained by a standardized procedure and analysis of that material for specific substances by standard methods. It is normally of a long-term nature and thus differs from a survey, which is usually short-term and often comprises only one period of sampling at each sampling site. Surveys are needed before starting a monitoring programme, to establish the magnitude of particular parameters, whether they be numbers of an organism per unit area or volume, or the concentrations of chemical substances. The sampling and analytical methods to be used in monitoring can then be designed to provide data with an appropriate degree of accuracy.

A monitoring system provides numerical data from the chemical or physical measurements. These must be of sufficient accuracy and reproducibility for subsequent mathematical or statistical analysis. In particular, the nature of the sample material and the times at which samples are taken must be clearly defined and rigidly adhered to, so that differences due to changes in the nature of samples or to the season in which they are taken do not invalidate the comparisons made from the data. Repetitive measurements from a suitably designed programme of sampling may:

a. indicate the change in contamination level with time;
b. indicate the metabolism or degradation of a contaminant over a period of time;
c. reveal the presence of new pollutants;
d. enable comparisons to be made of contamination levels in different areas;
e. identify areas where contamination is high, perhaps leading to the identification of an unknown source of pollution;
f. in conjunction with biological measurement, provide information on the possible effects of pollutants on species or ecosystems;
g. where maximum acceptable limits are established, as in human food, drinking water or air, enable action to be taken to maintain quality;
h. where controls are in operation to protect the environment, indicate the effectiveness of such controls.

A monitoring system must not be regarded as sufficient in itself to protect the environment, or any part of it, from the effects of pollution. It is unlikely to reveal localized areas of contamination or 'hot spots', as the number of sampling sites required for such a purpose would be far too numerous. Identification of sources of discharge or disposal of pollutants, or the sites of application of high concentrations of pesticides or other toxic substances, must form part of a complementary system of environmental protection and should be included in national systems of control.

III. TYPES OF PERSISTENT ORGANIC POLLUTANTS

Although several forms of stable organic pollutants have probably been present in our environment since the Industrial Revolution, those substances now considered to be potential (or actual) hazards to our environment have been developed and produced in quantity almost entirely within the last forty years. Organic compounds which are chemically stable, and hence persistent, are recognized as presenting an element of risk to one or more forms of life.

Persistence cannot be defined precisely, but it is doubtful whether chemicals surviving less than six months should be so classified. The term should, however, be applied to the chemical, not to its presence in a particular tissue, or geographical locality. Thus, while PCBs may disappear from water and enter fish and subsequently birds or mammals, their disappearance from any one component of the system does not imply that the substances are non-persistent.

The major groups are:

a. some organochlorine pesticides and their metabolites (e.g. DDT, DDE, DDD, dieldrin, isomers of BHC, hexachlorobenzene, chlordane, toxaphene);
b. polychlorinated biphenyls (PCBs) and terphenyls (PCTs);
c. polychlorinated naphthalenes (PCNs);
d. chlorinated aliphatic hydrocarbons (e.g. chlorinated paraffins and olefins, and waste products from PVC manufacture);
e. halogenated solvents, certain refrigerants, aerosols, fire retardants;
f. some stable herbicides (e.g. paraquat, simazine);
g. phthalic acid esters (plasticizers);
h. straight-chain surfactants;
i. petroleum hydrocarbons;
j. polynuclear aromatics (e.g. benzpyrenes);
k. chlorinated dibenzodioxins and dibenzofurans;
l. organometallic compounds (e.g. of mercury and tin).

Of the substances referred to some have yet to be confirmed as persistent. Certain PCBs and petroleum hydrocarbons are currently believed to be extremely stable under environmental conditions. Others may be regarded as fairly persistent but easily inactivated, as is paraquat on soil particles. Other very stable compounds are known to have been discharged to the environment, although techniques for their detection have not yet been fully developed, or used in environmental studies. This appears to be the case for PCTs, PCNs and some of those in groups d and e, for example.

Organic forms of metallic elements have been included, although some, such as methyl mercury, are believed to be produced by natural processes from inorganic forms to a significant extent (Wood et al., 1972). Phenyl mercury is discharged industrially but is not very persistent, and is probably converted to methyl mercury via the inorganic form (Noren and Westöö, 1967). Some metals are complexed as carbamates in agricultural fungicides, but few are considered to be very persistent.

The list given above is not intended to be exhaustive, but illustrates the wide variety of stable organic compounds which may be present in our environment. Very few of these are at present the subject of detailed studies in surveys or monitoring programmes. Only DDT, its metabolites DDE and DDD, dieldrin, PCBs and methyl mercury have been extensively determined (Edwards, 1973a). Some evidence is now being accumulated on petroleum hydrocarbons in marine species (Goldberg, 1972), but most of the other groups of compounds have been the subject of only one or two localized investigations. The sections which follow therefore are based mainly on experience in monitoring for certain organochlorine pesticides and PCBs in international studies sponsored by the Organization for Economic Cooperation and Development (Holden, 1970, 1973a).

IV. SELECTION OF SAMPLING MATERIAL

The sample materials which can be considered for monitoring pollutants are the natural media, air, soil and water, as in the surveillance of atmospheric or water pollution, and the multitude of components of the biosphere, whether plants, invertebrates or vertebrates. Soils can be used in certain instances, such as on agricultural land, or where particulate deposition from air may occur. Underwater soils (muds) can also provide valuable information on rates of deposition from the overlying water. Air and water have several advantages, because they are normally unlimited in quantity, require relatively simple analytical techniques, and standards of quality have been established for many pollutants. Organic pollutants, however, are often found in much greater concentrations in biological tissues than in the air or water in which the organisms live (see Chapter 2). Furthermore, the effects of pollutants on organisms depend directly on the amounts absorbed, and only indirectly on the amounts in the physical environment, and thus the analysis of tissues or organs may have a more direct relevance to these effects than the analysis of the external media. Organisms which accumulate pollutants to a considerable degree may act as sensitive indicators of the 'state of health' of the general environment, and in some instances, if the individuals of a species range widely whilst feeding, may integrate the geographical variation in contamination levels. Biological sampling has been of particular importance in the study of pollution by DDT and PCBs (Edwards, 1973a), and relatively little information has been obtained on the distribution of these substances in air and water (Södergren, 1972).

Organic pollutants may be soluble in aqueous or non-aqueous media, depending particularly on their polarities. Such properties are important in determining the distribution of pollutants in the physical environment.

Intake by biological tissues is also affected by polarity (see Chapter 3). Thus water-soluble compounds may be expected to disperse readily in water, and to dissolve in rain. Other less polar compounds, as typified by most organochlorines, have very low solubility in water, but are more readily soluble in lipids. Organochlorines in fact are rapidly removed from water by biological material, and concentrated in fats and waxes, but may also be lost from water surfaces by evaporation (Hartley, 1969), a property which is partly responsible for the significant quantities of DDT and PCB found in the atmosphere.

V. ORGANOCHLORINE CONCENTRATIONS AND SELECTION OF SAMPLES

Before discussing the design of a monitoring programme, it is useful to consider the magnitude of the concentrations of the common organochlorine residues such as DDT and its metabolites DDD and DDE, and PCBs, which are found in various types of potential sample material. Selection of the most suitable types of specimen for regular sampling depends in part on the ability to determine, with acceptable accuracy, the actual concentrations of pollutants which are present. As far as possible, therefore, an attempt should be made to select material for analysis, of an appropriate type and quantity, which is likely to yield detectable and determinable residue concentrations, at least of the contaminants considered most important.

Monitoring species should reflect the degree of contamination of the physical environment by one or more pollutants, through the relatively high concentrations of those pollutants which they have accumulated in their tissues, as compared with the natural or background (baseline) levels. Not all species will contain high concentrations, as some may have means of avoiding, excreting or metabolizing particular pollutants. Moreover, it may be necessary to select a particular organ or tissue in which the pollutant is concentrated preferentially, e.g. cadmium in renal tissue, methyl mercury in association with certain proteins, or organochlorines in triglyceride lipids.

While the ability to absorb and retain relatively high concentrations of pollutants can make a species useful for monitoring, it must not be assumed that because concentrations found may appear relatively high this necessarily implies that some detrimental biological effect may have resulted. Changes in growth, behaviour or fecundity may have been measurable in laboratory or controlled field experiments, but rarely in natural populations. We cannot, for example, measure declines in the growth rate of fish, the clutch-size of birds, or the populations of mammals, with sufficient accuracy to detect changes which may be ecologically significant over a prolonged period. Sudden changes, such as those created by mass mortalities of adults or the complete failure of a reproductive stage, are more obvious, but monitoring programmes are intended to give warning of more subtle trends than these. In consequence, we are only able at present to measure, at most, changes in the level of contamination in a species, with little chance of deducing any biological effect. Too little research on effects correlated with tissue concentrations, at levels well below those which are lethal, has been carried out. Even when specimens are analysed after death it is often difficult or impossible to confirm that the residue levels found could have been responsible for the mortality. The only sublethal biological effect so far extensively correlated with environmental contamination is that of the eggshell thickness of certain species of birds which have accumulated high concentrations of DDE and other organochlorine residues (e.g. Ratcliffe, 1970; Cooke, 1973).

The samples taken for monitoring programmes are often inadequate. However, the acquisition of large numbers of samples, taken with no special consideration of the biological variables capable of influencing the residue concentrations, can not only become a burden to the analyst but may yield analytical data incapable of the necessary evaluation. Calculation of the arithmetic means of several series of samples may suggest that differences exist between the series, but unless care was taken in selecting the samples these differences, even if statistically significant, may be due to factors other than external contamination levels. For example, PCB or mercury levels in some species are known to increase with age (Johnels et al., 1967; Addison et al., 1973). If sample selection ignores age as a critical parameter, different age distributions in the various population samples may themselves influence the mean values obtained, and obscure true differences in environmental contamination levels. Again, if the contaminant is fat-soluble, and the proportion of fat in the body varies with sexual maturity, or availability of food, both characteristics being seasonally-dependent, the time at which samples are obtained will be of considerable importance.

The analyses obtained from many series of samples of populations of several species have been examined statistically during the course of the OECD collaborative studies, and it is frequently found that the distribution of the residue data from the populations is non-Gaussian (Holden, 1970). Often it appears to be lognormal and after appropriate transformation the means and variances calculated enable comparison to be made between populations. Large numbers of individuals are required in each sample, to ensure that even a moderately large difference between means can be detected with appropriate significance. Thus, for populations of both northern pike (*Esox lucius*) and starlings (*Sturnus vulgaris*) examined in the second OECD study it was calculated that 50 individuals from each population would require to be analysed separately in order to be able to detect a 25 per cent difference between the geometric means. The samples involved in this particular study were not selected for sex, age or size, each of which could have been responsible for part of the variance. The two latter parameters could be expected to contribute to skewness, because a random sample is likely to contain fewer larger, older specimens than smaller, younger ones. The method of sampling may itself produce some bias in the sample. The capture of fish by nets could, for example, be selective for size, the smallest and youngest often passing through the meshes.

Several criteria must therefore be considered in selecting a species suitable for monitoring. The species must also be sufficiently numerous to enable relatively large numbers of individuals to be taken from each population for analytical purposes, without making any significant reduction in the total population. The species should therefore be one which occurs at high population densities, either locally (in flocks or shoals) or over large areas, as with many invertebrate species. Nestlings or eggs of birds, however, can often be sampled without affecting population size. This also avoids the problem of age determination which is encountered with adults. Ideally, it would be advantageous to include species from different trophic levels in an ecosystem, in order to obtain information on transport mechanisms through food chains, but other restrictions on species selection are likely to preclude this.

For global monitoring purposes, it is rarely possible to select a species which occurs in all parts of the world. Related species which fulfil the same ecological role, and have similar characteristics in respect of their environmental requirements and food organisms, are generally accepted as equivalent, as for example two species of European starlings *Sturnus vulgaris* and *S. unicolor*, the freshwater perch *Perca fluviatilis* and *P. flavescens*, the marine mussels *Mytilus edulis* and *Modiolus demissus*, or the herring *Clupea harengus* and sprat *C. sprattus*. Nevertheless, such alternatives have so far been selected only for Europe and North America, and other species would be required in South America, Africa and Asia. This aspect of species selection has not yet been adequately considered, and it is doubtful whether the required knowledge of the ecology of appropriate species exists at the present time. It should be emphasized, however, that only if comparisons are to be made *between* areas are equivalent species required. Changes *within* any one area could be monitored by appropriate species representative of that area—a much simpler problem of selection.

To eliminate some of the variables which may influence residue concentrations, it should be easy to age and sex individuals. Selection of individuals of a specific sex and age, with perhaps the additional restriction of size or weight range, can normally only be made if a much larger number of individuals are sampled initially. Clearly the choice of age or size must be made carefully, with prior knowledge of the distribution of these two parameters in appropriate populations. Thus the decision to use four-year-old fish to provide sufficient material for analysis, when the average population of the particular species is dominated by two- or three-year-old fish, would necessitate the acquisition of very large numbers of fish initially, and rejection of most of the individuals, perhaps destructively, in order to obtain the requisite number of fish of the selected age group.

In a recent OECD programme it was decided to use perch as a monitoring species for fresh waters, two-year-old fish being selected as they are normally distinguishable by length alone from younger or older fish. This simplified the problem of age determination (which is time-consuming) but individual fish do not always provide enough material for the analyst to complete the full analysis required. In consequence, it was decided where necessary to take two separate samples (each of 25 fish) from each population at the same time, one sample being used for organochlorines and the other for certain metal contaminants. As there was no intention to correlate organochlorines and metal residues within individual fish, this procedure did not lose any useful information, and did not require much additional effort in obtaining the necessary sample.

One problem which often arises is to know whether individuals have acquired their residues from the area in which they are taken, or from some other area. Sedentary organisms, such as mussels, or plants, can only receive their contamination from their immediate environment, but fish, birds and mammals, which may range over considerable distances within relatively short periods, should be regarded as monitoring species for areas, rather than sites. Unless the species migrates over long distances, the information obtained will in some way be relevant to the level of occurrence of the contamination in the sampling area. Migratory species present some difficulty in the evaluation of the residues they may acquire, as it can never be certain whether concentrations measured after migration were acquired in the area where the individuals are sampled, or in the area from which they have migrated.

A. Soils and Sediments

Sampling of soils is appropriate for the monitoring of terrestrial environments which have been contaminated by the usage of pesticides for agricultural purposes, and techniques for representative sampling have been standardized for soil surveys in many countries (Wiersma *et al.*, 1971). Concentrations of persistent pesticides may be found in the range 1–100 ppm in such soils (Edwards, 1973b). Samples from control areas, where pesticides are known not to have been used at any time, should indicate the extent of contamination by atmospheric fallout, though in uncultivated soils residues will probably be confined to a relatively thin surface layer, and the sampling technique must take account of this. Consequently the use of soil as a medium for global monitoring, in which most areas could be assumed to contain the lowest concentrations of contaminants (less than 0·1 ppm of total DDT, for example), is probably less appropriate, as it is difficult to measure accurately the depth of the contaminated surface layer which may be only a few millimetres thick. However, such samples could indicate the existence of local contamination arising from nearby sources, and the concentrations might be better expressed in terms of unit area.

Soils have been sampled regularly in the United States National Pesticide Monitoring Programme (Sand *et al.*, 1967) at 23 locations where pesticide usage is considerable, and at 35 low- and non-use sites. Depending on the type of area sampled, one or fifty cores may be taken per acre in each plot sampled. Sampling is intensive in some areas, to give more precise data on accumulation or depletion of residues, and to develop data on rates of movement of pesticides with water. The cores are taken to a depth of three inches (7·5 cm), and include surface cover, and composites are made from groups of cores. Results are reported in parts per million dry weight down to 0·01 ppm. The United States Programme involves the collection of about 3,000 samples annually and the survey includes information on pesticide usage.

Correlation between the rates of application of arsenic, DDT and dieldrin, and the residues found were examined for those states having the highest residues (Wiersma *et al.*, 1972). Of the pesticides investigated, dieldrin occurred the most frequently in cropland soil, followed by DDT residues, aldrin and chlordane. In non-cropland soils, DDT residues were most often detected, followed by dieldrin. Whether the DDT residues had persisted from much earlier pesticide usage, or from fallout, is not clear.

No routine sediment sampling from rivers or lakes appears to be in operation, the method of sampling itself being a difficult problem. If the sediment is well-mixed, as in some rivers, the grab sample might be adequate, but for stratified sediments a sample of the upper layer, possibly only a few millimetres deep, would be essential to give information on relatively recent deposition of residues.

B. Water

Concentrations in natural waters of organochlorines such as DDE, DDT or PCB (expressed in terms of a commercial formulation such as Aroclor 1254) are generally of the order of 1 ng/l (1 pp 10^{12}) or less, except where local pollution exists. In the latter case, concentrations up to 1,000 ng/l may be detected, but often only 10–100 ng/l. Published analyses of many rivers in the U.S.A. indicate that few exceed 10 ng/l of DDT, or 5 ng/l of DDE (Manigold and Schulze, 1969), and in the predominantly unpolluted rivers of Scotland the author's laboratory has measured concentrations of DDT, DDD, DDE and dieldrin in the range 1–3 ng/l. PCB levels were below 1 ng/l. For such analyses, extracts from the samples must be concentrated until they represent preferably a 10,000-fold increase from the original aqueous concentration. This may require 10-litre samples, and a very high standard of laboratory cleanliness, to avoid artefacts. New methods of concentration are under development, but the practical difficulties presented by this stage of processing, and the uncertainty regarding the proportion of the contaminants in true solution, adsorbed to particulate matter, or contained in living microorganisms, limits the value of the information obtained from the analysis. A high proportion of the contaminant may be in the particulate fraction, but determination of this depends on filtration or centrifugation. Material retained on the filter may remove part of the contaminant originally in solution.

The only monitoring programme which includes samples of fresh water as indicators of environmental contamination appears to be that of the United States. In its National Pesticide Monitoring Programme (Green and Love, 1967), a network of 53 sampling locations on major rivers was established, and the manner of sampling, preservation, storage and despatch of samples defined. Analyses for a wide variety of pollutants were proposed, with limits of detection set at the 5 or 10 parts per 10^{12} level. The subsequent reports (Brown and Nishioka, 1967; Manigold and Schulze, 1969; Schulze et al., 1973) indicated that several variations from the original proposal had been made, including a change from grab samples to depth-integrated sampling, and modifications of the analytical procedure. PCBs were not sought or allowed for in the early years of the programme. Despite the low limits of detection, the majority of samples showed no detectable amounts of any organochlorine residues.

This programme may be adequate for the safeguarding of public water supplies (for which the permissible limits of organochlorines are well above the limits of detection), but does not enable any trends in contamination level to be detected, or help to relate residues in fish to levels in water. One major difficulty when sampling flowing waters is in deciding whether to sample for particulate-bound residues quantitatively, or to avoid such residues as far as possible. The concentration of suspended material depends on flow rate, and increases with depth. A knowledge of particulate-bound residues is important when transport mechanisms in the aquatic environment are being investigated, but otherwise sampling sediment independently of water probably gives more useful information.

C. Air and Precipitation

The techniques for sampling air and precipitation for organic pollutants are still being developed, and no regular monitoring is yet in progress. Södergren (1972) has, however, been using a nylon screen sampler for particulate deposition at several sites in different countries. Precipitation and particulate deposition has also been sampled by the author's laboratory at four sites in Scotland since 1972, but the concentrations determined are extremely low, and the technique requires improvement before it could be used for routine monitoring. Södergren (1973) found that in Sweden the greatest proportion of both DDT and PCB is deposited in the particulate fraction.

D. Vegetation

Terrestrial vegetation, apart from that receiving direct application, is less suitable for monitoring many types of pesticides, as the intake of most such chemicals from soils is low (Finlayson and MacCarthy, 1973). However, some species could be considered for monitoring the levels of pollutants in the atmosphere and the influence on plant growth of certain pollutants such as sulphur in the air, and heavy metals in the soil, is a well known phenomenon. The chemical analysis of plants and soils for monitoring atmospheric levels of metal contaminants has been described by Goodman and Roberts (1971). In the marine environment, seaweeds have been used to monitor the levels of metallic elements in coastal waters (Preston et al., 1972).

The concentrations of organochlorines such as DDT, DDE and PCBs found in plant material, whether terrestrial or aquatic, will vary widely according to the exposure to dust, sprays or effluent discharges. The presence of cuticular wax on the surface, or the adherence of absorbent particulate matter, may result in surface concentrations of contaminants which are unrelated to concentrations present in the plant tissues, although washing procedures should reduce the significance of such surface concentrations. So far as is known, plants have not yet been considered in this role for organochlorine monitoring, but few of such compounds are even slightly systemic, and accumulation within plant tissues is therefore unlikely. Concentrations should be expressed on a dry weight basis, as the moisture content of fresh specimens could be variable, but the possibility of loss of residues on drying should not be overlooked.

E. Invertebrates

Invertebrates, whether terrestrial or aquatic, do not appear to have been widely used for monitoring purposes, but would seem to be appropriate for the examination of the effects of agricultural sprays or disease control in public health programmes, as well as monitoring the effects of local discharges in rivers, estuaries or coastal areas. Edwards and Thompson (1973) summarized the information available on the occurrence of pesticides in soil fauna, and found that many species concentrate pesticides to a considerable extent. Different species of earthworms concentrate residues to different degrees, and identification of earthworm species for monitoring purposes might be difficult. Other soil invertebrates do not seem to have been investigated as monitoring organisms.

Animal species living in water usually concentrate organochlorines from the water by several orders of magnitude. Thus marine zooplankton may contain at least 0·01 ppm, an easily determined concentration if a sufficient sample is obtainable. This should be a minimum of 10 g, but often a considerable effort is required to collect such a sample in the normal size of townet. Moreover, the species variation in both phyto- and zooplankton populations at different times of the year, or in different areas, is considerable. Marine plankton have been sampled to provide information on their significance in the accumulation of organochlorine residues by plankton-eating fish. Harvey et al. (1972) and also Williams and Holden (1973), found gross differences in the degree of contamination of different areas of the sea by organochlorines. The plankton was sampled by nets of various mesh sizes and different constructional materials, but samples are liable to include non-biological material, including tar balls and detritus. In shallow water, where currents are strong, bottom sediments might also be disturbed. Furthermore, contamination may arise from the surface film of the sea, in which organochlorines are concentrated (Seba and Corcoran, 1969), nylon nets (Harvey and Teal, 1973) and boat paint (Jensen et al., 1972).

Ware and Addison (1973) have shown that organochlorine concentrations per unit weight of plankton are greater for smaller organisms. Södergren (1968) found that DDT was absorbed, rather than adsorbed, to algal cells, suggesting that intake is not primarily a surface phenomenon. As the species composition of plankton populations is variable, it is impossible to obtain the same proportion of a number of species at the same time at different locations, or alternatively samples of the same species at different sites. Concentrations expressed in terms of lipid content rather than wet weight might be more relevant, but as yet there is no good evidence that this is so. Finally, it is desirable that at least five grammes of plankton should be obtained in each sample for analysis, and for much of the year this can necessitate collection over considerable distances by the standard type of plankton net.

Similar difficulties arise in fresh water if plankton is used, and if the microbenthos is sampled it is necessary to select species, e.g. of amphipods or molluscs, which are of widespread occurrence. Species of *Gammarus*, *Asellus* or *Limnaea* might, for example, be appropriate, being available at any time of year, but the age of specimens is likely to be variable. Södergren et al. (1972) used *Gammarus pulex* as an indicator organism in a regional study of chlorinated hydrocarbon residues in streams in southern Sweden. Seasonal changes seem to be correlated with run-off conditions, and only diffuse relationships between residue levels and age of organisms in a stream ecosystem were found.

All large invertebrates used in monitoring programmes so far are marine molluscs. The mussel *Mytilus edulis* has been used for coastal monitoring in OECD studies in 1967–1969 (Holden, 1970) and 1969–1971 (Holden, 1973a). In the United States, Butler (1973) has used ten species of molluscs, including *M. edulis*, to monitor pesticides in 15 coastal states, the most widely-distributed species being the eastern oyster *Crassostrea virginica*, found in 12 states. Monthly sampling demonstrated a marked seasonal pattern in DDT residues in Florida, correlated with usage of the pesticide on crops. Average yearly levels also showed a marked decline of DDT over six years.

The levels of intake and flushing rates of organochlorines in molluscs vary with species (Butler, 1966), and consequently a monitoring species must be chosen with care. Oysters can accumulate residues of DDT from an aqueous concentration of 10 pp 10^{12}, and can show a 25,000-fold accumulation from 1 pp 10^9 in water in 96 hr (Butler, 1973). Up to 90 per cent of the residues can be lost by flushing in clean water for a week. Thus residue levels found in molluscs exposed to varying aqueous concentrations will present difficulties in interpretation. Nevertheless these species, being sedentary, have the considerable advantage that they can usually be sampled more easily than fish or birds. In the OECD programmes, however, problems arose from the particulate material accumulated by mussels, and the variable amount of water in the shells. Both water and sediment were discarded as far as possible, but in the latest study to be reported (Holden, 1973a) specimens sampled in ostensibly clean areas showed higher organochlorine levels than some from areas considered to be badly polluted by sewage or industrial discharges.

F. Vertebrates

1. Fish

Aquatic organisms, and fish in particular, can accumulate organo-chlorine residues directly from water through their respiratory processes, and also from food. Fish species from one area vary widely in the residue levels which they may contain, and these may be correlated with the large differences in lipid content of the tissues, although the nature of the food organisms must also play an important part. Thus the flesh of the cod (*Gadus morhua*) may only contain organochlorine residues of the order of 0·01 ppm, whereas that of the clupeoids such as the herring (*Clupea harengus*) in the same water may contain levels of about 0·1 ppm. Both species, however, may be abundant, and each individual fish can provide ample material for analysis.

Many species of fish congregate in shoals, making them useful for monitoring. Marine species may be exploited commercially, simplifying to some extent the problem of obtaining samples. There are also several freshwater shoaling species, which can be sampled by netting or trapping. In the earlier OECD programmes, the northern pike (*Esox lucius*) was monitored because of its predatory habit, and it was assumed that this would lead to relatively high residue concentrations. In fact, even in Europe, where the species is common, it was not very easy to obtain 10 fish of similar age or size prior to spawning (when the fish should be in good condition). Often the lakes inhabited by pike were still partly frozen, and sampling impossible, at the scheduled time.

In the latest OECD Programme (1972–75) a selection is made from three shoaling species in fresh waters, the common perch (*Perca fluviatilis*), yellow perch (*P. flavescens*), and the roach (*Leuciscus rutilis*). Twenty-five two-year-old fish of one sex must be obtained each year from each population, the sex also being the same for all years. One or other of these species is fairly common in both Europe and North America. In the marine environment, herring (*Clupea harengus*) or sprat (*C. sprattus*) have been chosen.

The eel (*Anguilla anguilla*) might be considered as a useful monitoring species for fresh waters, as it accumulates high organochlorine residues (Holden, 1973a). From information obtained on this species in Scotland, however, it is not certain that the residues found reflect recent contamination.

In the United States National Pesticide Monitoring Programme a large number of freshwater species of fish have been chosen for monitoring (Henderson *et al.*, 1969, 1971), each being sampled where sufficiently abundant, but the information obtained from such a wide variety must make interpretation of the analytical data difficult. A few species, however, occur in most states, and these are probably more useful. The original list of species, selected from those near the top of the food chain, comprised carp, buffalo, black bass, channel catfish, green sunfish, yellow perch, rainbow trout and squawfish. As some difficulty was experienced in obtaining some of these species, the list was expanded to include suckers, other catfish, other trout, etc. Of the species named, only carp, yellow perch and rainbow trout (or closely related species) occur to any significant extent in Europe, and none are suitable for monitoring other parts of the world.

At each sampling site, five whole fish of each available species were taken as a sample, and the length, weight and estimated age of each fish in each sample recorded. The five individuals were then combined, and ground to a homogeneous mixture. Such a procedure gives no information on residue levels in the edible parts of the fish, as the viscera and stomach contents, which could be expected to vary considerably among individual fish, are included in the total samples. Additional variability is thus included in this method, which could be avoided if a specific tissue, such as muscle, were selected for analysis. Henderson and his co-workers found that in some waters the fish showed consistently high residues of DDT, dieldrin and other organochlorine insecticides, particularly where they drained from agricultural or highly industrialized areas. They also found a considerable variation in residue levels in different samples, which they thought could be caused by variation in analysis, or between individual fish. Because of such variations, they advised caution in using and interpreting the data. DDT residues in fish have been found to increase with age (Youngs et al., 1972), and thus age selection could be important in reducing the variation among individuals.

A different approach to species selection for monitoring the marine environment was proposed by Berner et al. (1972), as part of a national programme for marine monitoring in the United States. The environment was divided into coastal and marine zones, and species representative of each trophic level selected for each zone. The fish species chosen in the coastal zone were three plankton-feeding fish (herring, menhaden and anchovy), two bottom-feeding flatfish (yellowtail flounder and dover sole) and two top carnivores (striped bass and silver salmon). All but the striped bass are fished commercially, and that species is exploited by sport fishermen. Of the species referred to, the herring is available on both sides of the North Atlantic, and the anchovy could be an equivalent species for the Pacific. Various species of flounder, all bottom-feeders, occur in both Atlantic and Pacific waters, but, because they breed in fresh water, the striped bass and silver salmon are of doubtful value as monitoring species, as is the Atlantic salmon (*Salmo salar*) which is commercially exploited in the coastal waters of the eastern Atlantic and North Sea.

The species suggested by Berner et al. for oceanic zone monitoring were yellowfin tuna, albacore tuna and pink salmon, which are commercially exploited carnivores at the ends of food chains. None of the species have ecological equivalents suitable for monitoring the eastern Atlantic and North Sea waters, although the bluefin tuna is fished in a few areas.

It is clear from the above suggestions that no consideration has yet been given to species appropriate for monitoring the oceans of the southern hemisphere. In coastal waters, where most monitoring could be concentrated, various species of hake (genus *Merluccius*) occur on both sides of the North Atlantic and South Atlantic, on the Pacific coast of North and South America, in the Mediterranean and around New Zealand. These species inhabit the continental shelf, and feed upon small fish and squid. Species of cod occur on both sides of the North Pacific and North Atlantic. Several species of clupeoids, such as herring, pilchards, sardines and sprats, are available on both sides of the North Atlantic and North Pacific as well as in the Australasian, South African, Mediterranean, South West Atlantic and South East Pacific waters. Tuna species occur in the central Pacific, East African and central Atlantic waters. Neither Arctic nor Antarctic waters have species suitable for monitoring which are common to both areas, and in much of the Indian Ocean information on available species appears to be sparse.

Generally speaking, the coastal waters in the equatorial zone would probably require special consideration, the coral reef environments having different species from those in temperate zones.

Most surveys of pollutants in biological materials have been made in North America and Western Europe, and experience in species selection probably has little relevance to the environments of the greater part of the earth's surface. Before any global monitoring system can be designed, much more information is required on the ecology of the various species of fish and invertebrates in the marine environment in the different oceans. It also seems unlikely that appropriate species can be obtained from commercially exploited stocks in all areas, and special arrangements may therefore be necessary in many areas to obtain the necessary samples in a global monitoring programme.

2. Mammals

Small mammals would seem to be the only forms likely to be suitable for large-scale monitoring, if appropriate widely distributed species could be selected. Robel et al. (1972) trapped rodents of a number of species in Kansas over five years, in a study of the possible effects of commonly used insecticides on the population dynamics of rodents. Nine species were analysed for residues, dieldrin being the most common and heptachlor epoxide the only other insecticide detected. DDT residues were not found, but this insecticide was not used in the study area during the period of study, although diazinon, parathion, methyl parathion, heptachlor, endrin and aldrin were used. Thus it would seem that even in a treated area the levels of contamination of rodents by various organochlorine and organophosphorus insecticides can be low. Unless the sensitivity of the method of analysis is increased, it would seem that such mammals are not very suitable as monitoring organisms, because they have rather low residue levels. Mice and voles, however, apparently accumulate organochlorines to a much smaller extent than shrews (Dimond and Sherburne, 1969). Larger animals, with a greater life span, would probably be too few for appropriate numbers of the same age to be obtained. In the marine environment, seal pups have been analysed after culling. Such specimens are of known age and sex, but they can only monitor limited areas, and there is some indication that they reflect the residue levels of the parents, which may have migrated considerable distances, often from unknown areas (Holden, 1972).

3. Birds

Individual birds, especially from the larger species, yield sufficient muscle tissue for analysis, although livers are often used for monitoring purposes, partly because concentrations of organochlorines are usually much higher in liver. In many species, particularly those of raptors, concentrations in the muscle may exceed one ppm and are often much higher. Such samples present no major difficulty to analysts, at least from the aspect of detecting residues.

More studies have been made on the residue levels and effect of organochlorines on birds than on any other vertebrate group. In several instances, the chronic toxic effects of certain pesticides such as dieldrin and DDT were observed in birds before investigations were begun into their effects on other forms of wildlife. It is not surprising, therefore, that all programmes designed to monitor contamination in wildlife should include at least one species of bird. Yet some of the most serious effects of organochlorines are demonstrated in the raptorial species, which by their nature are not particularly numerous or accessible, and thus not very appropriate for monitoring purposes. The decline in numbers of a species such as the peregrine (*Falco peregrinus*), caused by organochlorine residues, was found to occur in both Great Britain and North America. The species was never abundant, and nests not very accessible, but once the decline in numbers could be demonstrated it could clearly never be considered a suitable species for monitoring purposes. Likewise, the American bald eagle (*Haliaetus leucocephalus*), similarly affected by organochlorines, is a species which could not be sampled for the purpose of studying residue levels in the environment, although specimens found dead have been used for this purpose.

The species which have been selected for monitoring mostly occur in flocks, or are at least very common. None, however, seem likely to show any symptoms of chronic toxicity, except in extreme cases, and can only be used as indicators of the general level of contamination in their locality. The starling (*Sturnus vulgaris*) has been proposed as a useful monitoring species in several programmes, as it usually occurs in large flocks and is found in Europe, North America and Australasia. However, there is some migration in autumn from north to south, when some flocks may contain both migratory and sedentary individuals for a period, making this an unsuitable time for sampling. When the flocks have returned to their breeding areas, it cannot be certain whether the residues they contain have been acquired in their winter quarters or more recently in the sampling areas. It has been suggested that nestlings are more likely to reflect ambient concentrations, in consequence of being fed with food material obtained locally, rather than the residue levels of the female parent which are to some degree passed to the egg. For this reason, and to avoid the difficulty of ageing adults, nestling starlings have been selected for the 1972–1975 OECD Programme, but as an individual nestling will yield insufficient material for the analyses required, a fixed number of nestlings (usually three or four) is being taken per nest and the tissues combined to provide a sample representative of each nest.

Starlings have been used in all OECD studies on organochlorines since 1966 (Holden, 1970, 1973a). The species has also been used in the United States since 1967 for monitoring mercury and lead (Martin, 1972) and organochlorines (Martin, 1969; Martin and Nickerson, 1972). The OECD study of 1967–1969 called for 30 individuals, 20 to be pooled in groups of 5 and 10 to be analysed individually, the birds being adults taken prior to nesting and muscle tissue being selected for analysis. There was good evidence of skewness in the distribution of residues of organochlorines among individuals in several of the samples.

The United States Programme involves the random sampling of the birds in 40 blocks at intervals of 5° latitude and longitude, and at up to four sites per block. Ten birds are taken at each site as far as possible, each being skinned, and the beak and wings removed. The 10 pooled carcases are minced in a Hobart food chopper and aliquots taken for analysis. These samples would thus include stomach contents and viscera, the variable proportions of which could be a source of variance among individuals. In both this and the OECD Programme it has not always been found easy to sample the species in some areas. The results obtained in the United States Programme up to 1970 indicated the decline in some organochlorine pesticides since 1967, but this was not statistically significant.

The United States Pesticide Monitoring Programme also employs the wings of wild mallard (*Anas platyrhynchos*) and black duck (*A. rufipes*) taken by sportsmen (Heath, 1969). Adult and immature wings are separated, flight feathers are removed and groups of 25 wings homogenized for analysis. In this survey, DDE has been the predominant residue, followed by DDT, DDD and dieldrin. The results have been sufficiently precise to show differences in levels between flyways, groups of states and often between individual states. About 12,500 wings are taken annually (Johnson *et al.*, 1967).

The eggs of birds can sometimes be sampled instead of the birds themselves, particularly when the latter are insufficiently numerous to sacrifice. Many species will lay more eggs to replace those lost. However, there is some risk that the first egg laid may contain higher residue levels than subsequent eggs, and unless a nest is under continuous observation this egg cannot be identified. The variability created by the first egg could be reduced if several eggs per clutch, or complete clutches, can be taken but again this would depend on the species concerned.

Moore (1966) considered a number of species of birds which, because of their wide distribution throughout the world, might be suitable for an international monitoring system. His list of such species, all of which have been shown to contain moderate to high organochlorine residue levels, included the cormorant (*Phalacrocorax carbo*), which in some countries feeds mainly on freshwater fish and in others on marine fish. This variation in feeding habit renders it unsuitable for global monitoring, although it might be appropriate for a regional programme. The little tern (*Sterna albifrons*) is cosmopolitan, but not numerous enough, as is the oyster catcher (*Haematopus ostralegus*), the osprey (*Pandion haliaëtus*), stilt (*Himantopus himantopus*), peregrine (*Falco peregrinus*), barn owl (*Tyto alba*) and the buzzard (*Buteo buteo*). Moore, however, suggested that the eggs of the cormorant, little tern and oyster catcher might be suitable for use as international indicators of environmental contamination. For a more limited national programme, he proposed the eggs of the cormorant and species of terns and auks.

Other bird species suggested by Moore for monitoring purposes, usually by sampling eggs, include herons (*Ardea cinerea*) and guillemots (*Uria aalge*). Herons could be expected to indicate fresh water contamination in many areas, but near the coast they are often marine feeders. Guillemots feed on marine invertebrates and small fish, and consequently their residue levels could reflect contamination at this trophic level. Their nests are not particularly accessible, but they or a related species occur along all coasts of northern Europe and North America, and in the Pacific up to the Bering Strait. Eggs of the species *U. aalge* have been analysed over several years in the United Kingdom (Parslow, 1973).

VI. ORGANIZATION OF MONITORING PROGRAMMES

So far, this chapter has discussed the requirements of monitoring in terms of sampling procedures and the possible types of sample. It has been assumed that the necessary analytical facilities and expertise are available for the operation of a monitoring programme, but many problems arise between the planning and the fulfilment of the programme; these include the assessment of the results obtained. At the present time, neither the analytical facilities nor the expertise exist for anything more than a very modest monitoring scheme, as has become very obvious during the past seven years in the operation of the OECD studies. Laboratories carrying out this work in the various countries have found it difficult to obtain all of the required samples, or to complete the analyses according to schedule, either because of practical difficulties, or because it has not been possible to give sufficient priority to the analysis of the samples obtained in the international programme. Permanent monitoring programmes would require the setting-up of specialist laboratories, perhaps associated with those already in existence which have the necessary expertise, but nevertheless laboratories established for the sole purpose of carrying out the necessary analyses of samples obtained from the monitoring programme.

In both the United States National Programme and the OECD Programme, it has not always been possible to get the complete samples required. A decision is often necessary as to whether an incomplete sample is adequate for the purpose or whether that sample should be excluded. Problems also arise if samples are taken at an incorrect time, when the individuals may be in a different physiological condition, introducing a further variable into the already difficult final stage of interpretation of the data. The timing of the actual analysis of the sample material is also dependent on the availability of the necessary personnel, and the capacity of the laboratory to carry out this operation, but long intervals between sampling and analysis may permit the residue content of the samples to change whilst in storage (Jefferies and Walker, 1966).

The analytical stage provides the bulk of the numerical data from the samples, and is obviously a critical part of the entire operation, but the numerous sources of error which may arise during analysis are not always appreciated. It is essential that any variation due to analytical procedures, including that between analysts, should be much less than the true difference between samples.

When a single laboratory is responsible for the analysis of all samples acquired in a monitoring programme, the variance due to the analytical technique will be less than that which arises if a number of laboratories are involved. However, it is still essential that the single laboratory so designs and tests its analytical methods that it minimizes analytical errors. Most laboratories do in fact test their own techniques, usually by the use of spiked samples, and can show that the efficiency of recovery of particular residues from the samples is at least 85 per cent, and often appreciably higher. In a large scale monitoring programme, it is unlikely that a single laboratory can undertake all the analyses, and consequently a number of different laboratories, probably in several different countries, will be involved. In this situation, it is essential that adequate and regular check samples are circulated among all laboratories involved, to establish the extent of the differences in analytical results between laboratories.

Even the check samples themselves present problems, as the material should preferably be of natural origin. For example, muscle tissue or fish oil must be homogeneous and prepared in such a way that it is not likely to decompose. If a part of the sample can be spiked with known quantities of particular contaminants, this gives an opportunity for the analyst to compare his own analytical results with the known values for the added contaminants.

It may sometimes be possible to standardize the complete analytical technique, so that differences between laboratories may be minimized. However, it is not uncommon to make minor modifications even to a standard method, and laboratories in different countries may not be able to agree on one standard method. For this reason, it was agreed at the commencement of the series of OECD programmes in 1966 that no attempt would be made to standardize on analytical methods for organochlorines, but rather to examine the extent of agreement which analysts in different laboratories, using their own selected methods, could achieve on one check sample. If the agreement proved to be close, the fact that different methods were being used became unimportant. Such a comparison of the analytical ability of analysts in different countries also enables one to test whether there is agreement on the identification of different residues present in the check samples. In the analysis of organochlorine residues, particularly where there is interference from polychlorinated biphenyls (PCBs), there are several possibilities of confusing the identity of individual residues. For example, unless the appropriate GLC columns are chosen for analysis, it is possible to get confusion between the following pairs of contaminants; DDE and dieldrin, hexachlorobenzene and α- or γ-BHC, op'-DDT and pp'-DDD, op'-DDT and endrin, heptachlor epoxide and dibutyl phthalate, sulphur and aldrin, and various PCBs with DDE, DDD, DDT and dieldrin (Holden, 1973b).

Quantification of PCB residues presents a further difficulty. In general, the GLC chromatogram of a wildlife sample produces a PCB pattern which does not resemble that from any commercial PCB formulation very closely, but it is common to select the formulation which provides the nearest match, and use that for calculation of PCB concentrations. There are a number of ways of making the calculation, but the better methods involve the measurement of peak height or peak area of a number of peaks in both sample and standard (Holden, 1973a). The analytical procedure normally ensures that PCB residues have been separated, prior to the GLC analysis, from most of the other organochlorine residues to avoid confusion with them.

Check samples give an adequate means of comparing the accuracy of analyses from different laboratories, but if a proportion of all analyses, whether from check samples or environmental samples, are also made in duplicate it is possible to assess the reproducibility of the analytical technique which can be achieved in each laboratory. This is important when attempting to assess whether the variance among values from individuals in a population results largely from analytical error.

For major monitoring programmes, as in the United States, OECD and any future United Nations programme, many laboratories will be involved in different parts of the world, and all the data acquired must be collated by some central unit. This unit must have the authority to demand the results, to establish a time schedule, to organize the analytical check sampling, and to provide standard report forms on which the data are supplied to them. If the data are given in suitable form, it should be possible to make appropriate statistical analyses with a computer. Before passing the information for computer storage, however, data must be examined for anomalies, for the possibility of mixed populations of individuals, for any irregularities in the presentation of the data, or for the omission of essential information. To enable an adequate statistical analysis to be made of the results, particularly in comparing mean contamination levels in different areas, or at different times, it is essential that as few 'not detectable' returns are made as possible. To achieve this, the detection limits must be set so low that such a result is rare. The statistical analysis should contribute valuable information to the final report by the central unit, and could where necessary suggest action to reduce pollution, or to control the undesirable use of certain chemicals. With experience, it should be possible to improve the monitoring system, reducing the number of sampling sites as necessary, or perhaps establishing new sites in areas where unexpectedly high levels of contamination were detected.

In all sampling and analytical procedures, there is a great risk of human error. It would be difficult to automate the sampling of wildlife material, although this is often done in both air and water monitoring. The analytical techniques currently used for contaminants such as organochlorines are not yet amenable to automation, and consequently are particularly susceptible to human error. Routine analysis is tedious, especially when the results are commonly at or below the limit of detection. Yet with the increasing sensitivity of techniques which are being developed, there will be more sources of error or interference, requiring an increased vigilance in laboratories. The inevitable changing of staff may in itself result in changes in analytical reproducibility, but as methods are improved, and staff become more experienced in the technique, the variance resulting from a particular technique will probably decrease. Sensitivity may also be increased, and new data may not therefore be easily compared with earlier information.

Finally, the cost of such operations is rarely mentioned in the planning of monitoring programmes. For a limited number of organochlorine analyses, including for example, the DDT group, two or three other organochlorine pesticides and the PCB group, the overall cost of analysis per sample is usually of the order of 50–100 dollars, depending on the country and laboratory. The sampling operation, transport of samples, clerical and computer time after analysis involve additional expenditure. For a programme involving, say, 25 samples from each of two populations of a species, and from each of ten areas, a total of five hundred analyses, costing 25,000–50,000 dollars for the analysis is involved, and the overall cost is probably two or three times greater. This is only for one group of pollutants in one species. For a wide variety of species and pollutants, although some analytical processes may be much cheaper, the total programme would cost several million dollars annually. Whilst a significant reduction in cost could be made by reducing the number of analyses if several individuals from one population are obtained, and a homogenate of these prepared for a single analysis, no estimate of the variation between individuals can be obtained.

It should also be obvious that much of the analytical activity, and the expense, will be wasted if the sampling procedure is inadequate, or incorrect. Biologists are thus very important, and must give full attention to the quality and accuracy of the samples which they obtain, for example by ensuring that the samples are taken at the correct time, are of the required age, and that sufficient numbers of the correct species are supplied to the analyst.

Finally, it cannot be stressed too often that more biological research is required to provide the basis upon which any assessment of monitoring data can be made. The acquisition of such analytical data is not the ultimate objective, but is sought only to establish the possibility of environmental effects, most of which are essentially biological. Chemical, and in particular analytical, science is far ahead of a full biological understanding of the effects of pollution, even though many more pollutants are probably as yet undetectable. Laboratory investigations on biological effects, both physiological and biochemical, should be greatly intensified, to identify the effects of chronic exposure and to establish by associated chemical analyses the concentrations in tissues, not merely the concentrations in the external environment, at which effects occur. The information obtained would, with the use of accepted safety factors, enable maximum permissible levels to be agreed upon for environmental components. Even if the maximum permissible level can only be one order of magnitude less than the minimum concentration producing effects, this would provide considerable safeguards for our environment.

REFERENCES

Addison, R. F., Kerr, S. A., Sale, J. and Sergeant, D. E. (1973). *J. Fish. Res. Bd Can.* **30,** 59–600.

Berner, L. Jr., Martin, J. H., McGowan, J. and Teal, J. (1972). *In* 'Marine Pollution Monitoring: Strategies for a National Program' (E. D. Goldberg, ed.), pp. 11–16. National Oceanic and Atmospheric Administration, U.S. Department of Commerce.

Brown, E. and Nishioka, Y. A. (1967). *Pestic. Monit. J.* **1,** 38–46.

Butler, P. A. (1966). *J. appl. Ecol.* **3** (Suppl.) 253–259.

Butler, P. A. (1973). *Pestic. Monit. J.* **6,** 238–362.

Cooke, A. S. (1973). *Environ. Pollut.* **4,** 84–152.

Dimond, J. B. and Sherburne, J. A. (1969). *Nature, Lond.* **221,** 486.

Edwards, C. A. (1970). *In* 'Critical Reviews in Environmental Control', pp. 1–67. Chemical Rubber Co., Cleveland, U.S.A.

Edwards, C. A. (1973a). 'Environmental Pollution by Pesticides', Plenum Press, London.

Edwards, C. A. (1973b). *In* 'Environmental Pollution by Pesticides' (C. A. Edwards, ed.), pp. 409–439. Plenum Press, London.

Edwards, C. A. and Thompson, A. R. (1973). *Residue Rev.* **45,** 1–79.

Finlayson, D. G. and MacCarthy, H. R. (1973). *In* 'Environmental Pollution by Pesticides' (C. A. Edwards, ed.), pp. 57–86. Plenum Press, London.

Goldberg, E. D. (1972). 'Baseline Studies of Pollutants in the Marine Environment and Research Recommendations'. The IDOE Baseline Conference, New York, 1972.

Goodman, G. T. and Roberts, T. M. (1971). *Nature, Lond.* **231,** 287–292.

Green, R. S. and Love, S. K. (1967). *Pestic. Monit. J.* **1,** 13–15.

Hartley, G. S. (1969). *Adv. Chem. Ser.* **86,** 115–134.

Harvey, G. R. and Teal, J. M. (1973). *Bull. environ. Contam. Toxicol.* **9,** 287–290.

Harvey, G. R., Bowen, V. T., Backus, R. H. and Grice, G. D. (1972). *In* Nobel Symposium 20: 'The Changing Chemistry of the Oceans' (D. Dyrrsen and D. Jagner, eds), p. 177. Almqvist and Wiksell, Stockholm.

Heath, R. G. (1969). *Pestic. Monit. J.* **3,** 115–123.

Henderson, C., Johnson, W. L. and Inglis, A. (1969). *Pestic. Monit. J.* **3,** 145–171.

Henderson, C., Inglis, A. and Johnson, W. L. (1971). *Pestic. Monit. J.* **5,** 1–11.

Holden, A. V. (1970). *Pestic. Monit. J.* **4,** 117–135.

Holden, A. V. (1972). *In* 'Marine Pollution and Sea Life', pp. 266–272. Fishing News (Books) Ltd., London.

Holden, A. V. (1973a). *Pestic. Monit. J.* **7,** 37–52.

Holden, A. V. (1973b). *Pestic. Sci.* **4,** 399–408.

Jefferies, D. J. and Walker, C. H. (1966). *Nature, Lond.* **212,** 533.

Jensen, S., Renberg, L. and Olsson, M. (1972). *Nature, Lond.* **240,** 358–360.

Johnels, A. G., Olsson, M. and Westermark, T. (1967). *Vår föda* **7,** 67.

Johnson, R. E., Carver, T. C. and Dustman, E. H. (1967). *Pestic. Monit. J.* **1,** 7–12.

Manigold, D. E. and Schulze, J. A. (1969). *Pestic. Monit. J.* **3,** 124–135.

Martin, W. E. (1969). *Pestic. Monit. J.* **3,** 102–114.

Martin, W. E. (1972). *Pestic. Monit. J.* **6**, 27–32.
Martin, W. E. and Nickerson, P. R. (1972). *Pestic. Monit. J.* **6**, 33–40.
Moore, N. W. (1966). *J. appl. Ecol.* **3**, 261–269.
Noren, K. and Westöö, G. (1967). *Vår föda* **2**, 13–17.
Parslow, J. L. F. (1973). *Rep. Lundy Fld Soc.* **23**, 31–37.
Preston, A., Jefferies, D. F., Dutton, J. W. R., Harvey, B. R. and Steele, A. K. (1972). *Environ. Pollut.* **3**, 69–82.
Ratcliffe, D. A. (1970). *J. appl. Ecol.* **7**, 67–115.
Robel, R. J., Stalling, C. D., Westfall, M. E. and Kadoum, A. M. (1972). *Pestic. Monit. J.* **6**, 115–121.
Sand, P. F., Gentry, J. W., Bongberg, J. and Schechter, M. S. (1967). *Pestic. Monit. J.* **1**, 16–19.
Schulze, J. A., Manigold, D. E. and Andrews, F. L. (1973). *Pestic. Monit. J.* **7**, 73–84.
SCOPE (1973). Global environmental monitoring system (GEMS) *SCOPE* **3**, Special Committee on Problems of the Environment (Royal Society, London) 130 pp.
Seba, D. B. and Corcoran, E. F. (1969). *Pestic. Monit. J.* **3**, 190–193.
Södergren, A. (1968). *Oikos* **19**, 126–138.
Södergren, A. (1972). *Nature, Lond.* **236**, 395–397.
Södergren, A. (1973). *Vatten* **2/73**, 90–107.
Södergren, A., Svensson, Bj., and Ulfstrand, S. (1972). *Environ. Pollut.* **3**, 25–36.
U.N. (1971). Report of the First Session of the Intergovernmental Working Group on Monitoring or Surveillance. A/CONF. 48/IWGM, 1/3, United Nations, Geneva. 31pp.
Ware, D. M. and Addison, R. F. (1973). *Nature, Lond.* **246**, p. 519.
Wiersma, G. B., Sand, P. F. and Cox, E. L. (1971). *Pestic. Monit. J.* **5**, 63–66.
Wiersma, G. B., Tai, H. and Sand, P. F. (1972). *Pestic. Monit. J.* **6**, 194–228.
Williams, R. and Holden, A. V. (1973). *Mar. Pollut. Bull.* **4**, 109–111.
Wood, J. M., Penley, M. W. and De Simone, R. E. (1972). *In* 'Mercury Contamination in Man and his Environment', pp. 49–65. Report No. 137, IAEA Vienna.
Youngs, W. D., Gutenman, W. H. and Lisk, D. J. (1972). *Environ. Sci. Technol.* **6**, 451–452.

2. Exposure and Residues

F. MORIARTY

Institute of Terrestrial Ecology,
Monks Wood Experimental Station,
Abbots Ripton, Huntingdon, England

I. INTRODUCTION

Living organisms sometimes contain high concentrations of organochlorine insecticides and of other pollutants too. Barker (1958) established this point very clearly when he investigated how large numbers of robins (*Turdus migratorius*) had died of DDT poisoning on the university campus in Urbana, Illinois. Elm trees (*Ulmus americana*) had been sprayed with DDT twice in 1949 in an attempt to control insect vectors of two elm diseases. Soil samples were taken from beneath these trees in 1950, after the trees had been sprayed for a third time. Most of the DDT was found within the top two inches of the soil, and the highest concentration, of 17·8 ppm (parts per million), occurred in the top quarter-inch. Earthworms sampled at the same time contained 33–164 ppm of DDT. They presumably ingested much of their dose from fallen leaves, and leaf samples taken in the autumn of 1950 had 20–30 ppm DDT. Dead robins, with a modal concentration of 60–70 ppm DDT in the brain, presumably obtained their lethal dose by eating earthworms.

There have been many other instances where animals have acquired unexpectedly large, and sometimes toxic, residues of pollutants, e.g. Minamata disease caused by mercury (Löfroth, 1969), PCBs in guillemots (*Uria aalge*) (Holdgate, 1971), organochlorine insecticides and their metabolites in the peregrine falcon (*Falco peregrinus*) (Ratcliffe 1970, 1972), an organophosphorus insecticide and a mercurial fungicide in grey-lag geese (*Anser anser*) (Bailey *et al.*, 1972). The size of these residues must depend in part on the degree of the organisms' exposure and we need to understand the relationships between exposure and residues before we can interpret fully the significance of the residues measured in monitoring schemes.

The dominant theory has been that persistent pollutants accumulate in food webs and increase in concentration as they pass from prey to predator. This theory was stimulated chiefly by an incident at Clear Lake, California, where western grebes (*Aechmophorus occidentalis*) died from DDD poisoning. The grebes contained up to 1,600 ppm DDD in their fatty tissue whereas the water contained, at least in theory, 0·02 ppm (Hunt and Bischoff, 1960). There have been many subsequent field and laboratory data for organochlorine insecticides which have been quoted as evidence for this theory, but the argument involves some faulty logic and a confusion between causes and correlations (Moriarty, 1972). One has first to distinguish between aquatic and terrestrial species. The evidence suggests that, with organochlorine insecticides, what matters for aquatic species is direct intake from the physical environment, and that any pollutant ingested with the food is of minor significance. Food could be a significant source if the prey species has had a greater exposure in its physical environment than the predator, but we do not know whether this is an important factor for wildlife. For terrestrial animals, except perhaps for soil inhabitants, food is presumably the important source. Here too it is conceivable, although not yet certain, that position in a food web is of minor importance and that the important determinants are the rates at which a species takes in and eliminates pollutants. The important factor here appears to be the ratio of rate of intake with food, to rate of turnover of the pollutant (Moriarty, in press). Although small active predators may well have higher residues than their prey, this does not depend simply on position in the food chain but basically on rates of intake and loss.

Residues of organochlorine insecticides within animals can therefore be more usefully described by a compartmental model than by position in the food web. This model should also be applicable to other pollutants. Atkins (1969) gives a beautifully clear exposition of the model, which has been developed extensively in physiology and for pharmacology. It has recently been applied to some work with insecticides, particularly by Robinson and his co-workers (Robinson and Roberts, 1968). I shall discuss the theory, assumptions and defects of this model. I shall also use the model to analyse experimental data: there is a great deal of published data that has never been analysed satisfactorily, because suitable methods have not been available. Finally, I shall consider how we can use this model to help predict the residues that exposure to new pollutants could produce.

II. THE COMPARTMENTAL MODEL

Unlike the food chain model, compartmental analysis emphasizes an animal's own physiological processes, and the pollutant present within the body is assumed to occur in one or more compartments. In this context, a compartment can be defined as a quantity of pollutant that has uniform kinetics of transformation and/or transport, and whose kinetics are different from those of all other compartments.

A. Theory

1. Loss From One-Compartment System

To take the simplest situation, imagine a unicellular organism that contains a certain amount of DDE (Q), which we will consider as one compartment (compartment 1). We will suppose that if the cell is suspended in unpolluted water, then DDE will be lost from the cell by excretion, but that no metabolism occurs. We will also assume that the rate at which DDE leaves the cell is directly proportional to the amount present. Then the rate constant k_{01} is the amount of DDE excreted per unit amount of DDE present per unit time and is therefore expressed in units of time. The subscripts indicate that this rate constant refers to the passage of DDE from compartment 1 (the cell) to compartment 0 (the organism's surroundings). The total amount of DDE excreted in unit time, the turnover rate, is of course $Q.k_{01}$ units of mass/unit time.

One detail should be mentioned at this point: there is not a universally accepted convention for the order of the subscripts. I shall use the first subscript to indicate the compartment into which the pollutant is passing, whilst the second subscript indicates the compartment that the pollutant is leaving. Some authors use the reverse order.

If our model be correct, then the cell will lose DDE at an exponential rate. The manner in which the amount of DDE lost from the organism changes with time can be described by the differential equation

$$\frac{dQ}{dt} = -k_{01} \cdot Q. \tag{1}$$

When integrated, this becomes

$$Q = Q_0 \cdot e^{-k_{01}t} \tag{2}$$

where Q_0 is the amount of DDE in the cell when first placed in unpolluted water and t is the time that has elapsed since then.

Half-life $(t_{\frac{1}{2}})$ is a useful statistic that can easily be derived from this relationship:

$$t_{\frac{1}{2}} = \frac{\log_e 2}{k_{01}} = \frac{0.693}{k_{01}}.$$

By taking common logarithms on both sides of equation (2) we obtain

$$\log Q = \log Q_0 - 0.4343 k_{01}\, t\,.$$

The graph of log Q against t is a straight line, more generally stated as $y = a + bx$, where x is the independent variable (time), y is the dependent variable (amount of DDE) and b is the slope. The rate constant, k_{01}, is then easy to calculate:

$$k_{01} = \frac{b}{-0.4343}.$$

This transformation has at least one practical advantage: it is relatively easy to test experimental data for departures from linear relationships.

2. Intake into One-Compartment System

Let us now suppose that our unicellular organism is suspended in water that contains a constant concentration of DDE. Initially the cell contains no DDE, and DDE enters at a steady rate of R units of mass/unit of time (e.g. μg/hr). As before, DDE is excreted, but there is no metabolism. This simple one-compartment system can be depicted graphically (Fig. 1).

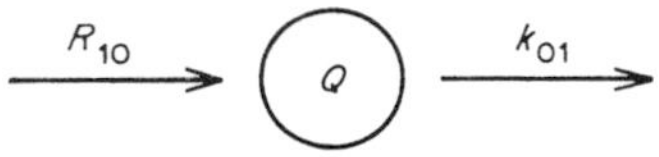

Fig. 1

The rate at which DDE is excreted will increase as the amount within the cell increases until eventually a steady state is attained, when the rate of intake equals the rate of loss. We have already assumed that DDE is excreted at a rate directly proportional to the amount present. It follows that in the steady state the turnover rate is $Q \cdot k_{01}$, and

$$Q \cdot k_{01} = R_{10}.$$

We can now develop a mathematical model. The rate at which the amount of DDE in the organism changes can be described by the differential equation:

$$\frac{dQ}{dt} = R_{10} - k_{01} \cdot Q.$$

When integrated, this becomes:

$$Q = \frac{R_{10}}{k_{01}} (1 - e^{-k_{01}t}) + Q_0 \cdot e^{-k_{01}t}$$

where t is the interval of time since exposure began, and Q_0 is the amount of DDE present when exposure began. In this instance we stated that

$Q_0 = 0$, so the equation can be simplified to

$$Q = \frac{R_{10}}{k_{01}} (1 - e^{-k_{01}t}).$$

As exposure continues, the value of $e^{-k_{01}t}$ must decrease. As $t \to \infty$, then $e^{-k_{01}t} \to 0$. In other words, when the value of $e^{-k_{01}t}$ becomes sufficiently small to be ignored, then

$$Q = \frac{R_{10}}{k_{01}} = Q_\infty$$

the steady state.

This can be illustrated graphically (Fig. 2).

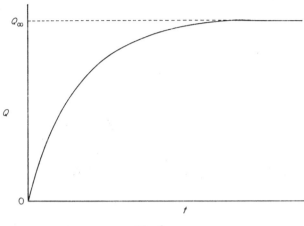

Fig. 2.

It is worth considering the effect of changes in the values of the parameters in this equation. The shape of the curve is determined solely by the value k_{01}, and the larger the rate constant, the sooner any percentage of the asymptotic value is reached (exemplified by Fig. 9). The value of Q_∞ only affects the absolute values. The rate of intake (R_{10}) equals the product of the rate constant (k_{01}) and the asymptotic value (Q_∞). When $t = 0$, then $dQ/dt = R_{10}$. Graphically this means that the rate of intake (R_{10}) forms the tangent to the curve at its origin.

If the organism already contains some DDE when exposure begins, then

$$Q = Q_\infty - Be^{-k_{01}t}$$

where $B = Q_\infty - Q_0$, which can be illustrated graphically (Fig. 3).

The latter parts of the two curves are of course identical.

Data of this type are frequently published with a logarithmic vertical scale for concentration instead of an arithmetic scale. This can give a misleading impression that the concentrations have almost reached the asymptotic value, which is often reinforced by the subjectively chosen line of 'best fit'.

In practice, nearly all pollutants can be metabolized as well as excreted. This does not necessarily affect our example very much. The rate at which DDE is removed from the organism will still be proportional to the amount of DDE present, if both the rate of metabolism and the rate of excretion are proportional to the amount of DDE. Of course, if enzyme induction occurs, the model will have to be more complicated.

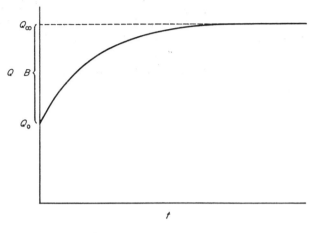

Fig. 3.

3. Systems with Two or More Compartments

Usually we are concerned with multicellular animals, often with vertebrates. Pollutants in such animals are often considered to be divided between several compartments. In practice, compartments are usually synonymous with specific tissues or organs, such as blood, liver, muscle and depot fat. However it should be remembered that the prime criterion of a compartment is not histological, but of a mass of pollutant with distinctive kinetics.

One practical advantage of compartments being synonymous with tissues is that instead of working in units of mass, one can, for some purposes, work in units of concentration, commonly in parts per million. This does assume of course that the volume of distribution is constant. If it were varying, the concentration of pollutant could alter even though there were no net gain or loss of pollutant in that tissue. The assumption of constant volume would probably still be important if one used units of mass. If the volume altered, then the rate constant could alter. Strictly, this is a false way of considering the matter. By definition the rate constant cannot alter. Rather, a fresh set of differential equations would be needed, which would produce different rate constants. There has been at least one experimental study (Davison, 1973) designed specifically to show that compartmental volumes are in fact of constant size.

Even with only two compartments, there are several possible ways of connecting the compartments to each other and to the environment. In practice the mammillary system is commonly used, in which one central compartment (compartment 1) can exchange material with all of the other, peripheral, compartments and with the environment, but there is no direct exchange between any of the peripheral compartments, which exchange material only with the central compartment (Fig. 4).

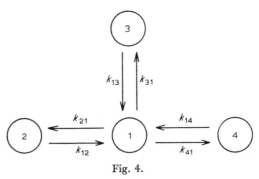

Fig. 4.

This scheme makes good physiological sense. Compartment 1 is the blood, one of whose functions is the transport of material within the body. The model also assumes that pollutants are transferred to and from the environment via the blood. Transport will be discussed in greater detail in the next chapter.

When the system contains more than one compartment then the changes in residues with time become more complicated. Consider a system with one central and one peripheral compartment, after exposure has ended (Fig. 5).

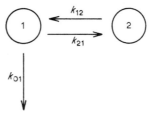

Fig. 5.

The rate of change for the amount of a pollutant in the blood (Q_1) is:

$$\frac{dQ_1}{dt} = k_{12}Q_2 - (k_{21} + k_{01})Q_1$$

and the rate of change for the amount of pollutant in the other compartment (Q_2) is:

$$\frac{dQ_2}{dt} = k_{21}Q_1 - k_{12}Q_2.$$

These can be integrated to

$$Q_1 = X_1 e^{-\lambda_1 t} + X_2 e^{-\lambda_2 t}$$

and

$$Q_2 = X_3 e^{-\lambda_1 t} + X_4 e^{-\lambda_2 t}.$$

These equations are of the same general form as for a one-compartment system, but there are two exponential terms instead of one. Therefore, even if the logarithm of quantity is plotted against time, the relationship will not be linear.

The constants are all derived from the rate constants and the initial amounts in compartments 1 and 2 $(Q_{1,0}$ and $Q_{2,0})$:

$$\lambda_1 = \frac{(k_{21} + k_{12} + k_{01}) + \sqrt{(k_{21} + k_{12} + k_{01})^2 - 4k_{12}k_{01}}}{2}$$

$$\lambda_2 = \frac{(k_{21} + k_{12} + k_{01}) - \sqrt{(k_{21} + k_{12} + k_{01})^2 - 4k_{12}k_{01}}}{2}$$

$$X_1 = \frac{Q_{1,0}(\lambda_1 - k_{12}) - k_{12} \cdot Q_{2,0}}{\lambda_1 - \lambda_2}$$

$$X_2 = \frac{Q_{1,0}(k_{12} - \lambda_2) + k_{12} \cdot Q_{2,0}}{\lambda_1 - \lambda_2}$$

$$X_3 = \frac{Q_{2,0}(k_{12} - \lambda_2) - k_{21} \cdot Q_{1,0}}{\lambda_1 - \lambda_2}$$

$$X_4 = \frac{Q_{2,0}(\lambda_1 - k_{12}) + k_{21} \cdot Q_{1,0}}{\lambda_1 - \lambda_2}.$$

In physiological terms, the interesting values are the rate constants, which give some insight into the dispersal of pollutants within the body.

$$\lambda_1 + \lambda_2 = k_{21} + k_{12} + k_{01}$$

and

$$\lambda_1 \lambda_2 = k_{12} \cdot k_{01}$$

so, provided there are adequate data, the rate constants can be estimated. In practice however, with pollutant studies, the data are usually inadequate for the calculation of rate constants.

So far we have been working with units of quantity (mass) within compartments. Invariably pollution studies have measured concentrations of pollutants within compartments. When a pollutant enters one compartment from another, the rate at which the concentration of pollutant rises in that compartment depends not only on the rate constant for intake, but also on the relative volumes of the two compartments. So:

$$\frac{dC_1}{dt} \neq k_{12}C_2 - (k_{21} + k_{01})C_1$$

but

$$\frac{dC_1}{dt} = k_{12}C_2 \cdot \frac{V_2}{V_1} - (k_{21} + k_{01})C_1$$

where C_1, C_2 and V_1, V_2 are the concentrations and volumes for compartments 1 and 2. The net result is that the equations for X_1, X_2, X_3 and X_4 acquire an extra constant. For example:

$$X_1 \text{ becomes } \frac{C_{1,0}(\lambda_1 - k_{12}) - k_{12}C_{2,0} \cdot \dfrac{V_2}{V_1}}{\lambda_1 - \lambda_2}.$$

This distinction between concentration and quantity has not always been appreciated (e.g. Robinson et al., 1969).

For many practical purposes however, we are more interested to know the overall rate at which pollutant disappears from a compartment. The exponential constants are far more useful for this purpose. There is of course no such distinction between rate constant (k) and exponential constant (λ) for a one-compartment system with a single exponential term—the two are then synonymous.

This use of exponential constants can be illustrated by some data from a study on rats (Robinson et al., 1969). The rats were fed 10 ppm dieldrin in the diet for 8 weeks. Blood samples were then analysed at intervals from 0–71 days after exposure. The data were fitted to an equation with two exponential terms of the type just described (Fig. 6):

$$C_1 \times 10^4 = 542e^{-0 \cdot 535t} + 298e^{-0 \cdot 0529t}$$

The blood's dieldrin can now be considered in two parts. That part which is lost more rapidly has a half-life of 1·3 days ($0 \cdot 693/\lambda_1$), whilst the slower part has a half-life of 13·1 days. One is also interested in the relative magnitudes of the exponential coefficients (X). In this example the rapid component is almost twice as large when exposure stops as the slow component (542:298, or about 9:5). The higher this ratio, the more rapidly most of the HEOD disappears.

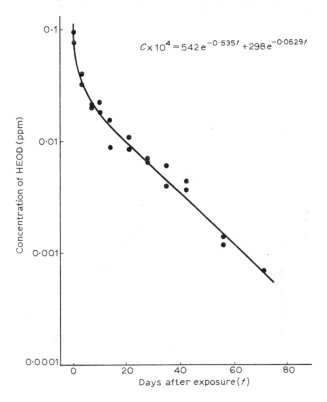

$$Cx10^4 = 542e^{-0·535t} + 298e^{-0·0529t}$$

Fig. 6. Decrease in the concentration (C) of dieldrin in rats' blood during the first 71 days after exposure. Data fitted to an equation with two exponential terms (data and equation from Robinson *et al.*, 1969).

It is important however to realize that the exponential constants do not indicate discrete physiological processes—they are mathematical consequences of the original model. Robinson *et al.* (1969) deduced that, because their data gave an adequate fit to an equation with two exponential terms, after an initial period of rapid loss from the central compartment (blood), it is the transfer of dieldrin from the peripheral compartment to the blood that controls the loss of dieldrin from the body. This is a slightly distorted way of considering the matter. We have seen that two compartments entail two exponential terms for loss after exposure. In other words, if one supposes that there are two compartments, there is bound to be a 'fast' and a 'slow' phase of elimination. It would be more accurate to say that the rate of loss depends on the values of all three rate constants, and their interactions are far from simple, as the equations for the coefficients and exponential constants show.

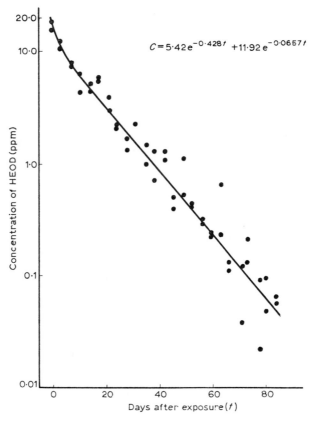

Fig. 7. Decrease in the concentration (C) of dieldrin in rats' adipose tissue during the first 84 days after exposure. Data fitted to an equation with two exponential terms (data from Robinson *et al.*, 1969).

Robinson *et al.* (1969) also measured the concentrations of HEOD in adipose tissue from 0–84 days after exposure (Fig. 7) and fitted the data to a single exponential term ($13 \cdot 5 e^{-0 \cdot 067 t}$). This gave a very adequate fit to the data but, if the two-compartment model be applicable, there should be two exponential terms and the exponential constants should be the same as for the blood. This single term is obviously comparable to that for the 'slow' component of the blood, which suggests that there should be a more rapid loss of HEOD during the first few days after exposure. The data for days 0 and 3 do support this suggestion, and an additional term can be introduced. Computation by the least squares method, with data weighted in inverse proportion to their magnitude, gives the following result:

$$C_2 = 5 \cdot 42 e^{-0 \cdot 428t} + 11 \cdot 92 e^{-0 \cdot 0657t}.$$

In contrast to blood, the larger exponential constant has the smaller coefficient, so that its effect is barely noticeable. However, the estimates of the two exponential constants agree reasonably well with the estimates obtained from the blood samples.

These equations for C_1 and C_2 after chronic exposure are of similar pattern to those for concentrations during exposure, when

$$C_1 = X_5 - X_6 e^{-\lambda_1 t} - X_7 e^{-\lambda_2 t}$$

and

$$C_2 = X_8 - X_9 e^{-\lambda_1 t} - X_{10} e^{-\lambda_2 t}.$$

More complicated models, with three or more compartments, will produce similar equations but with more exponential terms.

4. Fitting Data to Compartmental Models

Because of the amount of work involved, a computer is needed to fit data accurately to equations that have more than one exponential term. In practice it may be difficult to fit data. In contrast to many physiological and pharmacological studies, the rate constants in compartmental models for persistent pollutants have a time scale measured in days or weeks instead of minutes or hours. Perhaps because of this extended time scale, with the consequent increased risk of environmental changes, the data often have a considerable residual variation about any line, which makes it difficult to estimate more than one, or perhaps two, exponential terms. Important factors include the ratio of the exponential constants, the residual variation of the data, and the quantity of data (Atkins, 1969). Even in drug studies it is rarely possible to fit data to equations with more than three exponential terms (Brown, 1970).

This difficulty is particularly marked for intake during chronic exposure. Most of the available data can only be fitted to an equation with a single exponential. An exception was the experiment by Davison (1970), who fed sheep with dieldrin at the rate of 2 mg/kg body weight/day. Blood samples were analysed at intervals. A single exponential is clearly inappropriate, whereas a double exponential gives a remarkably good fit (Fig. 8). It would not need very much scatter of points about this line however, for it to be difficult to use more than a single exponential term, or to decide whether more than one term

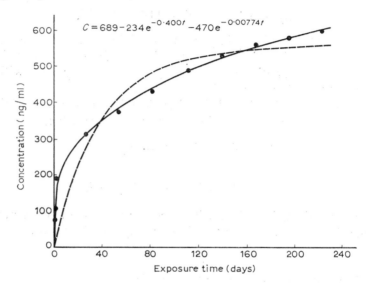

Fig. 8. Increase in the concentration (C) of dieldrin in sheeps' blood whilst ingesting 2 mg dieldrin/kg body weight/day. ———, line derived from equation with two exponential terms; – – –, line derived from equation with one exponential term (data from Davison, 1970).

was appropriate. There are very few sets of data as good as this and I do not know of any insecticide data that have been fitted to an equation with more than two exponential terms.

In theory one might expect to need a model with several compartments for adequate fitting of accurate data. In practice it has been found with drug studies that a two-compartment model often gives an adequate representation of absorption, metabolism and excretion (Riegelman *et al.*, 1968). We do not yet have sufficient data with which to test this possibility for persistent pollutants.

We have already seen that it is impossible to estimate the rate constants unless we know the volumes of the compartments as well as the concentrations of pollutant. However, it is still possible to estimate the ratios of the rate constants to and from the central compartment and any one of the peripheral compartments. When a steady state is established during chronic exposure the rate of intake into each compartment equals the rate of loss. Therefore, if compartment 1 be the central compartment, its relationship to any peripheral compartment (x), whilst a steady state is maintained, is:

$$C_1 k_{x1} = C_x k_{1x}$$

or

$$\frac{C_x}{C_1} = \frac{k_{x1}}{k_{1x}}.$$

Fatty tissues invariably have the highest concentrations of organochlorine insecticides in steady-state conditions, and therefore must have the highest ratio of rate constants for intake and loss.

Apart from this comparative measure, we have to accept that at present we have almost no information about rate constants, but do have some measures of exponential constants. These have some predictive value, but often the theoretical basis is rather uncertain. For example, residues in whole fish can be fitted to equations with single exponential terms. This is mathematically convenient but it is unrealistic, in physiological terms, to suppose that a whole fish can be considered as a single compartment and so it is uncertain how widely we can apply any conclusions.

Little heed has been paid to metabolism. This is not too serious with a one-compartment model—effectively it will be included with the rate constant k_{01}. Most metabolism of pollutants in vertebrates occurs in the liver (see Chapter 3). Robinson $et\ al.$ (1969) concluded that the liver could be considered as part of the central compartment and if this be generally true the effects of metabolism, until they are clearly distinguished, will again be attributed to the rate constant k_{01} and estimates of the other parameters will not be seriously affected.

B. Assumptions of the Mammillary Model

So far we have discussed the theoretical model without too much consideration of the assumptions. I shall now discuss some of these assumptions and, where appropriate and possible, test them against published experimental data.

Some of these published data are presented numerically but much is given in graphs. The original data have then, in most instances, been estimated from these graphs.

When equations include exponential terms, parameters and their standard errors were estimated by a least squares iterative calculation. One detail should be noted: since the estimates of the parameters are not normally distributed, the standard confidence tests cannot usefully be used. Furthermore, some of the earlier data need to be treated with caution because analytical methods were sometimes not very reliable.

1. The Central Compartment

It is generally assumed for vertebrates that blood acts as the central compartment via which organochlorine insecticides enter and leave the body from and to the physical environment. The same assumptions had been made for insects too, but recently Gerolt (1969) and Quraishi and Poonawalla (1969) suggested that lateral movement within the cuticle is of great importance and that transport by the blood is unimportant. It now seems reasonably well established that organochlorine insecticides are transported round the insect body by the blood (Moriarty and French, 1971). Benezet and Forgash (1972) have shown that the organophosphorus insecticide malathion is also probably distributed by the blood to other tissues in insects.

2. Relationships Between Compartments

We have already seen (Section A.2.) that, for a system with only one compartment, the concentration during exposure can be expressed as $C = C_\infty(1 - e^{-k_{01}t})$. The Mrak report (1969) concluded, from the data available for mammals, that this relationship fitted the results for changes in different tissues during exposure. They deduced from this premise, quite logically, that the concentrations in different tissues are correlated and Robinson (1970) extended this conclusion to include birds too.

Two comments are relevant. It is unlikely that the one-compartment model is appropriate to many situations. This is often not a practical objection because the residual variation in experimental data often precludes the use of more complicated models. It does seem physiologically absurd though to use, say, three one-compartment models to predict the concentrations in three different tissues within one organism. It is mathematically convenient but the values of k will have little biological meaning. However, even with this simple model, the relative concentrations in different tissues change with length of exposure. Thus, as a rule of thumb, it may be reasonable to say that when steady-state concentrations for organochlorine insecticides have been reached, the ratio of concentrations in blood, liver and fat will be of the order of 1:10:100. But the same ratio will not apply before the steady state is established.

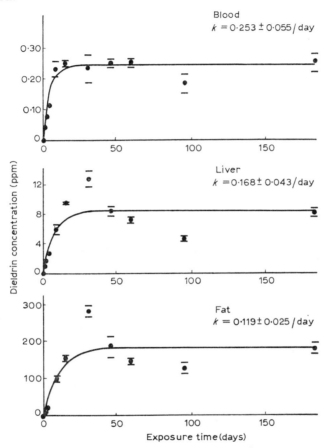

Fig. 9. Changes in the concentration of dieldrin in the blood, liver and fat of rats whilst fed on a diet containing 50 ppm dieldrin. Data fitted to equations with one exponential term. The horizontal bars indicate the standard errors of the means (data from Deichmann *et al.*, 1968).

These ideas were illustrated quite clearly when week-old rats were fed on a diet containing 50 ppm dieldrin (Deichmann *et al.*, 1968). Groups of 4–6 rats were killed at intervals and the blood, liver and fat were analysed for dieldrin. The results for blood (Fig. 9) conform quite well to the predicted pattern, although there is a more pronounced deviation on day 95. The values for fat and liver deviate from the predicted pattern more markedly, on days 31 and 95. These could be explained as experimental variation. One alternative possibility is that these deviations are oscillations about the final steady-state concentration. If the diet induces production of an enzyme that metabolizes dieldrin, the high value on day 31 indicates build-up towards the steady-state concentration that would occur without enzyme induction. The induced enzyme then increases the rate of loss, and so finally a different, lower, steady-state concentration is achieved. Other explanations too are possible of course. However, whatever their cause, the deviations from the predicted concentrations do not appear to unduly disturb the estimates of C_∞. If this simple one-compartment system be appropriate, the data suggest that the value of k is larger for blood than for liver or fat. Consequently, there is a more rapid rise towards the final steady-state concentration. This implies that the ratio between the concentrations in the different tissues changes with time. When conditions are near the steady state, the ratio changes very little, but tissues with different values for k approach the steady state at different rates and during this phase the ratios of concentrations between tissues change rapidly (Table I). Deichmann *et al.* (1968) tabulated these ratios for the measured concentrations and obtained a

Table I

Predicted concentrations of dieldrin in tissues of rats fed on a diet with 50 ppm dieldrin

Days fed	Blood ppm	ratio	Liver ppm	ratio	Fat ppm	ratio
1	0·047	1	0·91	19·3	1·8	38·7
2	0·093	1	2·10	22·6	22·3	239·8
4	0·156	1	3·95	25·3	56·5	362·1
9	0·225	1	6·59	29·3	113·7	505·2
16	0·248	1	7·97	32·2	153·5	619·8
31	0·252	1	8·54	33·9	178·9	709·7
45	0·252	1	8·58	34·0	183·1	725·9
60	0·252	1	8·59	34·0	183·9	729·1
95	0·252	1	8·59	34·0	184·1	729·7
183	0·252	1	8·59	34·0	814·1	729·7

Concentrations expressed in absolute units (ppm) and as ratios of the concentration in blood. Calculated from data of Deichmann *et al.* (1968).

similar pattern. The more dissimilar the values for k, the greater the change in the ratios until the steady state is reached.

There is one important practical implication. Wildlife specimens often have only one or a few tissues analysed. The important concentrations are those at the sites of action (see Chapter 4) and predictions of these concentrations from known concentrations in other parts of the body cannot be made safely unless one also knows how near or far the animal was from a steady-state concentration.

3. Homogeneity Within Compartments

The model assumes that as additional molecules enter a compartment they mix instantaneously and homogeneously with those already present. In practice it is important that the mixing time be short compared to the speed with which they leave the compartment again.

Kinetic studies with drugs often assume that the drug is uniformly distributed throughout the body water. Such an assumption is clearly impossible for the lipophilic organochlorine insecticides, but as a first approximation one has to assume that they are uniformly dispersed throughout the compartments. This has been demonstrated to be untrue for blood.

The organochlorine insecticides are characterized by very low water solubility: pp'-DDT is estimated to form a saturated solution at 25°C in water at 3.4×10^{-10} molar (Bowman et al., 1960). It is difficult to distinguish between true solution and colloidal suspension (Biggar et al., 1967) but Moss and Hathway (1964) found that dieldrin and telodrin are several thousand times more soluble in rabbit serum than they are in water. The major part of these compounds in blood is associated with haemoglobin in the erythrocytes and with soluble proteins in the serum. DDT and DDE present a similar picture (Morgan et al., 1972; Schoor, 1973).

A similar situation occurs with many drugs, which rely on protein-binding for transport in the blood (Brown, 1970) (see Chapter 3). This can affect excretion. The concentration of drug in the blood might be expected to decrease exponentially after exposure but often the rate of loss decreases with time and this can sometimes be explained by relatively slow transfer from plasma protein to plasma water (Krüger-Thiemer et al., 1966). This is an instance where one tissue, the blood, should properly be considered as two distinct compartments, of which one, the plasma protein, is dispersed throughout the other continuous compartment, the plasma water. There is little experimental evidence,

at least as yet, to suggest that this situation exists with the organochlorine insecticides. Despite their uneven distribution in blood, the
kinetics appear to be adequately represented by the assumption of even
distribution.

4. Random Activity

The model assumes that the molecules of pollutant within each compartment act in a random manner: there is no distinction between
molecules based on time since their arrival in the compartment.

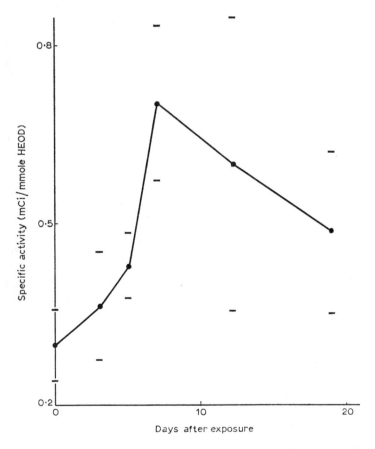

Fig. 10. Changes in the specific activity of dieldrin in rats' adipose tissue during the
first 19 days after exposure. The horizontal bars indicate the standard errors of the means
(data from Baron and Walton, 1971).

Baron and Walton (1971) have recently found an apparent exception. Rats were fed on a diet that contained 25 ppm HEOD until the concentration of HEOD in their retroperitoneal adipose tissue became steady at about 50 ppm. HEOD was then removed from the diet but on each of the first four subsequent days the rats were dosed orally with a similar amount of HEOD to that previously ingested with their food. Some of this 'new' HEOD was labelled with C^{14}. Half of the rats were then fed on uncontaminated food, whilst the other half continued on a diet with 25 ppm of C^{12}-HEOD. As might be expected, the latter group maintained a fairly steady concentration of HEOD in their fat, whilst rats on a normal diet free of HEOD lost insecticide exponentially from their fat.

The unexpected result was that the specific activity of the HEOD in rats fed on a normal diet continued to rise for a week after dosing had stopped (Fig. 10). The specific activity then decreased, but had not dropped to the initial level by the time of the last measurement, 19 days after the end of exposure. Baron and Walton concluded that 'old' dieldrin is probably lost more rapidly than 'new' dieldrin. In other words, the loss of dieldrin molecules is not a random process, which indicates, presumably, that the dieldrin molecules only dispersed slowly within the adipose tissue cells.

This experiment also produced another interesting result which is more appropriately discussed in the next section.

5. Rate Constants During and After Exposure

The second unexpected result from Baron and Walton's work concerned the loss of C^{14}-dieldrin. Even though the rate at which dieldrin molecules are lost from the fat tissue depends on how long they have been there, one might expect the rate of loss to be unaffected by continued exposure to dieldrin. The evidence (Fig. 11) suggests that dieldrin of a specific 'age' is lost more rapidly when the diet still contains dieldrin than when exposure ceases: the regression coefficients are significantly different $(t_{10} = 3 \cdot 91; \ P < 0 \cdot 01)$. The authors were inclined to dismiss the difference as a statistical artefact (personal communication), but a similar result was obtained in a rather different situation.

Goldfish (*Carassius auratus*) were fed C^{14}-dieldrin in their diet for 32 days (Grzenda *et al.*, 1972). In one group the C^{14}-dieldrin was then replaced by C^{12}-dieldrin while the other group had a residue-free diet. The latter group had half-lives for C^{14}-dieldrin (plus any C^{14}-metabolites) in various tissues of about 3–4 weeks, whereas goldfish still on a contaminated diet lost 62–100 per cent of their C^{14}-dieldrin (plus C^{14}-metabolites) after 2 weeks.

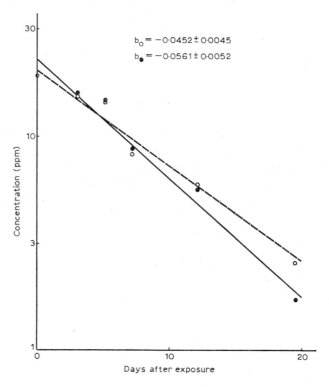

Fig. 11. Linear regressions for the loss of C^{14}-dieldrin during the first 19 days after exposure. ●————●, rats fed on a diet with C^{12}-dieldrin; ○– – –○, rats fed on a diet with no dieldrin (data from Baron and Walton, 1971).

These results suggest several possibilities: enzyme induction during continued exposure to dieldrin could play a part; molecules of dieldrin might exchange between tissues more rapidly during than after exposure; the rate of turnover depends on the combined concentration of 'old' and 'new' molecules, but the 'old' molecules may be lost preferentially. Alternatively, results during and after exposure may require different models. If this be true, estimates of k derived from rate of loss after exposure should be smaller than those derived from measurements of initial rate of intake and steady-state concentration.

6. The Steady State

It is an essential part of the compartmental model that a steady state will develop if exposure continues for long enough. Whilst a steady state persists, the removal rate of a pollutant equals its replacement rate in all compartments, so that concentrations are constant. There are plenty of data to support this idea, at least to a first approximation, but some qualifications are needed.

Man appears to be a special case. DDT did not reach a steady state during 21·5 months exposure (Hayes *et al.*, 1971), nor did dieldrin during two years (Hunter *et al.*, 1969). In both instances the authors concluded that a steady state was attained, but their data do not support their conclusions: in fact concentrations rose steadily all the time (Moriarty, 1974).

Quaife *et al.* (1967) were critical of the then available experimental evidence to support the idea that aldrin and dieldrin reach and maintain a steady-state concentration during chronic exposure, and their scepticism was well founded. Later work on beagle hounds (Walker *et al.*, 1969) showed that, despite the authors' original interpretation, a steady state is not maintained during two years' chronic exposure to dieldrin (Moriarty, 1974). A steady state was clearly established within six months, but a second rise in concentration occurred after 18 months exposure. Davison (1970) obtained a similar result in a much shorter time. Sheep fed 0·5 mg dieldrin/kg body weight/day attained a stable concentration in their blood within four weeks. The concentration then started to rise again within the next twelve weeks (Fig. 12). This increase was not so abrupt as in the beagles, and it did not occur with higher dose rates, of 2·0 mg dieldrin (Fig. 8) and 1·0 mg dieldrin. This increase, after a steady state has existed for some time, may not be a universal phenomenon. Rhesus monkeys were fed DDT for 7·5 years, when the abdominal fat reached and maintained a steady-state concentration within six months (Durham *et al.*, 1963). There was some decrease during the last few years but this could have been an artefact from the death of some animals. Brown *et al.* (1965) fed two hens for two years on a diet containing one ppm of dieldrin or aldrin. The amount of dieldrin in the eggs rose steadily for about nine months and then dropped again later on.

Organisms age all the time and this process may sometimes affect the steady state. Hayes (1965) suggested that one relevant factor with rats could be that mature animals eat less and so ingest less pollutant.

Experimental results are usually obtained in rather stable environmental conditions. Exposure to a second insecticide can be sufficient to upset a steady state (Deichmann *et al.*, 1971). Conditions fluctuate much more in the field and some of these fluctuations will affect residues. Dale *et al.* (1962) first showed that starvation releases DDT residues from fat reserves, which then increase the concentrations in

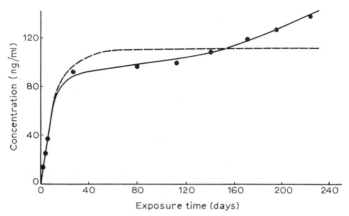

Fig. 12. Changes in the concentration of dieldrin in sheeps' blood whilst ingesting 0·5 mg dieldrin/kg body weight/day. ———, line derived from equation with two exponential terms; – – –, line derived from equation with one exponential term (data from Davison, 1970).

various tissues, including the body fat, of DDT or related metabolites. This has been amply confirmed (Findlay and de Freitas, 1971). Normal physiological events such as breeding activity (Anderson, 1970; Deichmann *et al.*, 1972) and hibernation (Jefferies, 1972) can also reduce the fat reserves, with repercussions on residue levels. The effects of other factors have scarcely been studied yet in any species but may be important. For example, salinity affects the amount of DDT residues in *Gambusia affinis* (Murphy, 1970).

7. Exclusion of Other Models

The mammillary model has been developed partly because the derived equations accord reasonably well with the experimental data and also because it does not contradict physiological principles too grossly. It should be remembered though that these two criteria are not sufficient to exclude other models. It is not inconceivable that other theories could be developed, also making good physiological sense, whose different derived equations would also accord with the experimental data.

Certainly it is possible to fit residue data to other equations. McCully
et al. (1966) fed DDT to steers and analysed omental fat for residues at
various times after the end of exposure. They found a linear relationship between the logarithm of the concentration and the logarithm of

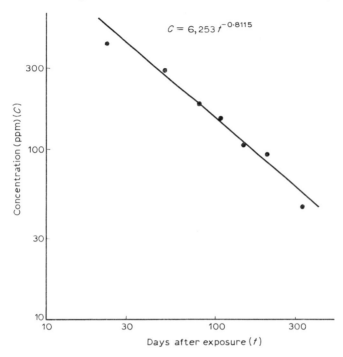

Fig. 13. Linear regression for the loss of DDT from steers' omental fat after exposure.
Both scales are logarithmic (data from McCully *et al.*, 1966).

the time after exposure (Fig. 13). I have reanalysed these data graphically (Atkins, 1969) and fitted the data to an equation with two exponential terms (Fig. 14). The same data fit both equations quite
well, and preference for the compartmental model rests solely on its
theoretical basis. Abundant accurate data are needed before one can
distinguish between mathematical models.

III. EXPERIMENTAL DATA

We have already discussed why the available data are of limited value
for fitting to compartmental models (Section II.A.4.). However, a
selection from them can give us some idea of the properties of persistent

pollutants. Some data have been ignored because the chemical analyses do not distinguish the original pollutant from its metabolites. I will consider results for different species in three separate categories: aquatic species, terrestrial species and birds.

A. Aquatic Species

Many of the published papers refer to fish. For all species, data obtained from static tests are of little use for at least two important reasons. First, the actual concentration in the water is usually decreasing, and much less than the nominal concentration, during exposure: much of the pollutant, at the low concentrations used, may be adsorbed onto surfaces. Second, individuals can acquire pollutant from other individuals within the same container (Gakstatter and Weiss, 1967). This implies that an isolated individual will lose pollutant more rapidly, if the surrounding water is replaced continuously, than in static water and results will therefore be less consistent in static tests. Both of these difficulties are best overcome by a continuous-flow system.

Table

Loss of residues from aquatic species after expos

Species	Pollutant	Tissue analysed	Initial concentration (ppm)	Period covered analyse (days)
Cottus perplexus (reticulate sculpin)	Dieldrin	whole fish	2·3	89
Lebistes reticulatus (guppy)	Dieldrin	whole fish	11	30
Leiostomus xanthurus (spot)	Aroclor 1254 (PCB)	whole fish	28	84
Tubifex sp. (tubificid worm)	Dieldrin	whole worm	149	16
Amblema plicata (bivalve mollusc)	Dieldrin	gills	0·056 16·8	84 84
Esox lucius (pike)	Hg^{203} as methyl mercury:			130
Anguilla vulgaris (eel)	i) nitrate	whole fish	Single dose, by injection either into the stomach or into the dorsal muscle	130
Pleuronectes flesus (flounder)	ii) protein-bound			100
Lampsilis siliquoidea (bivalve mollusc)	Dieldrin	whole body except shell	1·4	14
Anodonta grandis (bivalve mollusc)	DDT	whole body except shell	1·5	28

Few data are available for rates of loss after exposure (Table II). I have included, for comparison, some data for methyl mercury, which is notable for its great persistence after the first phase of loss. Confirmatory results in more natural conditions have been obtained for *Esox lucius* (Lockhart *et al.*, 1972).

There are rather more results for rates of intake during exposure. One of the most interesting sets of data was obtained for the intake of dieldrin by *Cottus perplexus* (reticulate sculpin) (Chadwick and Brocksen, 1969). Fish were exposed for up to 32 days, in a continuous-flow system, to one of six concentrations of dieldrin, and the concentration of HEOD in whole bodies increased at a virtually steady rate for the entire experimental period. I therefore estimated the rates of intake by linear regression (Table III). The rates of intake do not increase in proportion to the external concentration but the two can be related by a power function (Fig. 15) which indicates that a tenfold increase in the concentration of dieldrin in the water increases the rate of intake 6·4-fold.

It is of interest to compare these values with those for other species and pollutants (Table IV). Relevant data are scanty but do support the idea that the ratio of rate of intake to external concentration

...en kept in continuous flow systems

Number of exponential terms	λ (per day)	$t_{\frac{1}{2}}$ (days)	Comments	Reference
1	0·020	34·7		Chadwick and Brocksen (1969)
1	0·0047	148		Reinert (1967)
1	0·017	40·8	Half-lives for various tissues fall within the range 39·7–51·6 days	Hansen *et al.* (1971)
1	0·057	12·2		Chadwick and Brocksen (1969)
1	0·022	31·6		Fikes and Tubb (1972)
1	0·039	17·6		
2	half-life of slow phase 640–1,200 days		Analysis with a whole-body counter	Järvenpää *et al.* (1970)
2	half-life of fast phase about 2–4 days			
2				
1	0·20	3·5	Rate of loss much slower in third week after exposure	Bedford and Zabik (1973)
1	0·053	13·1	Similar results for muscle and viscera analysed separately	Bedford and Zabik (1973)

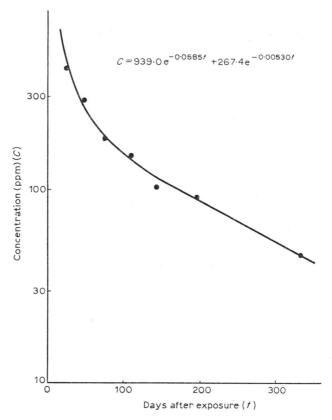

$$C = 939 \cdot 0\, e^{-0 \cdot 0585 t} + 267 \cdot 4\, e^{-0 \cdot 00530 t}$$

Fig. 14. Decrease in the concentration of DDT in steers' omental fat after exposure. Data fitted to an equation with two exponential terms (data from McCully et al., 1966).

Table III

The rates of intake of dieldrin by reticulate sculpins (*Cottus perplexus*)

Concentration of dieldrin in water (pp 10^9)	Period of exposure (days)	Rate of intake by fish (pp 10^9 per day)	Rate of intake ÷ concentration in water (per day)
0·017	32	8·4	494
0·086	24	24·3	283
0·17	32	41·2	242
0·86	32	220	256
1·7	24	324	191
8·6	10	1,049	122

Calculated from data of Chadwick and Brocksen (1969).

decreases as the concentration increases. This ratio is remarkably constant for several fish species exposed to several organochlorine compounds. The invertebrates had a far wider range of ratios, and to a large extent the more active organisms had the higher intake rates.

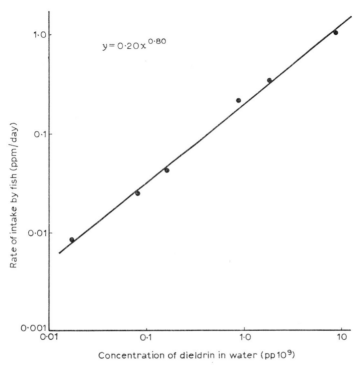

Fig. 15. Linear regression for the rate of intake (y) of dieldrin by reticulate sculpins (*Cottus perplexus*) in different ambient concentrations (x). Both scales are logarithmic (data from Chadwick and Brocksen, 1969).

Even if the one-compartment model be appropriate, it is not possible in many instances to estimate the value of k_{01} for the data in Table IV, because exposure was too short for a steady state to be attained. However, if the value of $\lambda(k_{01})$ be the same during and after exposure, then the values of λ in Table II can be used to calculate some of the expected steady-state concentrations in Table IV.

It can also be difficult to extrapolate the results of such experiments to field conditions, where the effective exposure may be difficult to determine. For example, much of a pollutant may be associated with particles, when turbulence may increase the effective exposure (Raymont, 1972). Moreover, the rate of intake by animals will depend greatly on the pollutant's physical state.

Table IV

Intake by aquatic species

Species	Pollutant	Concentration in water (pp 10⁹)	Rate of intake ÷ concentration in water (per day)	Estimated steady-state concentration (ppm)	Comments	Reference
			A. INTAKE FROM CONTINUOUS-FLOW SYSTEMS			
Lepomis macrochirus (bluegill sunfish)	Endrin	0·2 2·0	756 385			Bennett and Day (1970)
Cottus perplexus (reticulate sculpin)	Dieldrin	0·5	1,121	28	A different experiment from that of Table II	Chadwick and Brocksen (1969)
Lebistes reticulatus (guppy)	Dieldrin	0·8–1·1	1,064	230	Mean concentration in water assumed to be 1·0 pp 10⁹	Reinert (1967)
Salmo gairdneri (rainbow trout)	Toxaphene	0·84	1,123		Test in lake	Terriere et al. (1966)
Leiostomus xanthurus (spot)	Aroclor 1254 (PCB)	1·0	1,100	65	Also data for separate tissues	Hansen et al. (1971)
Tubifex sp. (tubificid worm)	Dieldrin	80	250	352	Rate of intake against time is a sigmoid curve—this estimate is a maximum	Chadwick and Brocksen (1969)
Daphnia magna	Dieldrin	2·1 4·5 12·8	8,790 13,200 10,350		Concentration in water fluctuated	Reinert (1967)
Amblema plicata (bivalve mollusc)	Dieldrin	0·02 20	165 75	0·055 16·9	Gills only were analysed	Fikes and Tubb (1972)
Crustacea ⎰ *Orconectes nais* (crayfish)	Aroclor 1254 (PCB)	1·1–2·8	480		Estimates for the rate of intake may be too low: they are based on the residues found after one day's exposure	Sanders and Chandler (1972)
Palaemonetes kodiakensis (shrimp)			7,900			
Gammarus pseudolimnaeus			10,600			
Daphnia magna			22,500			
Insect larvae ⎰ *Pteronarcys dorsata* (stonefly)			750			
Corydalus cornutus			1,270			
Culex tarsalis (mosquito)			12,600			
Chaoborus punctipennis			16,900			

Species	Pollutant			Comments		Reference
Ephemera danica (nymphs)	Clophen A 50 (PCB)	0·5	692		1·3	Södergren and Svensson (1973)
Tetragoneuria spp. (dragonfly nymph)	C^{14}-DDT	3·6 4·0 6·1 10·8 13·3 20·0	888 850 688 611 616 790	Static tests, but calculations alleged to compensate for loss of DDT from water Measures C^{14} i.e. DDT plus metabolites		Wilkes and Weiss (1971)
Salmo gairdnerii (rainbow trout)	Hg as phenyl mercuric acetate	0·005 0·010 0·020	25·0 22·5 20·0	Head, fins and internal organs removed before analysis		MacLeod and Pessah (1973)

B. INTAKE FROM FOOD

Species	Pollutant	Concentration in food (mg/kg body weight per week)	Rate of intake per day (pp 10^9)	Comments	Reference
Salmo clarki lewisi (cut throat trout)	DDT	1 3	34 193		Allison *et al.* (1964)
Leptodius floridanus (crab larvae)	Dieldrin	0·213 (ppm)	10 (dry weight)	Static test with nominal concentration of 0·5 pp 10^9 dieldrin in water gave intake rate of 191 pp 10^9/day	Epifanio (1973)

Residues usually refer to whole organisms and rates of intake were therefore estimated by linear regressions or by one-compartment models.

Table V

Loss of residues from

Species	Pollutant	Tissue analysed		Initial concentration (ppm)	Period covered by analyses (days)
Laboratory rat (♂)	Dieldrin	Adipose tissue		47·55	19
Laboratory rat	Dieldrin	♂ { Depot fat		22·6	
		Liver		3·5	
		Brain		0·95	
		Muscle		0·93	
					52
		♀ { Depot fat		121	
		Liver		5·0	
		Brain		2·5	
		Muscle		2·4	
Laboratory rat (♂)	Dieldrin	Adipose tissue		15·9	84
		Blood		0·076	71
		Liver		0·85	59
Laboratory rat	DDT	Adipose tissue			(months)
			♂ {	896	14
				540	14
				234	8
				115	14
			♀ {	3,028	8
				4,190	14
				459	14
				337	14
Laboratory rat	Heptachlor epoxide	Adipose tissue	♂	48·4	(days) 28
			♀	189·5	42
Beagle dogs	Dieldrin	Adipose tissue	{	56·1	(months) 12
				80·0	10
	DDT	Adipose tissue	{	1,295	8
				539	4
Steers and heifers	Dieldrin	Adipose tissue		78	(days) 224
Ewes	Dieldrin	Adipose tissue		79	252
Steers	pp′-DDT	Omental fat		419	308
Pipistrellus pipistrellus (pipistrelle bat)	pp′-DDT	Whole body		184·9 μg/bat	12·5
Rhesus monkey	pp′-DDT	Adipose tissue		2,650	(months) 35
Man	pp′-DDT (recrystallized)	Adipose tissue		325 ± 62	37·8
	pp′-DDT (technical grade)	Adipose tissue		281 ± 80	37·8
Man	{ Dieldrin	} Blood	{	0·11	2·5 years
	Endrin			c.0·1	a few days
	Telodrin			0·022	4 years
Man	pp′-DDT	Serum	{	0·383	(days) 320
		Serum		0·201	320
		Adipose tissue		118	320
		Adipose tissue		40	320
	pp′-DDE	Serum	{	0·15	245
		Adipose tissue		46	245
	pp′-DDD	Serum	{	0·01	120
		Adipose tissue		6	120

Number of exponential terms	λ (per day)				$t_{\frac{1}{2}}$ (days)		Comments	Reference
1	0·13				5·2		see Section II. B.4–5	Baron and Walton (1971)
1	0·069 0·091 0·073 0·069 0·055 0·052 0·046 0·067				10·1 7·6 9·5 10·1 12·7 13·4 15·1 10·3			Brown *et al.* (1967)

	X_1	X_2	λ_1	λ_2	half-lives (days)			
2	5·4	11·9	0·43	0·066	1·6	10·5	see Section II. A.3.	Robinson *et al.* (1969)
2	0·054	0·030	0·54	0·053	1·3	13·1		
2	0·71	0·23	0·54	0·068	1·3	10·2		

	λ(per day)	$t_{\frac{1}{2}}$ (days)		
1	0·012	57·4		Ortega *et al.* (1956)
1	0·012	58·5		
1	0·0097	71·9		
1	0·0066	104·9		
1	0·011	60·8		
1	0·0085	81·5		
1	0·0065	107·1		
1	0·0093	74·5		
1	0·094	7·3	Concentrations in fat are based on weight of extracted fat	Radomski and Davidow (1953)
1	0·070	9·9		
1	0·0055	126·6	Fed aldrin + DDT.	Deichmann *et al.* (1969)
1	0·0042	164·7	Fed aldrin. First analysis 2 months after the end of exposure	
1	0·017	42·0	Fed DDT + aldrin.	
1	0·040	17·4	Fed DDT	
1	0·0097	74·2	Analysis for organically bound chlorine	Claborn *et al.* (1953)
1	0·0073	97·3	Analysis for organically bound chlorine	Claborn *et al.* (1953)

	X_1	X_2	λ_1	λ_2	half-lives (days)			
2	939	267	0·058	0·0053	11·9	130·8	First analysis 23 days after the end of exposure	McCully *et al.* (1966)

	λ(per day)	$t_{\frac{1}{2}}$ days		
1	0·046	15·2	First analysis 2·5 days after a single oral dose	Jefferies (1972)

	X_1	X_2	λ_1	λ_2	half-lives (days)			
2	2,640	11·2	0·022	0·00046	32·1	1,520	Serial biopsies from 1 monkey. Data analysed graphically	Durham *et al.* (1963)

	λ/(per day)	$t_{\frac{1}{2}}$ (days)		
1	0·0015	461		Hayes *et al.* (1971)
1	0·0011	617		
1	0·0026	266	Data from factory workers after transfer to other activities	Jager (1970)
1	c.0·7	c.1·0		
1	0·00069	1,011		
1	0·0024	292		
1	0·0012	568		
1	0·0023	301		
1	0·00058	1,204		
1	no significant loss		Data from single human volunteers	Morgan and Roan (1971)
1	no significant loss			
1	0·014	49·5		
1	0·015	46·2		

The low rate of intake for phenyl mercuric acetate appears consistent with data from outdoor ponds and tanks (Hannerz, 1968), although muscle, which was the main tissue analysed, may be slower than many other tissues to acquire these residues (Giblin and Massaro, 1973).

B. Terrestrial Species

There are relatively few data for the effect of exposure on residue levels in invertebrates (Edwards and Thompson, 1973). Several studies have been made with earthworms but they nearly all refer to residues found at one specific time, with no information on changes with time. The cockroach (*Periplaneta americana*) has a 'half-life' for dieldrin of 29·4 days during the first eight weeks after exposure (Moriarty, 1972).

Most experimental results for mammals apply to specific tissues, not to whole organisms, so that the data are much easier to relate to compartments. However, most of these data can still only be interpreted in terms of a model with one compartment.

It is reassuring to find that different workers can obtain comparable results. Three estimates for the half-life of dieldrin in adipose tissue of male laboratory rats ranged from 5·2–10·5 days (Table V).

Table

Intake

Species	Pollutant	Tissue analysed	Exposure	Period cover by analyse (days)
Laboratory rat (♀)	Dieldrin	Blood ⎫ Liver ⎬ Fat ⎭	50 ppm in diet	183
Laboratory rat ♂ { 3 weeks old 15 weeks old	*op′* + *pp′*-DDT	Fat	5 ppm in diet	189 105
♀ { 3 weeks old 15 weeks old				189 105
Sheep	Dieldrin	Blood	0·5 mg/kg body weight/day	112
			1·0 mg/kg body weight/day	224
			2·0 mg/kg body weight/day	224
Beagle hound	Dieldrin	♂ Blood	{ 0·005 mg/kg body weight/day { 0·05 mg/kg body weight/day	548 548
	Dieldrin	♀ Blood	{ 0·005 mg/kg body weight/day { 0·05 mg/kg body weight/day	548 548
Beagle hound ♂	Dieldrin	Fat	0·3 mg/kg body weight/5 days per week	300

Morgan and Roan (1971) illustrated quite clearly that man appears to retain DDT far longer than do other mammals and the data in Table V suggest that man retains several organochlorine insecticides for longer than do other species. This implies that it should take a long time to establish steady states during chronic exposure. Results support this deduction. We know that man takes more than two years to reach a steady-state concentration for DDT and dieldrin (Section II.B.6.). This appears to be very slow—few of the studies summarized in Table VI continued for as long as one year and in all instances an approximation to a steady state was attained within a few months.

It is true that the rhesus monkey loses some of its DDT very slowly (Durham *et al.*, 1963) despite attaining a steady state within six months of exposure, but the slow component is a minute part of the total and could perhaps indicate continued low-level contamination of the food.

Exposure (Table VI) is measured either as the concentration of pollutant in the food, or as a weight of pollutant/unit of body weight/day. It is not possible, with either measure, to derive the rate of intake (R_{10}) into the body. Two major reasons are that an unknown percentage of ingested pollutant passes, unabsorbed, right through the gut whilst some of the absorbed pollutant may get no further than the enterohepatic circulation (see Chapter 3). I have therefore only included

mmals

Number of exponential terms	λ (per day)		Asymptotic concentration (C_∞) (ppm)	Comments	Reference
1	0·25 0·17 0·12		0·25 8·6 184	Data illustrated in Fig. 9	Deichmann *et al.* (1968)
1 1	0·025 0·026		58 —	Analysis by Schechter–Haller method	Laug *et al.* (1950)
1 1	0·013 0·0066		117 —		
1	0·12			Concentration tends to rise again after 112 days (Fig. 12)	Davison (1970)
	λ_1	λ_2			
2 2	0·42 0·40	0·029 0·0077	0·21 0·69		
1 1	0·0088 0·017		0·011 0·047	Asymptotic concentration estimated by extrapolation (Fig. 8)	
1 1	0·031 0·013		0·0083 0·048	Concentrations in blood tend to rise again after 548 days (Section II.B.6.)	Walker *et al.* (1969)
1	0·014		56	Also fed 12 mg DDT/kg body weight/day	Deichmann *et al.* (1969) (repeated in Deichmann and MacDonald, 1971)

results where a reasonable estimate can be obtained for the steady-state concentration. The values of λ are then of mathematical use but their physiological meaning is uncertain (see Section II.A.3.).

C. Birds

Cummings *et al.* (1966, 1967) described one of the most comprehensive experiments, in which four groups of 15 white leghorn hens were maintained on a basal diet for two weeks. The control group was kept on this diet for a further 18 weeks. The other three groups were fed for 14 weeks on a diet with either 0·05, 0·15 or 0·45 ppm each of lindane, heptachlor epoxide, dieldrin, endrin and DDT in combination. They were then fed the basal diet again for a further four weeks. There was less than 0·01 ppm of each insecticide in the basal diet. The insecticides were all of greater than 99 per cent purity and the DDT was a 70/30 mixture of *pp'*-DDT and *op'*-DDT.

Eggs were analysed at intervals. Single birds from each treatment were killed at about fortnightly intervals and the abdominal fat and heart muscle analysed for insecticides. Some treatment results are not included because either the final concentrations were not significantly greater than those in the control birds, or because the estimates had large standard errors. These large variations between individual results tend to occur mostly with the lower exposures.

Rates of loss after exposure are summarized in Table VII. It is a nice question whether eggs can be compared, as a compartment, with

Table VII

Range of 'half-lives' in days for the loss of residues of six organochlorine insecticides from hens after exposure to a mixture of all six compounds

Insecticide	Fat	Breast muscle	Eggs
Heptachlor epoxide	26–38	131–215	34–160
Dieldrin	25–61	100–139	50–57
Endrin	23–30	59–104	32–45
pp'-DDT	36–56	49–143	39–50
op'-DDT	11–19		
Lindane	7–13		12–31

Calculated from data of Cummings *et al.*, 1966 and 1967.

Table VIII

Intake of residues by hens during exposure to a mixture of six organochlorine insecticides at three different concentrations

Insecticide	Conc. in diet (ppm)	Fat		Breast muscle		Eggs	
		λ (per day)	C_∞ (ppm)	λ (per day)	C_∞ (ppm)	λ (per day)	C_∞ (ppm)
Heptachlor epoxide	0·05						
	0·15						
	0·45			0·022	0·043		
Dieldrin	0·05	0·053	0·56				
	0·15	0·049	1·65	0·035	0·021		
	0·45	0·030	5·28	0·035	0·052		
Endrin	0·05	0·029	0·4	0·097	0·0035	0·012	0·037
	0·15	0·055	1·1	0·047	0·029	0·017	0·120
	0·45	0·038	3·5			0·020	0·423
pp'-DDT	0·05	0·020	0·56			0·038	0·066
	0·15	0·074	0·80			0·049	0·101
	0·45	0·023	3·22			0·041	0·276
op'-DDT	0·05						
	0·15	0·030	0·04				
	0·45	0·012	0·18				
Lindane	0·05	0·08	0·08			0·049	0·013
	0·15	0·12	0·22			0·060	0·031
	0·45	0·15	0·77	0·21	0·010	0·062	0·091

Calculated from data of Cummings et al., 1966 and 1967.

body tissues but the results for eggs are intermediate between those for fat and for breast muscle. Results for intake during exposure are summarized in Table VIII.

Cecil *et al.* (1972) fed white leghorn hens *pp'*-DDT, *op'*-DDT or *pp'*-DDE in their diet for 28 weeks. Table IX summarizes the egg residue data. The

Table IX

Residues in eggs during exposure of hens to *pp'*-DDT, *op'*-DDT or *pp'*-DDE

Insecticide	Conc. in diet (ppm)	Eggs λ (per day)	C_∞ (ppm)
pp'-DDT	6	0·029	3·4
	25	0·026	18·5
	50	0·031	35·8
op'-DDT	5	0·040	0·6
	25	0·058	2·5
	50	0·044	5·7
pp'-DDE	5	0·012	11·3
	25	0·016	35·7
	50	0·022	70·1

Calculated from data of Cecil *et al.*, 1972.

dose rates are higher than those used by Cummings *et al.* (1966), and the steady-state concentrations for *pp'*-DDT can be combined (Fig. 16). The power function that relates the steady-state concentration in eggs to residues in the diet is of considerable interest because birds' eggs can be a very suitable material for monitoring (see Chapter 1), although it must be remembered that the chicken is an atypical species. In particular it lays eggs continually. It seems likely though that residues in the eggs of other species too will reach a steady state. Homing pigeons (*Columbia livia* var.) fed HEOD laid eggs with similar residue levels in two separate laying periods that were 38 weeks apart (Robinson and Crabtree, 1969). Residues in eggs laid after exposure during the second year decreased rather slowly, with a 'half-life' of 132 days.

There are few studies for loss of residues from birds after exposure (Table X). The most striking result is the great persistence of DDE in feral pigeons. This tallies with its great persistence in man (Table V) and may well explain the almost universal occurrence of DDE residues

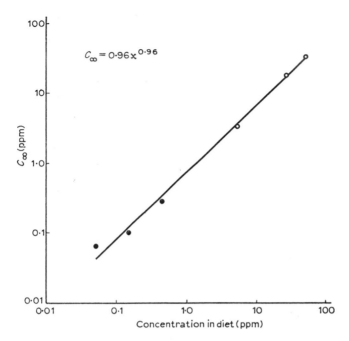

Fig. 16. Linear regression for the steady-state concentration (C_∞) of pp'-DDT in eggs of white leghorn hens on the concentration of pp'-DDT in the diet (x). Both scales are logarithmic. ●, values calculated from data of Cummings et al. (1966); ○, values calculated from data of Cecil et al. (1972).

in wildlife specimens. There have been other studies of the loss of DDE residues after exposure, but mathematical analysis is usually complicated because the precursor, DDT, is also present and the rate of conversion to DDE is unknown.

IV. CONCLUSIONS

We have seen that the mammillary model can provide a useful framework of ideas with which to analyse the results of studies on the intake and loss of organochlorine insecticides. It is true that some important assumptions deserve further study—the maintenance of a steady state, the constancy of the rate constants for loss during and after exposure, the random distribution of pollutant molecules within compartments. However, even if these assumptions are false, it should be possible to modify the model to take account of these factors.

Table X

Loss of residues from birds after exposures

Species	Pollutant	Tissue analysed	Initial concentration (ppm)	Period covered by analyses (days)	Number of exponential terms	λ (per day)	$t_{\frac{1}{2}}$ (days)	Comments	Reference
Columba livia (Feral pigeon)	DDT	7—all gave similar results	0·5–37·9	274	1	0·025	28		Bailey *et al.* (1969a)
	DDD	7—all gave similar results	3·8–770	92	1	0·029	23·8		
Columba livia (Feral pigeon)	DDE	7—all gave similar results	13–4,500	288	1	0·0028	250		Bailey *et al.* (1969b)
Columba livia (Feral pigeon)	Aroclor 1242 (PCB)	Muscle / Fat	c. 10 / c. 100	168 / 168	1 / 1	0·014 / 0·0055	50 / 125	Measurement of 'total PCB' is inevitably arbitrary	Bailey and Bunyan (1972)
Pigeon	Dieldrin	4—all gave similar results	8–450	250	1	0·015[a]	47·0		Robinson *et al.* (1967a)
Lonchura striata (Bengalese finch)	*pp′*-DDT	Whole body	107 μg/bird	25	1	0·069	10·1	First analysis 5 days after end of exposure	Jefferies (1972) and personal communication

[a] The original paper confuses λ with b (the linear regression coefficient) and gives both constants the same value. In fact $b = \log_{10} e \cdot \lambda$.

There have been few attempts so far to explain field results for residues of organochlorine pollutants in food webs by this type of analysis. It is therefore of interest to note that specimens of the shag (*Phalacrocorax aristotelis*) from around the Farne Islands had 5–40 times more dieldrin in their livers than samples from seven other vertebrate species (Robinson *et al.*, 1967b). This result may be linked with a low rate of metabolism for dieldrin: the shag is known to hydroxylate dieldrin very slowly (see Chapter 3).

This model can also be applied to other persistent pollutants whose characteristics differ from those of the organochlorine insecticides. For example, at least some aquatic species obtain inorganic compounds of heavy metals principally from their food, not from the physical environment, when concentrations tend to decrease as one passes along the food web (Pentreath, 1973). But the same principles should still apply.

Two other approaches should be mentioned. Hamelink *et al.* (1971) proposed that the accumulation of organochlorines by aquatic animals depends on the partition coefficients of these compounds between the environment and the tissue components. This might be true if movement of molecules depended solely on passive diffusion, but many active processes of transport, metabolism and excretion, are involved (see Chapter 3). Rates of transfer between compartments are therefore more relevant than partition coefficients.

Metcalf *et al.* (1971) have developed a 'model ecosystem', in which seven different species of plants and animals are kept in a tank with sand and water. Organisms, sand and water are analysed for residues 33 days after a single application of pesticide to the plants. This is an ingenious approach but it is difficult to see what advantages it has over other techniques. It is not a steady-state system, and in particular, one cannot measure the animals' exposure to the pesticide and its metabolites. Nor can the results be applied directly to any 'natural' ecosystem. Södergren (1973) has overcome some of these difficulties with a continuous-flow culture, or chemostat.

Relatively little use has been made of the mammillary model so far in studies on pollution. It should enable us, by estimates of the rate constants, to compare the intake and loss of different pollutants by organisms and to study the differences between species in the way they take in, distribute and lose residues. It should also be a useful first stage in the study of the effects of other variables on the intake, distribution and loss of pollutants. These are all vital studies if we are ever to understand and predict the distribution of pollutants in the environment.

ACKNOWLEDGMENT

I would like to thank Mr D. E. Walters, of the Agricultural Research Council's Statistics Group, University of Cambridge, for the computations.

REFERENCES

Allison, D., Kallman, B. J., Cope, O. B. and van Valin, C. (1964). *Res. Rep. U.S. Fish. Wildl. Serv.* **64**.

Anderson, D. W. (1970). Ph.D. Thesis, University of Wisconsin, pp. 168.

Atkins, G. L. (1969). 'Multicompartment Models for Biological Systems.' Methuen, London.

Bailey, S. and Bunyan, P. J. (1972). *Nature, Lond.* **236**, 34–36.

Bailey, S., Bunyan, P. J., Rennison, B. D. and Taylor, A. (1969a). *Toxic. appl. Pharmac.* **14**, 13–22.

Bailey, S., Bunyan, P. J., Rennison, B. D. and Taylor, A. (1969b). *Toxic. appl. Pharmac.* **14**, 23–32.

Bailey, S., Bunyan, P. J., Hamilton, G. A., Jennings, D. M. and Stanley, P. I. (1972). *Wildfowl* **23**, 88–91.

Barker, R. J. (1958). *J. Wildl. Mgmt* **22**, 269–274.

Baron, R. L. and Walton, M. S. (1971). *Toxic. appl. Pharmac.* **18**, 958–963.

Bedford, J. W. and Zabik, M. J. (1973). *Archs. environ. Contam. Toxicol.* **1**, 97–111.

Benezet, H. J. and Forgash, A. J. (1972). *J. econ. Ent.* **65**, 53–57.

Bennett, H. J. and Day, J. W. (1970). *Pestic. Monit. J.* **3**, 201–203.

Biggar, J. W., Dutt, G. R. and Riggs, R. L. (1967). *Bull. environ. Contam. Toxicol.* **2**, 90–100.

Bowman, M. C., Acree, F. and Corbett, M. K. (1960). *J. agric. Fd Chem.* **8**, 406–408.

Brown, S. S. (1970). *In* 'Foreign Compound Metabolism in Mammals' (D. E. Hathway, ed.), Vol. 1, pp. 98–129. The Chemical Society, London.

Brown, V. K., Richardson, A., Robinson, J. and Stevenson, D. E. (1965). *Fd Cosmet. Toxicol.* **3**, 675–679.

Brown, V. K. H., Robinson, J. and Richardson, A. (1967). *Fd Cosmet. Toxicol.* **5**, 771–779.

Cecil, H. C., Fries, G. F., Bitman, J., Harris, S. J., Lillie, R. J. and Denton, C. A. (1972). *Poult. Sci.* **51**, 130–138.

Chadwick, G. G. and Brocksen, R. W. (1969). *J. Wildl. Mgmt* **33**, 693–700.

Claborn, H. V., Bowers, J. W., Wells, R. W., Radeleff, R. D. and Nickerson, W. J. (1953). *Agr. Chem.* **8**, 37–39, 119, 121.

Cummings, J. G., Zee, K. T., Turner, V. and Quinn, F. (1966). *J. Ass. off. analyt. Chem.* **49**, 354–364.

Cummings, J. G., Eidelman, M., Turner, V., Reed, D. and Zee, K. T. (1967). *J. Ass. off. analyt. Chem.* **50**, 418–425.

Dale, W. E., Gaines, T. B. and Hayes, W. J. (1962). *Toxic. appl. Pharmac.* **4**, 89–106.

Davison, K. L. (1970). *J. agric. Fd Chem.* **18**, 1156–1160.

Davison, K. L. (1973). *Bull. environ. Contam. Toxicol.* **10**, 16–24.

Deichmann, W. B. and MacDonald, W. E. (1971). *Fd Cosmet. Toxicol.* **9**, 91–103.

Deichmann, W. B., Dressler, I., Keplinger, M. and MacDonald, W. E. (1968). *Ind. Med. Surg.* **37**, 837–839.

Deichmann, W. B., Keplinger, M., Dressler, I. and Sala, F. (1969). *Toxic. appl. Pharmac.* **14**, 205–213.

Deichmann, W. B., MacDonald, W. E. and Cubit, D. A. (1971). *Science, N.Y.* **172**, 275–276.

Deichmann, W. B., Cubit, D. A., MacDonald, W. E. and Beasley, A. G. (1972). *Arch. Tox.* **29**, 287–309.

Durham, W. F., Ortega, P. and Hayes, W. J. (1963). *Archs int. Pharmacodyn. Thér.* **141**, 111–129.

Edwards, C. A. and Thompson, A. R. (1973). *Residue Rev.* **45**, 1–79.

Epifanio, C. E. (1973). *Mar. Biol.* **19**, 320–322.

Fikes, M. H. and Tubb, R. A. (1972). *J. Wildl. Mgmt* **36**, 802–809.

Findlay, G. M. and de Freitas, A. S. W. (1971). *Nature, Lond.* **229**, 63–65.

Gakstatter, J. H. and Weiss, C. M. (1967). *Trans. Am. Fish. Soc.* **96**, 301–307.

Gerolt, P. (1969). *J. Insect Physiol.* **15**, 563–580.

Giblin, F. J. and Massaro, E. J. (1973). *Toxic. appl. Pharmac.* **24**, 81–91.

Grzenda, A. R., Taylor, W. J. and Paris, D. F. (1972). *Trans. Am. Fish. Soc.* **101**, 686–690.

Hamelink, J. L., Waybrant, R. C. and Ball, R. C. (1971). *Trans. Am. Fish. Soc.* **100**, 207–214.

Hannerz, L. (1968). *Rep. Inst. Freshwat. Res. Drottningholm* **48**, 120–176.

Hansen, D. J., Parrish, P. R., Lowe, J. I., Wilson, A. J. and Wilson, P. P. (1971). *Bull. environ. Contam. Toxicol.* **6**, 113–119.

Hayes, W. J. (1965). *A. Rev. Pharmac.* **5**, 27–52.

Hayes, W. J., Dale, W. E. and Pirkle, C. I. (1971). *Archs envir. Hlth* **22**, 119–135.

Holdgate, M. W. (ed.) (1971). 'The Sea Bird Wreck in the Irish Sea Autumn 1969'. Publ. Nat. Environ. Res. Counc. (GB) C. No. 4.

Hunt, E. G. and Bischoff, A. I. (1960). *Calif. Fish Game* **46**, 91–106.

Hunter, C. G., Robinson, J. and Roberts, M. (1969). *Archs envir. Hlth* **18**, 12–21.

Jager, K. W. (1970). 'Aldrin, Dieldrin, Endrin and Telodrin. An Epidemiological and Toxicological Study of Long-term Occupational Exposure'. Elsevier, Amsterdam.

Järvenpää, T., Tillander, M. and Miettinen, J. K. (1970). *Suom. Kemistilehti* **43**, 439–442.

Jefferies, D. J. (1972). *J. Zool.* **166**, 245–263.

Krüger-Thiemer, E., Diller, W. and Bünger, P. (1966). *In* 'Antimicrobial Agents and Chemotherapy—1965' (G. L. Hobby, ed.), pp. 183–191. American Society for Microbiology.

Laug, E. P., Nelson, A. A., Fitzhugh, O. G. and Kunze, F. M. (1950). *J. Pharmac. exp. Ther.* **98**, 268–273.

Lockhart, W. L., Uthe, J. F., Kenney, A. R. and Mehrle, P. M. (1972). *J. Fish. Res. Bd Can.* **29**, 1519–1523.

Löfroth, G. (1969). *Ecol. Res. Comm. Bull.* No. 4.

MacLeod, J. C. and Pessah, E. (1973). *J. Fish. Res. Bd Can.* **30**, 485–492.

McCully, K. A., Villeneuve, D. C., McKinley, W. P., Phillips, W. E. J. and Hidiroglou, M. (1966). *J. Ass. off. analyt. Chem.* **49**, 966–973.

Metcalf, R. L., Sangha, G. K. and Kapoor, I. P. (1971). *Environ. Sci. Technol.* **5**, 709–713.

Morgan, D. P. and Roan, C. C. (1971). *Archs envir. Hlth* **22**, 301–308.

72 F. MORIARTY

Morgan, D. P., Roan, C. C. and Paschal, E. H. (1972). *Bull. environ. Contam. Toxicol.* **8**, 321–326.
Moriarty, F. (1972). *Sci. total Environ.* **1**, 267–288.
Moriarty, F. (1974). *Environ. Qual. Saf.* **3**.
Moriarty, F. (In press). *In* 'The Ecology of Resource Degradation and Renewal' pp. 31–47. Blackwell, Oxford.
Moriarty, F. and French, M. C. (1971). *Pestic. Biochem. Physiol.* **1**, 286–292.
Moss, J. A. and Hathway, D. E. (1964). *Biochem. J.* **91**, 384–393.
Mrak, E. M. (1969). 'Report of the secretary's commission on pesticides and their relationship to environmental health'. U.S. Dept. of Health, Education, and Welfare.
Murphy, P. G. (1970). *Bull. environ. Contam. Toxicol.* **5**, 404–407.
Ortega, P., Hayes, W. J., Durham, W. F. and Mattson, A. (1956). *Publ. Hlth Monogr.* **43**.
Pentreath, R. J. (1973). *In* 'Radioactive Contamination of the Marine Environment'. pp. 421–436. IAEA, Vienna.
Quaife, M. L., Winbush, J. S. and Fitzhugh, O. G. (1967). *Fd Cosmet. Toxicol.* **5**, 39–50.
Quraishi, M. S. and Poonawalla, Z. T. (1969). *J. econ. Ent.* **62**, 988–994.
Radomski, J. L. and Davidow, B. (1953). *J. Pharmac. exp. Ther.* **107**, 266–272.
Ratcliffe, D. A. (1970). *J. appl. Ecol.* **7**, 67–115.
Ratcliffe, D. A. (1972). *Bird Study* **19**, 117–156.
Raymont, J. E. G. (1972). *Proc. R. Soc. B.* **180**, 451–468.
Reinert, R. E. (1967). Ph.D. Thesis, University of Michigan, Ann Arbor.
Riegelman, S., Loo, J. C. K. and Rowland, M. (1968). *J. pharm. Sci.* **57**, 117–123.
Robinson, J. (1970). *Bird Study* **17**, 195–228.
Robinson, J. and Crabtree, A. N. (1969). *Meded. Fakolt. Landbouwwetenschappen Gent.* **34**, 413–427.
Robinson, J. and Roberts, M. (1968). S.C.I. Monogr. No. 29, 106–119.
Robinson, J., Richardson, A. and Brown, V. K. H. (1967a). *Nature, Lond.* **213**, 734–736.
Robinson, J., Richardson, A., Crabtree, A. N., Coulson, J. C. and Potts, G. R. (1967b). *Nature, Lond.* **214**, 1307–1311.
Robinson, J., Roberts, M., Baldwin, M. and Walker, A. I. T. (1969). *Fd Cosmet. Toxicol.* **7**, 317–332.
Sanders, H. O. and Chandler, J. H. (1972). *Bull. environ. Contam. Toxicol.* **7**, 257–263.
Schoor, W. P. (1973). *Bull. environ. Contam. Toxicol.* **9**, 70–74.
Södergren, A. (1973). *Oikos*, **24**, 30–41.
Södergren, A. and Svensson, B. J. (1973). *Bull. environ. Contam. Toxicol.* **9**, 345–350.
Terriere, L. C., Kilgemagi, U., Gerlach, A. R. and Borovicka, R. L. (1966). *J. agric. Fd Chem.* **14**, 66–69.
Walker, A. I. T., Stevenson, D. E., Robinson, J., Thorpe, E. and Roberts, M. (1969). *Toxic. appl. Pharmac.* **15**, 345–373.
Wilkes, F. G. and Weiss, C. M. (1971). *Trans. Am. Fish. Soc.* **100**, 222–236.

3. Variations in the Intake and Elimination of Pollutants

C. H. WALKER

Department of Physiology and Biochemistry,
The University, Reading, Berkshire, England,

I. INTRODUCTION

The first two chapters of this book have dealt with two related issues—a. the residue concentrations of pollutants encountered in the field and b. the connection between the levels to which organisms are exposed and the residue concentrations in their tissues. In the present chapter we shall try to explain why different animals given similar exposures may build up different concentrations of residues. This means that we shall be concerned with the processes involved in the intake and elimination[1] of pollutants and the variation of these processes between species, strains, sexes and age groups.

---

[1] Elimination is taken to mean the removal of a compound by metabolism and/or excretion. The elimination of a pollutant does not necessarily involve the elimination of its metabolite(s).

Many persistent pollutants are very fat-soluble. Whereas compounds which are appreciably soluble in water are usually rapidly excreted, often without metabolic change, liposoluble compounds tend to be stored in fatty tissues (fat depots, hydrophobic areas of membranes) and are not readily excreted unchanged. The fate of liposoluble compounds in vertebrates will now be described in outline to put in perspective the later, more detailed, discussion of the processes involved.

To enter the body and to move between organs, tissues and cellular compartments within the body, liposoluble compounds must traverse membranous barriers. In most cases no specialized transport system is involved, and movement is due to passive diffusion (Parke, 1968). Small water-soluble molecules such as methanol and ethanol can move freely through hydrophilic pores of small diameter [0·35–0·45 mμ (3·5–4·5 Å)] which exist in some membranes, whereas molecules of larger size and very low water solubility are not able to do so but appear to move by partitioning into the membrane. Membranes are lipoprotein structures and the most generally accepted model for cellular membranes suggests a sandwich structure, with a layer of protein on either side of a bi-molecular layer of bimodal lipid (Stein, 1968). To cross such a barrier, diffusing substances would have to partition from a polar (hydrophilic) phase into a non-polar (hydrophobic) phase and back into a second polar phase.

In theory (Os *et al.*, 1964) the ability of liposoluble molecules to get across membranes should be related to their partition coefficients (C) between water and strongly non-polar liquids such as hydrocarbon solvents and oils:

$$C = \frac{\text{concentration in water}}{\text{concentration in non-polar liquid}} \simeq \frac{\text{solubility in water}}{\text{solubility in non-polar liquid}}$$

In general, this theory is borne out in practice. Molecules having a reasonable balance between solubility in water and solubility in non-polar liquids tend to move relatively easily across membranes. There is, however, considerable variation in composition from one biological membrane to another, and there are additional factors besides solubility that also affect the rate of movement across membranes (e.g. molecular weight and reactive groups). It should not be assumed that there is some optimal partition coefficient which indicates a maximal rate of penetration for liposoluble compounds through all biological membranes.

The removal of liposoluble compounds from the body usually depends upon conversion to water-soluble metabolites which can be readily excreted. The endoplasmic reticulum of the liver is a site of particular importance for the degradation of foreign compounds. Here a wide range of both foreign and endogenous liposoluble compounds partition into a hydrophobic environment in which various 'processing' (drug metabolizing) enzymes exist. Enzymic transformation produces water-soluble metabolites and conjugates, which then leave the endoplasmic reticulum and the liver cells, and which are eventually excreted in the bile and/or urine. Clearly species differences in metabolism may cause differences in both the persistence of liposoluble compounds and the rate of excretion of their water-soluble metabolites.

The metabolism of liposoluble foreign compounds does not necessarily proceed at a constant rate in a living animal. Many such compounds induce the liver enzymes which metabolize them, thereby increasing the rate at which they are degraded. This may be regarded as a natural defence mechanism which protects the animal against potentially harmful compounds. Studies with rats show that induction of liver enzymes is accompanied by an increased rate of biliary excretion of water-soluble metabolites and conjugates (Fig. 1).

Several aspects of the elimination of pollutants should be emphasized. Firstly, pollutants are not a unique class of compounds in any chemical or biochemical sense. The great majority of them are foreign compounds and are subject to the same processes as are other foreign compounds.

Secondly, there is good evidence that detoxication mechanisms have evolved in response to the selective pressure of foreign compounds. Since species differ from one another in their biochemistry, a normal metabolite to one species can be a foreign compound to another. Where such naturally occurring foreign compounds are appreciably toxic (as in the case of the plant metabolites atropine and muscarine for mammals), there is pressure for their elimination by the development of detoxication mechanisms. Such selective pressures must have existed since the early days of life on earth, and the ease with which vertebrates eliminate many foreign compounds of diverse structures points to the evolution of effective detoxication mechanisms. In the shorter term 'pre-adaptive' evolution of resistant strains of insects has occurred following exposure to insecticides. This occurs by selection of genes for resistance already present and not by the production of mutations (see Chapter 5).

Thirdly, interspecific differences in detoxication may reflect differences in dict or habitat. The absorption of foreign compounds may be either from the diet or directly from the physical environment (e.g. via gills, skin or lungs). These, therefore, may control the nature and quantity of the foreign compounds that exert selective pressures upon living organisms (Wit and Snel, 1968).

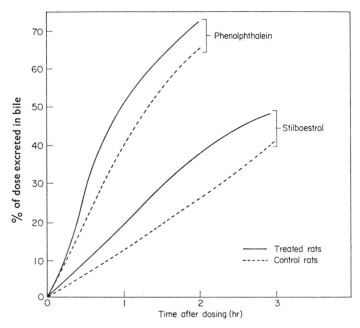

Fig. 1. The relationship between induction of liver enzymes and rate of biliary excretion in the female rat. Liver enzymes were induced in female rats by dosing with phenobarbitone. Liver weight relative to body weight was 0.030 ± 0.004 for control rats and 0.038 ± 0.005 for treated rats. Stilboestrol and phenolphthalein are excreted as glucuronides. A similar result was shown for biphenyl, which is metabolized by mixed function oxidation and glucuronidation before being excreted. Mixed function oxidases and glucuronyl transferases of the liver microsomes are induced by barbiturates. (After Levine et al., 1970.)

Where pollutants occur at concentrations that are toxic, the relationship between metabolism and toxicity is an important one. For this reason it is worthwhile considering the question of detoxication in a little more detail. Not all enzymic transformations of foreign compounds are detoxifying. For example, the oxidation of organophosphates such as malathion and parathion yields metabolites which are much more powerful anti-cholinesterases than the parent compounds and their formation *in vivo* represents an activation and not a detoxication. A metabolic conversion may have a detoxifying action in the whole animal for one or both of the following reasons: a. the metabolite is less toxic than the parent compound at the site(s) of action; b. the distribution of the metabolite is different from the parent compound and tends to keep the compound away from its site of action as with the transformation of liposoluble compounds to water-soluble metabolites. The metabolite is not necessarily less toxic than the original compound in the case of b., and there are cases where the reverse seems to be true. The hydration of dieldrin to produce aldrin *trans*-dihydrodiol in the nerves of both the German and the American cockroach may be an activating step since the metabolite rather than the parent compound appears to be neuroactive in isolated nerve preparations (Wang *et al.*, 1972; Matsumura, 1971). On the other hand, this metabolite is far less toxic than dieldrin when administered orally to the mouse and is the main excreted metabolite of dieldrin in the rabbit. Thus there is evidence that this conversion may be either activating or detoxifying, depending upon where it occurs in the body. In the vertebrate liver it aids excretion and protects the animal whereas in the cockroach nerve it appears to promote toxic action.

The importance of knowing not only the nature but the exact location and significance of enzymic transformations needs to be stressed in another context. In many *in vivo* studies upon the metabolism of insecticides by insects, analyses have only been done on whole bodies, so that the degree of metabolic change at or near the site of action is unknown. And yet a metabolic change at this site may be the crucial factor in determining the toxicity of a poison (e.g. in a resistant insect) and may occur to a much larger extent here than in the insect as a whole. Thus, a very small metabolic change in the whole insect may mask a larger and more critical metabolic change at the site of action.

In the following account pollutants are used as examples wherever possible, but in a number of cases references will be made to compounds that are not recognized as pollutants. This is unavoidable since much of the more fundamental work has been done upon compounds other than pollutants. Since we are concerned here with a limited number of processes that apply to a wide range of foreign compounds, this is unimportant. Many different compounds may be used as research tools to investigate these processes. Because of the particular interest in liposoluble compounds in the field of pollution many of the compounds chosen as examples are of this type.

The relevant processes will be considered under four major headings: factors affecting intake, distribution, metabolism and excretion. Vertebrates and invertebrates will be dealt with separately most of the time, but general principles applicable to both will be brought out as necessary. The nature of the biochemical and physiological processes involved, and their variation between species, strain, sexes and age groups will be discussed. The chapter will conclude with discussion of the interplay of factors which determines variations in the intake and elimination of pollutants (Section III) and of some of the effects of these differences upon toxic action (Section III) and residue levels

(Section IV). The emphasis will be upon variations between species and strains rather than variations between sexes and age groups.

II. FACTORS AFFECTING INTAKE AND ELIMINATION OF FOREIGN COMPOUNDS

A. Factors Affecting Intake

In spite of its importance, this subject has been only scantily researched. Intake across the integument has received some attention, notably in connection with insect resistance to insecticides; the intake of drugs from the gut has also been investigated, but very rarely from the comparative point of view. Little is known about movement across the gills of fish and the pulmonary epithelium of higher animals. Consequently a number of topics will only be considered in outline here to indicate where differences may be found; only those which have been investigated from the comparative point of view will be dealt with in more detail. Absorption from the gut and direct intake from the physical environment will be considered separately.

1. Absorption from the Gut

An important factor in determining the rate of absorption via the gut is the rate of intake of food and water. The rate of food intake in homoiothermic animals tends to be greatest where the body size is smallest, and where the temperature difference is greatest between body and surroundings. Thus birds are liable to have faster intake rates than mammals on account of their higher body temperatures. The rate of food intake is also dependent upon season and is likely to be relatively high when the environmental temperature is relatively low and when the animal is most active. Predators may take in relatively high levels of a pollutant because they select prey which behave abnormally as a result of their residue burden (see Chapter 5).

The membranes lining the gut are lipoprotein structures, and foreign molecules having some degree of liposolubility can readily partition across them into the blood stream, whereas those which are ionized or highly lipid-insoluble usually cannot unless they are small enough to move through pores 3·5–4·5 Å in diameter (Whittam, 1964). In the stomach of most mammals the low pH (1–2) causes weak acids to exist largely in their undissociated forms and weak bases to exist largely in their dissociated forms. The undissociated forms of acids and bases are usually non-ionized and liposoluble and are therefore readily absorbed in contrast to the dissociated forms (Fig. 2). Thus weak acids tend to be absorbed from the stomach more rapidly than weak bases. On the other hand the pH of the small intestine and colon are estimated to be 6·5 and 8 respectively. Conditions here are more favourable for the absorption of weak bases and less favourable for the absorption of weak acids.

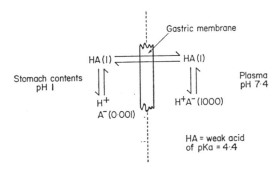

Fig. 2. The influence of pH upon intake of weak acids from the stomach. The figures in brackets indicate relative concentrations. HA = weak acid of pKa = 4·4. (After Os *et al.*, 1964.)

Ruminants differ from other mammals in possessing a specialized chamber of the stomach (rumen) of relatively high pH (6–7). In birds there are usually three compartments of the foregut with different levels of acidity. In the chicken, pigeon, pheasant, duck and turkey the pH values are 4·5–6·1 in the crop, 3·4–4·8 in the proventriculus and 2·0–2·6 in the gizzard (Sturkie, 1965). These pH differences are likely to affect the intake of weak acids and bases. Intake from the gut may also be influenced by the microflora which can often metabolize foreign compounds. Ruminants have an extremely active microflora.

The marked variation between groups in structure, physiology and microbiology of the gut suggests many possible reasons for interspecific differences of intake of foreign compounds, and the subject is ripe for investigation.

2. Direct Intake from the Physical Environment

The nature of the pollutants to which organisms are exposed and the efficiency of their intake is dependent upon habitat. Amongst the vertebrates, terrestrial species absorb airborne pollutants through the lungs and skin, and aquatic species absorb water-borne pollutants through the gills and skin. Insects absorb pollutants via the cuticle and tracheae. Soil animals come into contact with persistent pollutants associated with soil minerals as well as with substances dissolved in soil water.

The skin of vertebrates and the cuticle of insects both behave as lipoprotein barriers although they differ greatly in structure. Attention has been focused upon the absorption of insecticides after topical application to insects and mammals. O'Brien (1967) has reviewed this work and pointed out the serious limitations of much of it. Very often measurements of movement across the integument have been indirect. For example, it has been argued that the insect cuticle is much more permeable to certain compounds than the mammalian skin because the topical and injected LD_{50}s are similar in many insects but not in the rat and the rabbit. Direct measurements with DDT have contradicted this by showing that penetration rates are nearly the same in the rat and the American cockroach (*Periplaneta americana*). Again, penetration of the cuticle has often been determined by the 'wash off' technique which assumes that absorbed insecticide is that part not removed from the surface of the insect by a solvent rinse. This, and the associated procedure of extracting residues from the whole insect, measure the amount of insecticide going into and through the cuticle, and not merely the amount that has passed through the cuticle. Another complicating factor has been the different solvents in which the insecticide is applied. Sometimes application in an organic solvent can lead to more rapid penetration than is found with an aqueous system, presumably because the penetrating molecule moves more easily into the waxy layer of the cuticle.

Notwithstanding these difficulties several workers have shown that the movement of certain insecticides into and through the cuticle is greater in susceptible than in resistant strains (Table I). Penetration into the insect was some 1·8–5·0 times more rapid in the susceptible than in the resistant strain. With two diazinon-resistant strains of housefly, cross resistance was shown by larvae to DDT, DDD and methoxychlor, and this was probably due in part to a reduced rate of intake (Forgash *et al.*, 1962). With resistant larvae of the tobacco budworm there was some indirect evidence that reduced intake was connected with a relatively high level of sclerotin in the cuticle which may bind a proportion of the applied DDT (Vinson and Law, 1971). In a study of malathion-resistant and susceptible houseflies, penetration into and/or through the cuticle was reduced after treatment with

Table I

Cuticular absorption of insecticides by susceptible and resistant strains of insect

Species	Resistant strain	Compound applied to cuticle	Quantity absorbed by susceptible strain / Quantity absorbed by resistant strain	Time over which absorption was measured (hr)	Reference
Housefly third instar larvae (*Musca domestica*)	DDT-resistant Hawaian strain	DDT	5·0 2·5 1·9	1 24 196	Sanchez and Sherman (1966)
Tobacco budworm larvae (*Heliothis virescens*)	DDT-selected South delta strain	DDT	1·8	120	Vinson and Law (1971)
Housefly adults (*Musca domestica*)	R strain 18-fold tolerance to malathion	Malathion	2·7	< 1·20	Benezet and Forgash (1972)
Housefly adults (*Musca domestica*)	U strain diazinon-resistant	Diazinon	2·4	1	Forgash *et al.* (1962)
	A strain diazinon-resistant	Diazinon	3·2	1	

All insecticides were applied as acetone solutions.

silicic acid which can remove epicuticular wax, suggesting that the wax may speed up penetration (Benezet and Forgash, 1972).

In mammalian skin the lipoidal barrier lies in the epidermis, the dermis being freely permeable to most substances (Treherne, 1956). Ions and lipid-insoluble compounds show little tendency to cross the barrier, but they are able to enter the body through hair follicles and sebaceous glands.

When fish are kept in water containing very low concentrations of certain organochlorine insecticides they are able to build up remarkably high levels within their tissues (see Chapter 2). It is believed that intake of organochlorine compounds is mainly across the gills (Holden, 1962) and it appears that the gills of fish function as typical lipoprotein barriers to fat-soluble compounds.

Finally it should be mentioned that terrestrial animals inhale both gaseous and particulate airborne pollutants into the lungs and this can lead to efficient absorption. The pulmonary epithelium appears to differ from other body membranes in being freely permeable not only to liposoluble compounds but also to lipid-insoluble molecules and ions (Chasseaud, 1970).

B. Factors Affecting Distribution

After absorption, foreign compounds are distributed around the organs and tissues of the body by circulation in the blood and lymph (vertebrates) and the haemolymph (insects) and by movement across membranous barriers. The distribution pattern is dependent upon the compound, its metabolism and the route of intake as well as the species, sex, strain and age group. To aid discussion, four different types of location may be defined within the body for compounds possessing biological activity. These are: sites of storage, sites of action, sites of metabolism and sites of excretion. The distribution of compounds between these locations is important in determining their rate of elimination and their biological effect.

1. Sites of Storage

It is assumed that when a foreign compound is stored it is inert; it is not expressing biological activity, neither is it being metabolized. In practice, it is not always clear when a compound located in an organ or tissue is stored in this sense. Whilst depot fat nearly always acts as an inert store for liposoluble foreign compounds, the situation is more complex with membranes, which can be sites of storage, action or biotransformation or combinations of these three possibilities. Dieldrin, for example, is associated with membranes, but while the erythrocyte membrane appears to be just a storage site, the endoplasmic reticulum is a site of metabolism. The following account is largely restricted to plasma proteins and depot fat.

Liposoluble compounds tend to be associated with soluble proteins when they occur in the blood of vertebrates. Moss and Hathway (1964) found that most of the dieldrin transported in rat blood was located in the plasma (about 65 per cent) and the erythrocytes (about 35 per cent). Most of the dieldrin in plasma was associated with albumin, globulin and an unidentifiable protein. Whilst in the bound state a compound cannot diffuse into tissues, and can seldom be excreted or metabolized or express any toxic or pharmacological action. The binding is generally reversible and is part of a transport mechanism. Competition may exist for storage sites and bound molecules may be displaced by free molecules. There is some evidence of species differences in the extent of binding by plasma proteins (Chasseaud, 1970). Strong binding by plasma proteins is sometimes useful in pharmacology, e.g. the trypanocidal drug suramin owes its prolonged action to strong binding coupled with slow release.

The storage of fat-soluble compounds in depot fat has sometimes been related to toxic effect. With the small tortoiseshell butterfly (*Aglais urticae*), for example, the LD_{50} for dieldrin for fifth instar larvae was correlated with lipid content; the larvae with the highest lipid content showed the lowest susceptibility to the insecticide (Moriarty, 1968).

Contrasting with this, storage in depot fat can have a number of harmful effects in the longer term. Any factor which causes the rapid mobilization of the fat can also cause the release of a stored liposoluble compound and its transference to other tissues (see Chapter 2). Shortage of food, cold weather, migration, hibernation and the onset of egg laying and moult may all have this effect in the field (see Chapter 5). The dosing of females with sublethal quantities of dieldrin and/or DDT can produce lethal effects in the second generation in insects and birds. Such effects have been observed following the dosing of dieldrin to the desert locust (*Schistocerca gregaria*) and the Japanese quail (*Coturnix coturnix japonica*) and the dosing of DDT to the Bengalese finch (*Lonchura striata*) (Watts, 1969; DeWitt et al., 1960; Jefferies, 1971). They have been attributed, at least in part, to storage of dieldrin or DDT leading to transmission of quantities to the egg which are lethal to the developing embryo or to the young after hatching. Thus storage of a toxic compound may be protective in the short term yet hazardous in the longer term.

A number of specialized examples of storage require brief mention. Heavy metals such as lead and mercury in both the organic and inorganic states can combine with sulphydryl groups. Sulphydryl groups on enzymes tend to be sites of action rather than sites of storage and heavy metals can exert toxic action by combining with them. Bone acts as a storage site for lead, cadmium and the antibiotic tetracycline. Other examples of localization include mepacrine in liver, p-nitroaniline and certain unsubstituted sulphonamides in erythrocytes, and cadmium in seminiferous tubules. Triethyltin binds readily to rat haemoglobin but far less readily to haemoglobin of other species (see Chasseaud, 1970).

There have been one or two cases where resistance to insecticides has been associated with enhanced tissue binding. Gwiazda and Lord (1967) report this for a strain of diazinon-resistant houseflies, where the extractability of insecticide by organic solvents was used as an index of binding strength. A similar argument has been advanced for a strain of paraoxon-resistant houseflies (Mengle and Casida, 1960).

2. Sites of Action

The ease with which toxicants penetrate into and persist at their site of action is obviously important in comparative toxicology. The present discussion will be restricted to the nervous system since the sites of action located here have received most attention and are evidently of particular importance in the action of poisons and drugs.

With vertebrates, compounds must traverse the so-called blood–brain barrier to enter the brain. Many liposoluble compounds enter the brain rapidly by passive diffusion in contrast to ionized compounds and compounds of very low fat solubility which cannot enter unless there is a specialized intake mechanism for them. Pollutants that enter the brain readily include certain organochlorine, organophosphorus and organomercury pesticides and organolead compounds used as 'antiknocks' in petrol. One study has shown that the blood–brain barrier is considerably more permeable to sulfanilic acid in the dogfish and frog than in the dog (Cserr, 1967). It remains to be seen whether this represents a general difference between higher and lower vertebrates. As with intake, removal from the brain can occur by passive diffusion and there is also a non-specific filtration system which removes solutes from cerebro-spinal fluid by movement across the arachnoid villi (Chasseaud, 1970).

With regard to the peripheral nervous system of vertebrates, sites of action may be at synapses (e.g. organophosphates, carbamates, muscarine and atropine) or on the axon membrane itself (DDT and γ-BHC) (O'Brien, 1967). Comparative aspects of this remain unexplored, but there may be, for example, important differences between groups possessing both myelinated and non-myelinated fibres and groups that possess only non-myelinated fibres, in their response to poisons acting upon the axon.

The central nervous system of the insect, like the vertebrate brain, is more readily penetrated by liposoluble compounds than by ions and strongly polar compounds (see O'Brien, 1967), but the barrier to ions and polar compounds has not been identified. Present evidence suggests that the ganglionic sheath is not responsible. So far interspecific variations in the distribution and toxicity of insecticides have not been explained in terms of differences in penetration into the insect central nervous system (O'Brien, 1967).

3. Sites of Metabolism and Excretion

Sites of metabolism and excretion and the connection between metabolism and excretion are discussed in the next two sections.

C. Enzymic Systems which Metabolize Foreign Compounds

In vertebrates, the transformation of most foreign compounds takes place in two phases (Williams, 1959).

$$\text{Foreign compound} \xrightarrow[\substack{\text{(Usually} \\ \text{deactivation} \\ \text{occasionally} \\ \text{activation)}}]{\text{Phase I}} \text{Metabolite} \xrightarrow[\substack{\text{Endogenous} \\ \text{substrate} \\ \text{(deactivation)}}]{\text{Phase II}} \text{Conjugate}$$

There are certain departures from this scheme: sometimes foreign compounds and/or their metabolites are excreted without being conjugated and sometimes foreign compounds are conjugated directly. Dealing with Phase I reactions, these are commonly oxidations; sometimes they are hydrations, hydrolyses or reductions. The metabolites formed are usually, but not always, less toxic than their precursors. Where liposoluble molecules are involved, the metabolites so formed are almost invariably more water-soluble than the parent compounds and are therefore excreted more rapidly. Phase II transformation into conjugates nearly always leads to increased water solubility and diminished toxicity. Typically both Phase I and Phase II reactions occur in the livers of vertebrates although some of the enzymes involved e.g. esterases, are found in other locations as well. Many of the enzyme systems concerned with metabolizing liposoluble compounds are located in the endoplasmic reticulum of the liver.

The picture is less clear in insects, although many biotransformations are the same as in vertebrates.

The most important enzymic systems and their location are given in Table II.

1. Phase I Reactions

a. Mixed function oxidations. A wide range of oxidations are carried out upon foreign compounds by mixed function oxidation. This system appears to be the most versatile 'Phase I' process in both vertebrates and insects. Mixed function oxidations are so named because they involve the splitting of molecular oxygen, leading to the incorporation of one atom into a foreign substrate and the other into water (Mason, 1957).

$$X\text{H} + \text{NADPH} + \text{H}^+ + 0_2{}^* \rightarrow X\text{O}^*\text{H} + \text{NADP} + \text{H}_2\text{O}^*$$
$$* \text{ Labelled atoms}$$

They are carried out by microsomal fractions from various sources including liver, kidney, lung and adrenal tissue of vertebrates and from fat body, gut and Malpighian tubules of insects. The microsomal fraction from vertebrate liver is notably rich in mixed function oxidase activity and has been widely studied. It is derived almost entirely from the smooth and rough endoplasmic reticulum and is in the form of vesicles. It is possible to separate 'rough' from 'smooth' microsomes, and the smooth microsomes are found to have greater mixed function oxidase activity than the rough microsomes for certain drug oxidations (Remmer et al., 1968). The microsomes prepared from the liver should be distinguished from those from the adrenal cortex. The latter preparation contains both endoplasmic reticulum and mitochondria. Moreover, the mitochondria possess their own mixed function oxidase system concerned with steroid metabolism and which differs in certain respects from that in liver microsomes (Omura et al., 1965). Until recently most work upon mixed function oxidases in insects was with microsomes derived from the whole body, but the demonstration that insect homogenates can contain inhibitors of mixed function oxidation has called this approach into question (see Hook et al., 1968). Work with the southern army worm (*Prodenia eridania*) has shown that homogenizing the whole insect releases a proteinase from the gut which powerfully reduces microsomal oxidase activity (Krieger and Wilkinson, 1969).

The hydroxylation of aniline by insects involves mixed function oxidases and a study of this conversion by intact organs of the locust showed that about half of the total activity resides in the fat body, about one-third in the gastric caeca, and most of the rest in the fore,

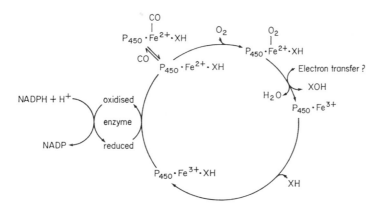

Fig. 3. Proposed scheme for mixed function oxidation. (After Estabrook et al., 1971.)

mid, and hind gut, and the Malpighian tubules (Hook et al., 1968). The following insect tissues have shown relatively high oxidative activity in other studies: the fat body of the locust (*Schistocerca gregaria*), cockroach (*Blaberus giganteus*) and blowfly larva (*Calliphora erythrocephala*); the mid gut of the southern army worm and the Malpighian tubules of the house cricket (*Acheta domesticus*) (see Brooks, 1972.)

The great majority of mixed function oxidation systems depend for their operation upon cytochrome P_{450}, a haemprotein which complexes both the substrate and molecular oxygen. It is so named because it forms a complex with carbon monoxide that gives strong spectral absorption at 450 mμ. A scheme for the involvement of cytochrome P_{450} in the mixed function oxidation of drugs by liver microsomes has been advanced by Estabrook et al. (1971) (Fig. 3).

NADPH reduces a flavoprotein ('NADPH-cytochrome c reductase') which directly or indirectly brings about the reduction of iron from the

Table II

Enzymic systems which metabolize foreign compounds

Enzymic system	Location	Compounds metabolized	Involvement in selective toxicity and resistance
Phase I Reactions			
Mixed function oxidases	Microsomes, notably from vertebrate liver and insect fat body	Many liposoluble compounds	Drug tolerance in humans sometimes associated with induction of this system. Resistance to various insecticides by certain strains of housefly is also associated with enhancement of it. These strains show marked cross resistance
Phosphatases	Present in nearly all tissues and subcellular fractions of species investigated	Organophosphorus insecticides and 'nerve gases'	
Carboxyesterases	In most tissues of insects and vertebrates	Malathion and malaoxon	Main reason for much lower toxicity of malathion towards mammals than towards insects. Malathion-resistant strains of housefly are also high in carboxyesterase activity

Epoxide hydrase	Microsomes—particularly mammalian liver microsomes	Epoxides—including dieldrin and heptachlor epoxide and various arene epoxides	
DDT dehydrochlorinase	Found in virtually all insects and vertebrates so far investigated	pp'-DDT and pp'-DDD	Most important single factor in DDT resistance in the housefly
Phase II Reactions			
Glucuronyl transferases	Mainly in microsomes, notably those from liver, adrenal cortex, and alimentary tract. Widespread in vertebrates other than fish but not in insects	Many compounds with labile hydrogen including hydroxylated metabolites of dieldrin, benzpyrene, chlorfenvinphos and biphenyl	Can be induced in the rat together with mixed function oxidases. Induction associated with more rapid excretion of conjugates
Glutathione-S-transferases	70,000 g supernatants of vertebrate liver homogenates. Also occur in insects	Many chlorinated compounds including γ-BHC and tetrachloronitrobenzene (TCNB). Some epoxides	Possibly involved in the development of γ-BHC resistance in certain strains of housefly

ferric to the ferrous state in cytochrome P_{450}. The substrate binds to cytochrome P_{450} in the ferric state, but the oxygen is only bound after reduction of the P_{450}-substrate complex to the ferrous state. Reaction seems to occur with an electron donor, perhaps to form a hydroperoxide $(-O_2^{2-})$ or superoxide $(^-O_2^-)$ complex. Finally one atom of oxygen is transferred to the substrate, the other incorporated into water, the oxidized substrate is released and cytochrome P_{450} returns to the ferric state.

Certain details of this scheme are not clear. The form(s) in which oxygen exists when bound to cytochrome P_{450} and the mechanism of electron transfer from NADPH to cytochrome P_{450} are not known. Whilst electron transfer from NADPH–cytochrome c reductase to P_{450} in adrenal cortical microsomes involves a non-haem iron protein, this does not appear to be so in liver microsomes.

Microsomal mixed function oxidases are characterized by dependence upon NADPH and molecular oxygen and by sensitivity to inhibition by carbon monoxide and methylenedioxyphenyl synergists such as sesamex and piperonyl butoxide.

Spectral studies suggest that there are different forms of cytochrome P_{450} within the same microsomal preparation showing different binding characteristics towards drugs. If so, this could provide a basis for variations in metabolism between species, strains, sexes and age groups.

Hepatic mixed function oxidases can be strongly induced by a wide range of liposoluble foreign compounds (Remmer et al., 1968). After a few hours of treatment with an inducing agent there is an increased rate of synthesis of cytochrome P_{450} in the case of the rat. In the longer term induction leads to the proliferation of the smooth endoplasmic reticulum, liver hypertrophy and an increased rate of microsomal oxidation (often greater than a twofold increase) for most liposoluble compounds. The increase in smooth endoplasmic reticulum ensures that there is an elevated cytochrome P_{450} level in the whole microsomal fraction, for the smooth microsomes are richer in cytochrome P_{450} than the rough microsomes. Furthermore, spectral K_m values suggest that the cytochrome P_{450} in the smooth microsomes has a greater affinity for certain drugs than has the cytochrome P_{450} in the rough microsomes (Remmer et al., 1968). This seems to explain why a mole of cytochrome P_{450} in smooth microsomes catalyses a more rapid oxidation rate for many drugs than does a mole of cytochrome P_{450} from rough microsomes.

The inducibility of liver enzymes can vary between sexes and species. Induction occurs more easily in female rats than in male rats (Remmer et al., 1968). In a study with male rats and female Japanese quail, the induction of cytochrome P_{450} by DDD was greater in the rat than in the quail (Bunyan *et al.*, 1972). This conclusion held both for levels fed and residue concentrations in tissues. The unsaturated compounds *pp'*-DDE and *pp'*-DDMU were better inducing agents, for a limited range of species, than the saturated compounds *pp'*-DDT and *pp'*-DDD (Bunyan *et al.*, 1970; Bunyan *et al.*, 1972).

On present evidence there is remarkable similarity between species in the products of mixed function oxidation. One of the few reported cases of a qualitative difference in metabolism involves coumarin. In a study with 10,000 g supernatants of liver homogenates, rats and mice were unable to hydroxylate this compound to form umbelliferone, although this conversion proceeded readily in a number of other vertebrates (Creaven *et al.*, 1965).

There are, however, very marked quantitative differences in mixed function oxidase activity between sexes, age groups, strains and species. Dealing with sex differences first of all, liver microsomes of male rats and quail convert aldrin to dieldrin (Fig. 4) much more rapidly than do liver microsomes from the females of these two species (Terriere, 1968). A similar difference between the sexes is found in the rat for barbiturates such as hexobarbitone (Remmer *et al.*, 1968). This difference accounts for the more rapid metabolism of barbiturates *in vivo* and the greater tolerance towards these and other drugs shown by male rats in comparison with female rats. The basis for the sex difference lies not so much in the actual concentration of cytochrome P_{450} in the liver microsomes, which is only some 20 per cent higher in males than in females, but rather in the much stronger binding affinity between cytochrome P_{450} and foreign compounds shown by the male (Remmer *et al.*, 1968). This illustrates how differences in susceptibility to a foreign compound may stem directly from basic differences in an enzyme system.

There are also examples of changes in oxidase activity with increasing age. Aldrin epoxidase activity in microsomes from the Malpighian tubules of the house cricket (*Acheta domesticus*) increases sixfold during the week following the final moult (Benke and Wilkinson, 1971). There is a deficiency in oxidase activity in newborn mice, rats, guinea-pigs and rabbits, but activity begins to appear within a few days of birth (Parke, 1968).

Some cases of resistance to insecticides are associated with differences in mixed function oxidase activity. A strain of houseflies resistant to DDT was found to have enhanced microsomal mixed function oxidase activity (Oppenoorth, 1965) (see Section III). Not surprisingly this strain showed cross resistance to certain other insecticides metabolized by mixed function oxidases.

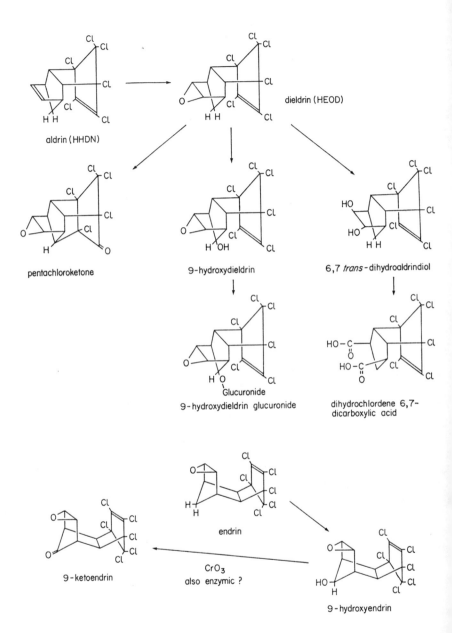

aldrin (HHDN)

dieldrin (HEOD)

pentachloroketone

9-hydroxydieldrin

6,7 *trans*-dihydroaldrindiol

Glucuronide
9-hydroxydieldrin glucuronide

dihydrochlordene 6,7–
dicarboxylic acid

endrin

9-ketoendrin

CrO$_3$
also enzymic ?

9-hydroxyendrin

Fig. 4. Metabolism of dieldrin and endrin. All of these transformations are known to occur in male rats *in vivo* with the following reservations. 9-hydroxydieldrin glucuronide has been reported as a metabolite *in vitro* with rat liver preparations—there is also evidence that it is excreted in the bile by rats but this is not conclusive. Although 9-ketoendrin is excreted *in vivo* by rats, its formation from 9-hydroxyendrin has not yet been proved.

An early indication of interspecific differences in microsomal oxidative ability came from the work of Brodie and Maickel (1961). They showed marked variations between species and groups with regard to the rate of NADPH oxidation. However, these results are of limited use, for they do not give a direct measurement of microsomal oxidase activity towards foreign compounds (Fig. 3). Much higher activity was found in mammals and birds than in fish or amphibia, with reptiles occupying an intermediate position. In later experiments oxidase activity was measured using aldrin (Table III), nitrotoluene and biphenyl as substrates (see Terriere, 1968). Aldrin was used with microsomal preparations and the other two compounds with centrifuged homogenates. The mammals and birds showed considerably more activity than the trout, the housefly and the locust. These and other results point to fish having relatively weak mixed function oxidase activity compared with land vertebrates (Bühler and Rasmusson, 1968; Terriere, 1968).

A comparative study of the hydroxylation of HCE, an assymetric dieldrin analogue, by liver microsomes showed a far lower rate of conversion in the shag (*Phalacrocorax aristotelis*) than in seven other vertebrates (Walker *et al.*, 1973; Table III). Human liver microsomes hydroxylate certain drugs much more slowly than do liver microsomes of the rat, mouse, rabbit, guinea-pig and cat (Remmer, 1970; Darby and Price-Evans, 1971). This seems to be due to the low level of cytochrome P_{450} in human liver microsomes ($0 \cdot 05$–$0 \cdot 07$ mμ mole/mg protein) compared with other mammals ($0 \cdot 38$–$0 \cdot 81$ in five mammalian species) (Remmer, 1970).

The study of the hydroxylation of aniline *in vivo* has also revealed interspecific differences (see Williams, 1971). All species studied excreted a mixture of *o*- and *p*-hydroxyaniline in the urine. A preference for forming *p*-hydroxyaniline was shown by the rabbit, the hen, and five species of rodent, but not by the cat, the dog or the ferret. Thus the last three species, which are all carnivores, contrast with the non-carnivores.

b. Hydrolytic enzymes. Many foreign compounds including some pollutants are esters, and there are esterases, phosphatases and amidases which can bring about their hydrolytic cleavage. Some examples are given in Fig. 5. For the most part these enzymes are not well characterized. Most of them have not been isolated, and their substrate specificity, cofactor requirement, and sensitivity to inhibitors have not been thoroughly investigated. Thus, it is seldom known whether they correspond to recognized enzymes concerned with normal metabolites (see O'Brien, 1967).

Table III

Species differences in microsomal oxidase activity

Species	Aldrin epoxidation mμ moles dieldrin formed/mg microsomal protein/min	HCE Oxidation			
		% substrate oxidized under standard conditions		Quantity of HHC (mμ moles) recovered/g liver used	
		30 min incubation	90 min incubation	30 min incubation	90 min incubation
MAMMALS (liver) Incubation temp. 37°C					
Rat (male)	0.30	28		25	35
Rabbit	0.34[a,a]				
Rabbit (male)	0.27[b,a]	73		50	
Pig	0.078[b,a]				
Mouse (male)	0.18[b,a]				
Mouse (female)					
BIRDS (liver) Incubation temp. 42°C					
Quail (male) (Coturnix coturnix)	0.11[b,c,a], 0.20	15		16	
Quail (female) (Coturnix coturnix)	0.009[b,c,a]				

Feral pigeon (male) (*Columba livia*)	0·078		90		
Rook (*Corvus frugilegus*)	0·31		50	22	17
Jackdaw (*Corvus monedula*)			85		
Fulmar (*Fulmarus glacialis*)			71		
Shag (*Phalacrocorax aristotelis*)	0·06	1·5	2·2	1·4	2·1
FISH (liver) Incubation temp. 37°C					
Rainbow trout (*Salmo gairdnerii*)	0·006[b,a]				
INSECTS Incubation temp. 30°C					
Housefly (whole) (*Musca domestica*)	0·041[b,c,d]				
Housefly (whole) (*Musca vicina*)	0·025[b,a]				
Blowfly (whole) (*Phormia regina*)	0·003[b,c,d]				
Southern army worm (gut) (*Prodenia eridania*)	2·15[b,a]				

Data from Walker *et al.* (1973).
Protein estimations by Lowry method unless otherwise indicated:

[a] Protein by microkjeldahl method.
[b] Protein by Biuret method.
[c] Incubation temperature 37°C.
[d] Data from Krieger and Wilkinson (1969).

The oxidase activity of trout liver microsomes was considerably higher at 20°C than at 37°C towards alkoxy biphenyls (Creaven *et al.*, 1967) so the figure given here should be regarded as an underestimate. Nevertheless there is good evidence that liver microsomes of trout and other fish have distinctly low oxidase activity compared with the rat, even allowing for differences in optimal temperature (Bühler and Rasmusson, 1968).

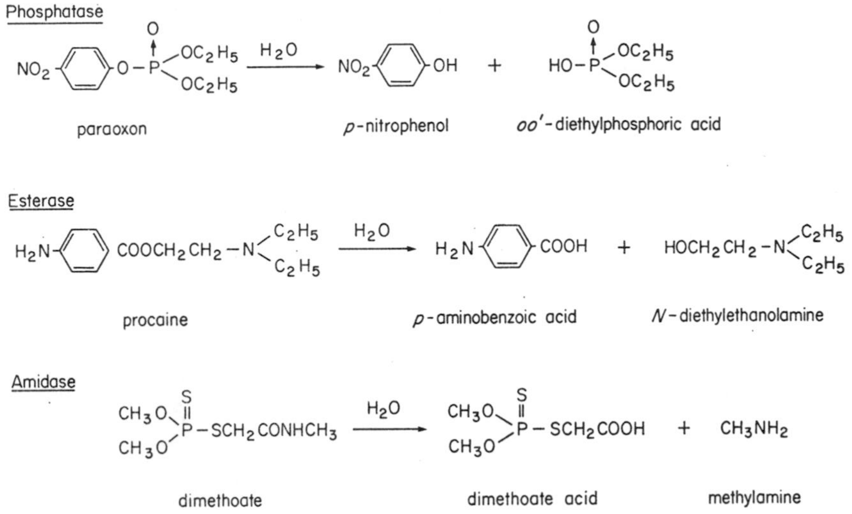

Phosphatase

$$NO_2\text{—}\langle\ \rangle\text{—}O\text{—}P\!\!\!\begin{array}{c}O\uparrow\\\diagdown\end{array}\!\!\!\begin{array}{l}OC_2H_5\\OC_2H_5\end{array} \xrightarrow{\ H_2O\ } NO_2\text{—}\langle\ \rangle\text{—}OH\ +\ HO\text{—}P\!\!\!\begin{array}{c}O\uparrow\\\diagdown\end{array}\!\!\!\begin{array}{l}OC_2H_5\\OC_2H_5\end{array}$$

paraoxon p-nitrophenol oo'-diethylphosphoric acid

Esterase

$$H_2N\text{—}\langle\ \rangle\text{—}COOCH_2CH_2\text{—}N\!\!\begin{array}{l}C_2H_5\\C_2H_5\end{array} \xrightarrow{\ H_2O\ } H_2N\text{—}\langle\ \rangle\text{—}COOH\ +\ HOCH_2CH_2\text{—}N\!\!\begin{array}{l}C_2H_5\\C_2H_5\end{array}$$

procaine p-aminobenzoic acid N-diethylethanolamine

Amidase

$$\begin{array}{l}CH_3O\\CH_3O\end{array}\!\!\!\begin{array}{c}S\\\diagup\!\!\!\diagdown\ \|\\P\end{array}\!\!\!-SCH_2CONHCH_3 \xrightarrow{\ H_2O\ } \begin{array}{l}CH_3O\\CH_3O\end{array}\!\!\!\begin{array}{c}S\\\diagup\!\!\!\diagdown\ \|\\P\end{array}\!\!\!-SCH_2COOH\ +\ CH_3NH_2$$

dimethoate   dimethoate acid   methylamine

Fig. 5. Examples of enzymic hydrolysis of foreign compounds.

Esterases and phosphatases are found both bound to membrane and in solution, and are widely distributed in nature. Esterases vary greatly in properties and activity between species, tissues and subcellular fractions, and their true function is often unknown. Classification has depended mainly upon studies of substrate specificity and sensitivity to inhibition but this has sometimes been misleading because different esterases can show essentially the same properties when looked at in this way (La Du and Snady, 1971). With more critical investigation it has become clear that the subject is a complex one requiring further detailed study. A similar situation exists with phosphatases, which are even less well characterized than esterases.

Many workers distinguish between aryl esterases and aliesterases although this classification is rather unsatisfactory and has been severely criticized (Junge and Krisch, 1973). Aliesterases (B esterases) (EC 3.1.1.1) catalyse the hydrolysis of aromatic and aliphatic esters, but they do not attack choline esters (La Du and Snady, 1971). They possess an imidazole group and a serine hydroxyl group at the active centre, but there is no complementary anionic site (of acetylcholinesterase). Like certain other hydrolytic enzymes with a serine hydroxyl group at the active centre, they are readily inhibited by organophosphates. Unlike lipases they act selectively upon water-soluble esters rather than liposoluble esters.

There are marked interspecific differences in the aliesterase activity of the plasma. Whereas aliesterase activity is high in the plasma of lower vertebrates, no activity is found at all in the plasma of humans, monkeys, dogs and pigs. It may be that cholinesterases have replaced aliesterases during the course of vertebrate evolution (La Du and Snady, 1971).

The organophosphate insecticide malathion and its toxic metabolite malaoxon are detoxified by carboxyesterase attack. Vertebrates tend to show greater carboxyesterase activity than insects, and this appears

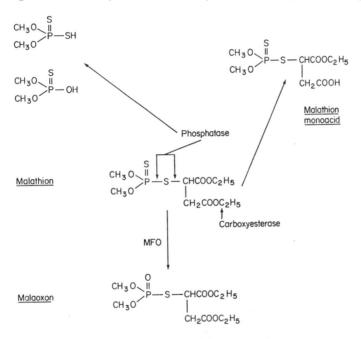

Fig. 6. Malathion metabolism. MFO = mixed function oxidation.

to be the main reason for the striking selective toxicity of malathion, insects tending to accumulate relatively high levels of malaoxon (Fig. 6) (O'Brien, 1967). The enzyme involved has been identified as an aliesterase in rat and human liver preparations and in rat serum, but this has not been established so far for carboxyesterases from other sources.

Aryl esterases (EC 3.1.1.2) act mainly, but not exclusively, upon aromatic esters. They are selective for esters which have a double bond of the alcohol moiety in the α position relative to the ester linkage. Because of this, aliphatic esters such as vinyl acetate having a correctly situated double bond can be hydrolysed by enzymes of this class. The double bond evidently interacts with a sulphydryl group on the enzyme to form a thiolester intermediate prior to cleavage of the ester bond (Augustinsson, 1961). Aryl esterases are not inhibited by organophosphates (cf. aliesterases).

In a comparative study of the esterase activity in 55 species of birds, phenyl acetate and triacetin were used as substrates (Bush *et al.*, 1973). Taking the results as a whole there was considerable interspecific variation in activity towards both substrates but no clear cut difference between orders, or between groups classified according to feeding habits. On the whole, species with high carcase weights had higher levels of esterase activity than species with low carcase weights. In the order Passeriformes, the lowest activities were recorded for vireos (*Vireonidae*), certain of the warblers (*Sylviidae*) and the scarlet tanager (*Piranga olivacea*), all of which are insectivorous. The highest activities were found in Pheuticus and Passer species, which are either herbivorous or omnivorous. Unfortunately it is not clear which esterases are involved. Esterase activity towards triacetin was strongly inhibited by eserine in 14 species tested, indicating that aliesterase (EC 3.1.1.1) is not involved. Furthermore the slow rate of hydrolysis of acetylcholine pointed to only a low activity of cholinesterase in these liver preparations.

Most, if not all, organophosphate insecticides are degraded by phosphatases. Enzymes of this class can attack *P-O-C*, *P-S-C* and *P-F* bonds. There has been some confusion about the nature of enzymatic attack upon *P-O-C* bonds in certain organophosphates, e.g. parathion and diazinon. Initial studies suggested that phosphatases were responsible for removing aryl groups but subsequent work has shown that mixed function oxidases are involved in what appear to be hydrolytic conversions (see Brooks, 1972).

An example of phosphatase attack upon an organophosphate is provided by the metabolism of paraoxon, the active metabolite of the insecticide parathion. In the rat liver at least three enzymes are involved in the hydrolysis of paraoxon (Fig. 7), and each of these shows different ion sensitivity and optimum pH. A comparative study of this transformation in samples of mammalian serum showed significant interspecific variations, the rates of degradation being placed in the following order: rabbit > ferret > sheep > rat > guinea-pig > goat, human > horse > mouse (Aldridge, 1953). Rabbit serum was approximately eight times more active than mouse serum.

c. Epoxide hydrase. A number of pollutants, including the persistent organochlorine compounds dieldrin and heptachlor epoxide, possess an epoxide group which can be attacked by an enzyme system located in liver microsomes. The epoxides are hydrated to *trans*-dihydrodiols

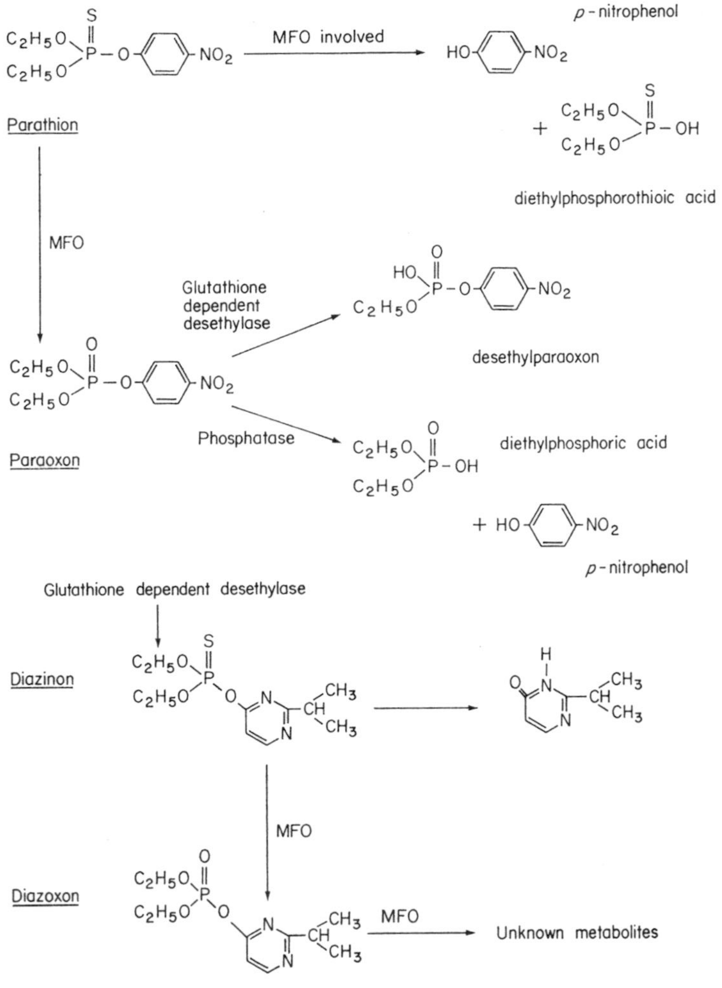

Fig. 7. Metabolism of parathion and diazinon. MFO = mixed function oxidation.

(Brooks, 1966; Oesch *et al.*, 1971a), and the enzyme which mediates this conversion is termed epoxide hydrase and may exist in more than one form (Oesch *et al.*, 1971b). As with mixed function oxidases, epoxide hydrase converts many liposoluble compounds into more water-soluble metabolites. In the guinea-pig, rat, and rabbit, hydrase activity towards arene epoxides was found to be high in the liver, low in the kidney and absent from most other tissues investigated (Oesch *et al.*, 1970). The activity in liver homogenates was located mainly in the microsomes.

Microsomal epoxide hydrase operates in the absence of any added cofactors, is not dependent upon NADPH or molecular oxygen, and is relatively insensitive to methylenedioxyphenyl inhibitors; features which distinguish it from mixed function oxidases. It is, however, inhibited by a number of epoxides and some organophosphates (Brooks, 1973). It can attack a wide range of substrates including a number of aromatic epoxides (e.g. naphthalene oxide, 11,12-epoxy-3-methyl-cholanthrene) and chlorinated cyclodiene epoxides (e.g. dieldrin) (Oesch *et al.*, 1971a; Brooks *et al.*, 1970). A fraction of microsomal epoxide hydrase can be solubilized with the aid of deoxycholate and the enzyme isolated by ammonium sulphate precipitation (Oesch *et al.*, 1971a).

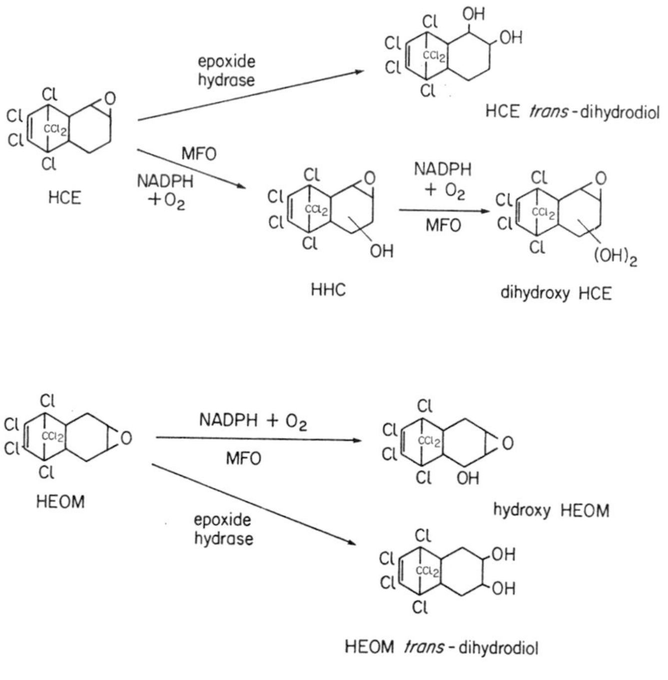

Fig. 8. Metabolism of HCE and HEOM by liver microsomes. MFO = mixed function oxidation.

Microsomal epoxide hydrase displays stereo selectivity. It has been shown that pig and rabbit liver microsomes can only hydrate up to approximately 50 per cent of HCE, an asymmetric analogue of dieldrin, and both the residual substrate and the diol show optical activity (Brooks *et al.*, 1970) (Fig. 8). Only the (+) enantiomer of HCE is readily hydrated by the enzyme. Hepatic microsomal epoxide hydrase can be induced to a small extent by phenobarbitone and 3-methylcholanthrene (Oesch *et al.*, 1970; Oesch *et al.*, 1972).

The rate of hydration varies greatly from compound to compound. Whereas dieldrin is hydrated very slowly, its analogue HEOM is attacked very rapidly (Brooks *et al.*, 1970). The only difference in structure between these molecules is that HEOM lacks an endomethylene bridge in the non-chlorinated ring (see Fig. 8). Some aromatic compounds e.g. naphthalene are converted to epoxides by mixed function oxidation, and these are rapidly metabolized by epoxide hydrase. There is evidence that the carcinogenic activity of certain polycyclic aromatic compounds (e.g. 3-methylcholanthrene) results from their conversion to unstable epoxides (Sims, 1973). If this is so, epoxide hydrase can serve the function of destroying carcinogenic metabolites.

There is great variation in the epoxide hydrase activity of liver microsomes between species as measured by HEOM hydration. In a comparative study of 18 vertebrate species, all mammals except the mouse showed greater activity than all birds, and three out of four fish showed no activity at all (El Zorgani *et al.*, 1970; Walker *et al.*, 1973) (Table IV). The rabbit was nearly 10,000 times more active than the rat. Sex differences were relatively small in the rat and the rabbit. The rabbit showed 6–8 times more activity than the rat and this may help to explain the difference between these two species in dieldrin metabolism. The principal excreted metabolites are a hydration product (aldrin *trans*-dihydrodiol) in the rabbit, but an oxidation product (9-hydroxydieldrin) in the rat.

Species differences are also shown in the hydration of HCE, the rabbit, pig and rook showing the greatest activity, the rat, fulmar, quail and jackdaw showing less activity and the pigeon and housefly showing no measurable activity (Brooks, 1969; Walker and El Zorgani, 1972; Walker and El Zorgani, 1974).

The significance of these *in vitro* species differences, with regard to rates of elimination *in vivo*, awaits investigation.

d. Dehydrochlorination. The dehydrochlorination of *pp'*-DDT to *pp'*-DDE (Fig. 9) is an unusual biotransformation in that it does not increase water solubility and the metabolite is more persistent than the original insecticide. Nevertheless DDE has been shown to be less toxic than DDT for many insects and its formation usually represents a detoxication. DDT dehydrochlorination appears to occur throughout the animal kingdom and DDE was found to be the most widespread and abundant of all organochlorine insecticide residues in British wildlife in surveys conducted in the 1960s (Edwards, 1970).

Table IV

Species differences in the epoxide hydrase activity of hepatic microsomes

Species	Sex	Epoxide hydrase activity mμ mol diol formed/mg microsomal protein/min
MAMMALS		
Rabbit	Male	34
	Female	50
Rat	Male	4·49
	Female	7·4
Grey squirrel (*Sciurus carolinensis*)	Male	7·6
Mouse	Male	0·45
Pig[a]		81
BIRDS		
Pigeon (*Columba livia*)	Male	0·0045
Japanese quail (*Coturnix coturnix japonica*)	Male	0·12
Domestic fowl (*Gallus domesticus*)	Male	0·30
Turkey (*Meleagris gallopavo*)	Female	0·22
Duck (*Anas platyrhynchos*)	Female	0·15
Jackdaw (*Corvus monedula*)	Male	1·26
Shag (*Phalacrocorax aristotelis*)	Male	0·33
FISH		
Pike (*Esox lucius*)	Female	0
Bleak (*Alburnus lucidus*)	[b]	0·029
Roach (*Leuciscus rutilus*)	Males and females	0
Grayling (*Thymallus vulgaris*)	Male	0

Data from Walker *et al.* (1973).
With the exception of the bleak, all specimens were adults.

[a] pH 8·4, 30°C. Brooks (1972).
[b] Immature specimen; sex could not be determined.

The fulmar (*Fulmarus glacialis*) has similar activity to the quail (*Coturnix coturnix japonica*) and the rook (*Corvus frugilegus*) has similar activity to the jackdaw (*Corvus monedula*). El Zorgani *et al.* (1970).

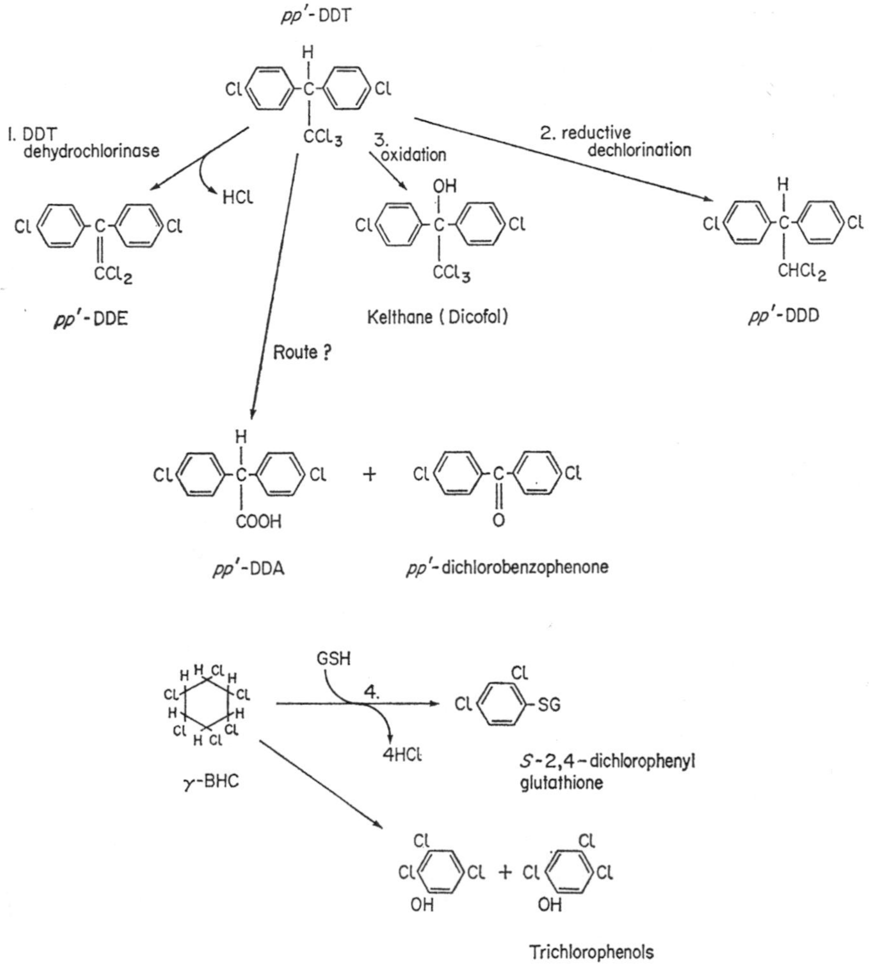

Fig. 9. Metabolic pathways for pp'-DDT and γ-BHC. 1. DDT dehydrochlorinase activity has been found in all species investigated so far with the possible exception of the rhesus monkey. 2. Reductive dechlorination of DDT is carried out by microorganisms and by dead vertebrate tissues, especially liver. It is not clear whether this conversion occurs in vertebrate tissues *in vivo*. 3. Oxidation of pp'-DDT to kelthane has only been demonstrated in invertebrates such as *Blatella germanica* and *Triatoma infestans*. The enzyme system appears to be a microsomal mixed function oxidase. 4. S-2,4-dichlorophenyl glutathione is formed from γ-BHC in a number of invertebrates. In the rat and rabbit trichlorophenols are excreted in the urine in both free and conjugated form.

DDT dehydrochlorinase has been isolated from houseflies (Lipke and Kearns, 1960). It is a relatively small protein, and depends upon glutathione (GSH) as a cofactor. It has been claimed that it consists of an aggregation of monomers having molecular weights of about 30,000 each (Dinamarca et al., 1969). The turnover number is very low, one molecule of the enzyme degrading only 2·5 molecules of DDT per minute. Turnover numbers of other enzymes with their natural substrates tend to be very much higher than this and the low efficiency of 'DDT dehydrochlorinase' is probably the result of the enzyme not dealing with its 'natural' substrate. Although dependent upon GSH, there is no net consumption of the cofactor during the formation of DDE. This may be because the conversion is initiated by conjugation with GSH when one chlorine atom is displaced and subsequent dissociation of the conjugate releases DDE and GSH (Brooks, 1972).

Dehydrochlorination also occurs when γ-BHC is metabolized, 2,4-dichlorophenyl-S-glutathione being the main metabolite in a number of insects (Clark et al., 1966) (Fig. 9). The exact mechanism is still in doubt but it seems likely that conjugation of γ-BHC with glutathione represents the first step in most insects and that dehydrochlorination follows. In view of the similarity between this process and DDT dehydrochlorination it has been suggested that both conversions are mediated by the same system. Direct studies upon DDT dehydrochlorinase from houseflies do not support this idea, for the enzyme shows no activity towards γ-BHC. On the other hand, acetone powders and partially purified enzyme systems from houseflies dehydrochlorinate pp'-DDT and convert γ-BHC into water-soluble metabolites. Furthermore, pp'-DDT and γ-BHC inhibited each other's metabolism in certain of these housefly preparations (Ishida and Dahm, 1965a,b). DDT dehydrochlorinase can be inhibited by analogues of DDT such as DMC and FDMC which can function as synergists for the insecticide. Differences in DDT dehydrochlorinase activity between strains of insects will be discussed in Section III.

2. Phase II Reactions—Conjugation

As we have seen, the products of Phase I reactions are normally converted into water-soluble conjugates in vertebrates, which aids excretion. Insects, too, are able to form conjugates.

Although some endogenous molecules are widely used for this purpose throughout the animal kingdom, others are only so employed by particular groups of animals. Interspecific variation is more pronounced in Phase II than in Phase I reactions on present evidence. Some of these differences arise from specialized features of metabolism e.g. arginine conjugation is well developed in Arachnida and Myriapoda, groups which show high tissue levels of this amino acid (see Parke, 1968).

The following account is restricted to two groups of conjugating enzymes. These are the enzymes which catalyse conjugation with glucuronic acid and glutathione. They provide a good illustration of the principles involved and are known to be important in the metabolism of liposoluble pollutants. Other conjugating enzymes which are involved in drug metabolism but are not dealt with here are those mediating the formation of alkyl and aryl sulphates, peptides and methyl derivatives (see Parke, 1968).

a. Conjugations with glucuronic acid. Glucuronide formation is the most common type of conjugation recognized in mammals, in contrast with insects which form glucosides rather than glucuronides. The subject has been recently reviewed by Dutton (1971). The formation of glucuronides is mediated by a range of glucuronyl transferases which are located principally in the microsomal fraction of such tissues as liver and adrenal cortex.

These enzymes catalyse the transfer of glucuronic acid from UDP-glucuronic acid to a group on a foreign substrate which contains a labile hydrogen atom (Fig. 10). Commonly, this is a hydroxyl group

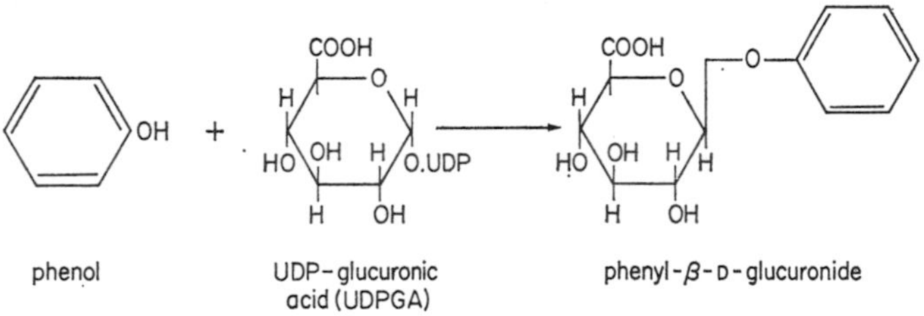

| phenol | UDP-glucuronic acid (UDPGA) | phenyl-β-D-glucuronide |

Fig. 10. Glucuronyl transferase—the conjugation of phenol.

but amino, imino and sulphydryl groups can also participate in glucuronide formation. Depending upon which element the link is established through, these enzymes are termed *O*-, *N*- or *S*-glucuronyl transferases. The carboxyl group in the C_6 position on the glucuronic acid contributes to the polarity of the conjugate and ensures that it is markedly water-soluble.

Glucuronide formation is important for the removal of both foreign compounds and endogenous substances such as certain steroids and catecholamines. There is evidence that some glucuronyl transferases handle both foreign and endogenous substances.

It appears that all mammals, birds and reptiles possess glucuronyl transferase activity as do the adult forms of those amphibians that are predominantly terrestrial. On the other hand amphibians that are predominantly aquatic show no activity whilst some fish show weak activity and others none at all. This tends to support the theory that species which are entirely aquatic have little need for metabolic conversion of liposoluble compounds to aid excretion (Smith, 1968).

There are differences between species and strains in glucuronyl transferase activity, which suggests that there are a number of different enzymes with overlapping specificities. Gunn rats are unable to produce a number of common O-glucuronides although they can form N-glucuronides. Similarly the cat cannot produce certain common O-glucuronides although it is not deficient in UDP-glucuronic acid and can synthesize certain other glucuronides. Some primates including man, the rhesus monkey and the baboon, can form the N-glucuronide of sulphadimethoxine, whereas the rat, rabbit, dog and guinea-pig evidently cannot (Adamson et al., 1966).

Recent evidence suggests that UDP-glucuronyl transferases operate in close association with mixed function oxidases at the microsomal level (Mehendale and Dorough, 1972). Like the microsomal oxidases they can be induced by 3,4-benzpyrene and 3-methylcholanthrene. Such an association is in keeping with the idea that most drugs are transformed in two phases. It should be added that dosing rats with barbiturates can lead to an increased rate of glucuronide excretion, presumably as the result of induction of either microsomal oxidases or UDP-glucuronyl transferases or both (Zeidenberg et al., 1967; Levine et al., 1970).

b. Conjugation with glutathione. Glutathione conjugation has been reviewed by Boyland (1971). It is important in the metabolism of pesticides such as γ-BHC and tetrachloronitrobenzene. In contrast to glucuronide formation it is usually the unchanged foreign compound which is converted into a conjugate. Many organohalogen compounds can combine directly with reduced glutathione with the elimination of hydrogen halide (Fig. 11).

The enzymes that catalyse glutathione conjugation are termed glutathione-S-transferases, and are typically found in the supernatants of liver homogenates after high speed centrifugation (usually at 70,000 g). There are at least ten different glutathione-S-transferases showing different substrate specificities and pH optima. The true function of these enzymes is uncertain, all their known substrates being foreign compounds. Possibly they have the protective function of removing foreign electrophiles which are able to attack cellular nucleophiles.

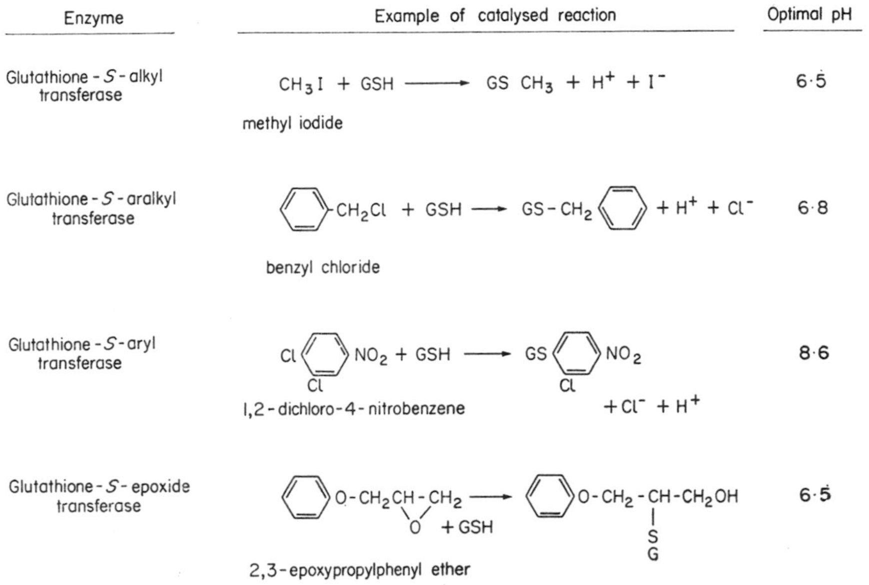

Fig. 11. Examples of glutathione-S-transferases.

Once formed, glutathione conjugates may undergo a number of biotransformations before they are finally excreted (Fig. 12). In vertebrates they are normally converted into acetyl cysteine derivatives (mercapturic acids) before being excreted (Boyland, 1971). In insects, on the other hand the glutathione conjugate and/or its cysteine derivative tend to be excreted rather than the mercapturic acid. Three glutathione-S-transferases will be discussed in a little more detail (Fig. 11).

Glutathione-S-epoxide transferase is unusual in that it mediates the addition of the whole molecule of reduced glutathione to the substrate without elimination of hydrogen. It catalyses the conjugation of 2,3-epoxyphenylpropyl ether, styrene oxide, and epoxides of polycyclic aromatic hydrocarbons. This latter group of compounds includes a number of pollutants which have carcinogenic activity (e.g. the epoxide of 3,4-benzpyrene).

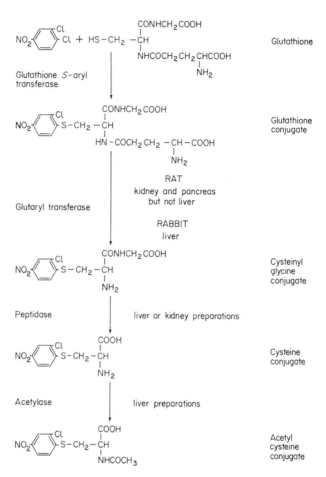

Fig. 12. The further metabolism of the glutathione conjugate of 1,2,dichloro-4-nitro-benzene. (After Boyland, 1971.)

Glutathione-S-epoxide transferase is widely distributed in vertebrates and there are considerable differences between species with regard to the activity found in supernatants of liver homogenates (Table V) (Boyland and Chasseaud, 1969). These data do not show any clear trends based upon phylogenetic classification, diet or habitat, nor is there any obvious correlation between the activity of this enzyme and the activity of other glutathione-S-transferases in different species. In another study Wit and Snel (1968) produced evidence for two different forms of the enzyme in wild birds. The conjugation of 2,3-epoxyphenyl-propyl ether and diethylmaleate appeared to be mediated by different

Table V

Glutathione-S-transferases in different species

| Species | No. of specimens and sex | Activity in dialysed supernatants of liver homogenates Activity μmoles thiol lost/min/g liver | | | |
		Alkyl	Aryl	Aralkyl	Epoxide
Guinea-pig	2 Male	1·3	1·3	7·4	2·1
Pigeon	6 Male	10·7	0·4	3·3	1·0
Rat	> 30 Female	3·0	0·5	2·3	2·1
Dog	1 Male	0·4	1·1	1·1	0·8
	1 Female	6·6	1·6	2·1	1·0
Mouse	20 Male	3·5	1·2	1·9	3·0
Hamster	5 Male	1·7	0·2	1·9	1·7
Rabbit	1 Male	1·1	0·7	1·1	0·3
Human	1 Female	0·8	0·04	0·5	0·4
Ferret	2 Male	0·4	0·5	0·3	0·8

After Boyland and Chasseaud (1969).

enzymes. In a sample of six birds, there was considerable variation in the rate of conjugation of epoxyphenylpropyl ether, the pheasant (*Phasianus colchicus*) showing much greater activity than the coot (*Fulica atra*), the tufted duck (*Aythya fuligula*), the great crested grebe (*Podiceps cristatus*), the goosander (*Mergus merganser*) and the common gull (*Larus canus*). There was far less variation in activity towards diethyl maleate, although the pheasant again displayed the highest activity. It has been argued that predominantly herbivorous species such as the pheasant encounter a wider range and larger amounts of foreign compounds in their diet than do carnivorous species and are therefore likely to have evolved more efficient detoxication systems. However, the relatively low activity for the coot, and the results shown in Table V, do not lend support to this idea.

Glutathione-S-aryl transferase catalyses the conjugation of various chlorinated aromatic compounds including the fungicide tetrachloro-nitrobenzene (TCNB). It is widely distributed in vertebrates and insects and there is evidence that it exists in more than one form, e.g. it has different properties in liver homogenates from the pigeon compared with those from the rat (Wit and Leeuwangh, 1969). Boyland and Chasseaud (1969) found that there was more interspecific variation with this enzyme than with the other glutathione-*S*-transferases in a study of nine vertebrates (Table V). The highest glutathione-*S*-aryl transferase activities were found in the female dog and the male guinea-pig and these were some 40 times greater than the value for adult humans.

Glutathione-*S*-alkyl transferase can handle a diversity of substrates including alkyl bromides, certain organophosphate insecticides (e.g. parathion, chlorfenvinphos) and β-propiolactone. With chlorfenvinphos, a methyl group is transferred to glutathione to yield methyl-*S*-glutathione.

The metabolism of the insecticide γ-BHC involves glutathione conjugation in both insects and mammals, but the enzyme type has not been established (Clark *et al.*, 1967). As we have seen, the main product of glutathione conjugation in insects is *S*-2,4-dichlorophenyl glutathione and the first step in its production is evidently direct conjugation of γ-BHC with reduced glutathione (Fig. 9) (Clark *et al.*, 1969). The rat and the rabbit seem to lack this activity, and couple glutathione to pentachlorocyclohexane, which is derived from γ-BHC by dehydrochlorination (Grover and Sims, 1965).

3. Microbial Metabolism in the Gut

Microbial metabolism requires brief mention in connection with the action of the gut microflora upon foreign compounds. The subject has been reviewed by Scheline (1968). Amongst the vertebrates, some interspecific differences in metabolism are due to differences in the gut microflora. Quinic acid is readily converted to hippuric acid by the gut microflora of man, the rhesus monkey, the baboon and the green monkey (the last three are all Old World monkeys). On the other hand New World monkeys and a range of other vertebrates carry out this conversion weakly or not at all (see Williams, 1971).

Metabolism in the gut will be mentioned later when discussing biliary excretion.

D. Factors Affecting Excretion

Since excretory processes have been more thoroughly investigated in vertebrates than in insects, much of what follows concerns vertebrates alone. In addition to excretion in urine and bile we shall consider the removal of substances by other means (e.g. in milk, eggs and sweat) which are excretory processes in fact if not in theory.

In insects and land vertebrates, the production of urine and/or bile raises problems of water conservation that do not exist for most aquatic vertebrates. Certain specialized features of the excretory system in different groups of terrestrial animals have the function of conserving water.

1. Urinary Excretion

Urinary excretion will first be described for mammals before discussing the special features of other groups.

When blood is filtered through the glomerulus of the kidney most of the plasma proteins are excluded from the resulting filtrate together with any foreign compounds tightly bound to them. Free metabolites and conjugates of foreign compounds pass through into the tubular lumen where they exist at similar concentrations to those originally present in blood. The walls of the kidney tubules act as typical lipo-protein membranes, and there is passive transfer of molecules of sig-nificant liposolubility between the glomerular filtrate and the blood stream. This can occur in both directions and the balance of intake and loss can change with passage down the kidney tubule. As water is reabsorbed from the tubules, so the concentration of liposoluble molecules rises inside them, encouraging diffusion back into the blood. Furthermore, the pH of the filtrate changes with movement down the tubule and this influences the state of dissociation of weak acids and bases and therefore the extent to which they exist in uncharged (i.e. liposoluble) forms. The production of the uncharged form of an acid or base leads to loss by diffusion across the tubule into the blood whilst the production of the charged form retards such loss. Additionally, conjugates may be broken down in the lumen to release liposoluble fragments which can be reabsorbed. Apart from these passive move-ments, a few foreign compounds which are strong organic acids or bases are actively transported into the tubular lumen. Two different systems have been recognized: one for strong acids, the other for strong bases. Both systems deal with endogenous and exogenous compounds so that, for example, hippuric acid and probenecid, choline and hexa-methonium are excreted by common active transport systems (see Parke, 1968). Thus the pattern of urinary excretion is complex and changes with movement down the tubule. Overall the system favours the excretion of water-soluble metabolites and conjugates of foreign compounds.

The anatomical structure of the kidney varies greatly between different groups of vertebrates. In view of this, and the dependence of excretion of foreign compounds upon such things as blood supply and properties of the tubular wall, there are likely to be marked inter-specific variations here.

Mammals are unusual amongst vertebrates in voiding urine independently of faeces. Reptiles, amphibians, birds and certain fish discharge urine into the cloaca where it is combined with faeces. Reabsorption of water from the cloaca in these groups aids water conservation. The extent to which metabolites and conjugates of foreign compounds are reabsorbed from the cloaca does not appear to have been investigated.

Freshwater fish contrast with marine fish in having no problems of water conservation and they produce hypotonic urine. In theory they are likely to be less efficient in reabsorbing foreign molecules of pronounced liposolubility than are groups which produce more concentrated urine.

The Malpighian tubules of insects produce what is essentially an ultrafiltrate of haemolymph. The movement of simple inorganic ions and water across the walls of Malpighian tubules has been reviewed by Maddrell (1971). Far less is known about the movement of organic molecules into Malpighian tubules. In the stick insect (*Carausius morosus*) there is evidence that simple organic compounds of low molecular weight such as glycine, urea and sucrose enter the Malpighian tubules by passive diffusion, their concentration in the urine often approaching but not exceeding their concentration in the bathing fluid. On the other hand certain dyestuffs with molecular weight > 400 appear to be concentrated by the Malpighian tubules of a wide range of insects. This process is not linked to fluid secretion and is evidently an example of active transport. Raising the pH from 6·5 to 7·5 increases intake, pointing to transport of the anionic forms (see Maddrell, 1971).

Urine from the Malpighian tubules is discharged into the hindgut which is divided into two regions—the ileum and the rectum. The hindgut has a cuticular lining which is impermeable to large molecules and here selective reabsorption of water and small molecules occurs. In the locust, for example, the cuticle of the rectum is impermeable to molecules exceeding $0·5–0·6 \ m\mu$ (5–6 Å) in diameter. It appears that the cuticle lining the rectum has the protective function of preventing the reabsorption of potentially toxic molecules greater than 300–500 in molecular weight.

The metabolism and excretion of *p*-nitrophenylchloride has been studied in the desert locust (*Schistocerca gregaria*) (Cohen and Smith, 1964). Glutathione-*S*-(*p*-nitrobenzyl) glutathione was the main product formed within the locust and this was converted into the corresponding cysteine conjugate by Malpighian tubules and hindgut. Both conjugates were found in the excreta.

γ-BHC is also converted into glutathione conjugates by insects. S-2,4-dichlorophenyl glutathione is the main transformation product of γ-BHC in the desert locust ($S.$ $gregaria$), housefly ($Musca$ $domestica$), grass grubs ($Costelytra$ $zealandica$), mature blow flies ($Lucilia$ $sericata$) and also in the cattle tick ($Boophilus$ $docolopatus$) (Clark et al., 1967; Clark et al., 1969) and S-conjugates similar or identical to this appear to be the main excreted derivates of γ-BHC in normal and resistant houseflies (Bradbury and Standen, 1956; Bradbury and Standen, 1959).

It seems that the production of glutathione conjugates is an effective detoxication mechanism in insects as well as in vertebrates, that these conjugates (like the other water-soluble organic molecules) are excreted in the urine, and that their reabsorption is prevented by the cuticular lining of the hindgut.

2. Biliary Excretion

The importance of this excretory route in higher vertebrates has only recently been recognized. A wide range of both foreign and endogenous compounds are excreted in the bile, usually as glucuronides, peptides or sulphates. The process of removal is remarkably similar for many foreign compounds and endogenous steroids (e.g. the bile salts and hydrophilic metabolites of testosterone and oestradiol). Although the existence of concentration gradients between bile and plasma for some compounds suggests that active secretion occurs, there is no conclusive evidence for this (Smith, 1971).

The extent to which water-soluble compounds are excreted in the bile can be influenced by molecular weight and chemical structure. A study of the excretion of 16 different organic anions by the rat, rabbit, and guinea-pig showed that molecules having a molecular weight > 500 were excreted mainly in the bile; those with a molecular weight of < 300 were excreted mainly in the urine (Hirom et al., 1972a). There were marked interspecific differences with regard to the preferred excretory route for intermediate molecular weights. There was a different molecular weight threshold for each species above which significant biliary excretion occurred (> 10 per cent of dose) but below which excretion was mainly via the urine (Fig. 13). The estimated thresholds were: rat 325 $\pm$ 50, guinea-pig 400 $\pm$ 50 and rabbit 475 $\pm$ 50. Other work suggests that the dog and hen have similar thresholds to the rat, whereas the rhesus monkey has a relatively high threshold similar to the rabbit (Abou El Makarem *et al.*, 1967). Above the threshold value, variations in the extent of biliary excretion have been found in the female rat for similar compounds (Hirom *et al.*, 1972b). These appear to be due to differences in stereochemistry and/or polarity.

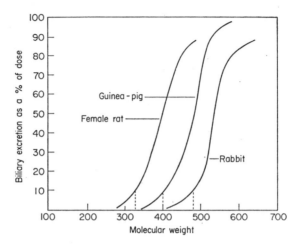

Fig. 13. The relationship between molecular weight and extent of biliary excretion. There was considerable scattering of points and the lines given are those of best fit judged by eye. Estimated threshold molecular weights are the values above which more than 10 per cent of the dose is excreted in the bile. (After Hirom *et al.*, 1972a.)

These differences between species may be the result of a selective filtration process. It has been suggested that a 'primary' form of bile is converted to a secondary form by selective reabsorption from the bile duct of molecules up to a particular molecular weight (Clark *et al.*, 1971). After reabsorption smaller molecules may be transported to the kidney to be excreted there. Recent experiments with retrograde biliary infusion in the rat have demonstrated selective reabsorption of ions as required by the theory (Clark *et al.*, 1971). Probably reabsorption occurs through pores, whose diameter is characteristic of a particular species. This can explain not only differences between species but also the importance of differences in chemical structure for compounds of similar molecular weight.

The preferred excretory route for conjugates and metabolites can be important toxicologically. In mammals, urinary excretion may be expected to lead to rapid and efficient removal from the body, whereas after biliary excretion compounds must pass through the alimentary tract before being voided with the faeces. Excreted foreign molecules may undergo biotransformation in the gut, often by microbial action.

Where water-soluble conjugates are broken down to release relatively liposoluble molecules (often the products of Phase I reactions) the latter tend to be reabsorbed. Commonly, most of the reabsorbed compound is returned directly to the liver, where it is reconjugated and excreted again in the bile, a process termed enterohepatic circulation; sometimes reabsorption leads to urinary excretion. Biotransformation in the gut may yield toxic metabolites e.g. chloramphenicol glucuronide is excreted in rat bile and then degraded to thyrotoxic metabolites in the gut (Smith, 1971). Thus it is clear that the preferred excretory route can be important in determining the ultimate fate of a pollutant and therefore the toxic effect of it or its metabolites in different species.

3. Other Excretory Routes

Insects can 'excrete' toxic substances by storing them e.g. uric acid is deposited in the urate cells of the fat body of many insect species. It should be emphasized, however, that storage of pollutants can lead to long term toxic effects (see Section II.B.).

An excretory process available only to females is the removal of unchanged fat-soluble compounds (e.g. dieldrin, DDT) in eggs and milk. After being excreted in this way, organochlorine insecticide residues are found mainly in the butter fat of cows milk and in the yolk of eggs, i.e. in non-polar, fatty phases. The significance of these excretory routes varies between species. The domestic fowl lays eggs continuously and can excrete far more organochlorine insecticide by this route than can most other birds, while the cow has an advantage over species that produce little or no milk.

Quite a wide range of compounds is excreted in cows milk, including thiouracil, erythromycin, isoniazid and some sulphonamides. Because the pH of milk ($c.$ 6·7) is lower than that of plasma, organic bases (but not organic acids) tend to be excreted in milk, following the principle already described for absorption from the stomach.

When fish are transferred from water containing dieldrin to clean water, unchanged insecticide is lost to the water, and the dieldrin level in the tissue falls markedly (Alabaster, 1969). This is thought to be due to simple diffusion across the gills and perhaps skin. A similar argument is advanced for aquatic amphibia. The possible significance of this route in relation to the development of metabolic systems was discussed earlier.

Finally, a curious excretory mechanism has been found in DDT-resistant larvae of the mosquito *Aedes aegypti*. When the peritrophic lining of the gut is rejected by the larva, it carries with it a considerable quantity of bound DDT (Abedi and Brown, 1961). This mechanism does not appear to have been investigated in other insects.

III. COMPARATIVE INTAKE AND ELIMINATION *IN VIVO*

For simplicity the factors which influence intake and elimination have been considered individually up to this point. We shall now use the limited available evidence to discuss the interaction of these factors *in vivo*. Firstly we will discuss differences in metabolism *in vivo* and some of the reasons for differences in persistence of residues. Secondly we will consider how selective toxicity may be the result of the interplay of these factors.

Comparative metabolic studies with amphetamine, phenol and dieldrin have revealed interesting species differences. The first two compounds are relatively non-persistent but they do illustrate the complexity of species variations in metabolism and the involvement of certain enzyme systems discussed in Section II; dieldrin provides an example of a persistent liposoluble pollutant.

Both amphetamine and phenol are relatively small molecules and all the metabolites and conjugates studied have molecular weights below 325, the threshold value for biliary excretion in the rat. The two initial lines of attack on amphetamine are (1) hydroxylation, (2) deamination (Fig. 14). Hydroxylation is followed by conjugation, and deamination by oxidation (major route), reduction and enolization (minor routes) and all products are eventually excreted as conjugates (see Williams, 1971). Hydroxylation is important only in the rat. Deamination is a major reaction in the guinea-pig and the rabbit, but the next step depends on the species. The rat produces mainly an oxidation product (benzoic acid) but the rabbit produces three different metabolites, two of which are not found in the other species studied. In humans, monkeys and dogs about a third of the amphetamine is excreted unchanged and another third is converted to benzoic acid.

The metabolism of phenol also illustrates differences between species (Fig. 15) (see Williams, 1971).

There are four major metabolic products, namely the sulphate and glucuronide of phenol and the sulphate and glucuronide of quinol. The pig forms no sulphate and the cat no glucuronide (the cat is known to be deficient in the appropriate glucuronyl transferase). The pig, the Indian fruit bat and the rhesus monkey are all unable to hydroxylate conjugated phenol to conjugated quinol. Other species produce three or all four of the conjugates mentioned.

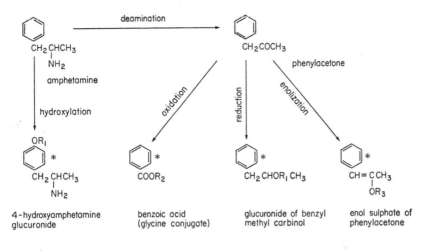

*Conjugates : $R_1 = C_6H_9O_6$, $R_2 = NHCH_2CO_2H$, $R_3 = SO_3H$

% of dose of drug excreted in 24 hr in different forms

ᴇCIES	Amphetamine	4-Hydroxy-amphetamine	Benzoic acid	Phenylacetone	Benzyl-methylcarbinol
ᴀn	30	3	20	3	0
ʜesus monkey	25	6	29	0	0
ᴐg	30	6	25	1	1
ᴀbbit	3	6	23	22*	8
ᴜinea-pig	18	1	65	0	0
ᴏuse	30	15	31	0	0
ᴀt	13	60	3	0	0

Fig. 14. Comparative metabolism of amphetamine. (After Williams, 1971.) No distinction is made between free and conjugated forms in table.* Probably present as enolsulphate.

There are no clear cut trends based on phylogenetic classification, diet or habitat, for either amphetamine or phenol metabolism.

Interesting interspecific differences in dieldrin metabolism and excretion were found between the male Carworth Farm E (CFE) rat, the male Carworth Farm 1 (CF1) mouse and the rabbit (Fig. 4) (Korte and Arent, 1965; Baldwin et al., 1972). The main excreted metabolite in urine and/or faeces in both rats and mice was 9-hydroxy-

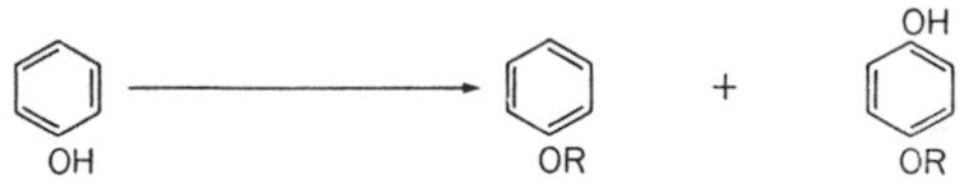

Phenol — Phenol conjugate + Quinol conjugate

$$R = C_6H_9O_6 \quad \text{or} \quad SO_3H$$

% of dose excreted in 24 hr in different forms

SPECIES	Glucuronide of		Sulphate of	
	Phenol	Quinol	Phenol	Quinol
RODENTS				
Guinea-pig	78	5	17	0
Hamster	50	25	25	0
Rat	25	7	68	0
Mouse	33	14	43	5
Gerbil	15	0	69	15
Lemming	38	15	35	12
Jerboa	26	4	61	12
PRIMATES				
Rhesus monkey	35	0	65	0
Squirrel monkey	70	19	10	0
Ring-tailed monkey	65	21	14	0
Man	23	7	71	0
OTHERS				
Cat	0	0	87	13
Ferret	41	0	32	28
Hedgehog	15	0	75	10
Indian fruit bat	90	0	10	0
Pig	100	0	0	0

Fig. 15. Comparative metabolism of phenol. (After Williams, 1971.)

dieldrin, which appears to be a product of mixed function oxidation (Matthews and Matsumura, 1969). The rabbit, on the other hand, excreted mainly the hydration product aldrin *trans*-dihydrodiol, which is only a minor metabolite in the other two species. Rabbit liver microsomes showed 8–11 times more epoxide hydrase activity than male rat liver microsomes towards the dieldrin analogue HEOM (Table IV).

Since studies on epoxide hydrase distribution in mammals show it to be concentrated in the liver microsomes (Oesch *et al.*, 1970; Walker *et al.*, 1973), it is likely that the preference for hydration of dieldrin shown by the rabbit is due to a relatively high activity of this enzyme in the endoplasmic reticulum. The rat also differs from the rabbit in excreting significant quantities of a pentachloroketone and dihydrochlordene 6,7-dicarboxylic acid. The latter metabolite can be formed by oxidation of aldrin *trans*-dihydrodiol in the rat, but this reaction hardly proceeds at all in the rabbit (Oda and Muller, 1972).

Excreted metabolites appeared mainly in the faeces with the rat and the mouse but mainly in the urine with the rabbit. In the case of the rat and the rabbit the same trend has been reported for other organochlorine compounds including heptachlor epoxide, chlordane and HCE (see Walker, 1974) and may be due to differences in threshold molecular weights for biliary excretion between the two species (see Section II.D.). With the rat, all of the metabolites and conjugates isolated from faeces and bile have molecular weights significantly above the threshold value. With the rabbit, the principal urinary metabolite (the diol) has a molecular weight below threshold. There are, however, minor urinary metabolites of dieldrin which appear to be conjugates and their molecular weights are unknown. Uncertainty about metabolic transformation (especially conjugation) in the kidney itself makes it difficult to base conclusions on the structure of urinary metabolites.

The pentachloroketone (mol. wt 351·5) formed by the rat is excreted in the urine and this compound falls within the range of threshold molecular weights cited by Hirom *et al.*, 1972a. It seems likely that this is reabsorbed from bile and excreted by the kidney although one cannot rule out the possibility that it is a metabolite formed by the kidney (Baldwin, 1971). With endrin too, a ketone (mol. wt 397) is the main metabolite in male rat urine, but in this case the molecular weight exceeds the upper limit of the cited range of threshold molecular weights. It should be noted, however, that threshold molecular weights were determined using non-chlorinated compounds of relatively large molecular size in relation to molecular weight (Hirom *et al.*, 1972a). If reabsorption from the bile is related to molecular size, the threshold molecular weight for strongly halogenated molecules could be considerably greater than 325 in the rat.

The levels of a liposoluble compound in tissues are influenced by the induction of liver enzymes. The concentration of butylated hydroxytoluene (BHT) in depot fat rises for 1–2 days when it is regularly administered to rats. Thereafter, as a consequence of enzyme induction, it quickly falls to about half of the maximum concentration reached (Gilbert and Golberg, 1965). Similarly the level of dieldrin storage in rat adipose tissue can be reduced by dosing with inducing agents such as pp'-DDT, pp'-DDE, pp'-DDD, pp'-DDMU, pp'-DDMS and hepta-barbital (Street, 1968). Reduced storage is associated with increased excretion of hydrophilic dieldrin metabolites and increased metabolism of hexobarbital *in vivo* and appears to be the result of enzyme induction. There are species and sex differences in inducibility (see Section II.C.). and these should be reflected in corresponding differences in residue accumulation.

The measurement of biological persistence is discussed in Chapter 2. Dieldrin and certain other organochlorine compounds are very persistent (see Chapter 2, Tables II and V) compared with drugs such

Table VI

Half-lives of foreign compounds in the blood of different species

Species	Half-life (hr)			
	Hexobarbitone	Phenylbutazone	Antipyrine	Meperidine
Man	5·5	72	12	5·5
Rhesus monkey		8	1·8	1·2
Dog		6	1·7	0·9
Rabbit	1·3	3		
Rat	1·0	6		
Rat	2·0			
Mouse	0·5			
Guinea-pig		5		
Horse		6		

After Burns (1970).

as hexobarbitone, phenylbutazone, antipyrine and meperidine (Table VI), and there are striking differences between species with regard to the persistence of the same compound. For example, dieldrin, and the four drugs are most persistent in man and this is correlated with a very low level of cytochrome P_{450} and of mixed function oxidase activity in human liver microsomes (Section II.C.).

The persistence of dieldrin requires further discussion. It is less persistent in male rats than in female rats and this is associated with relatively high mixed function oxidase activity in the liver microsomes of the males (Remmer *et al.*, 1968). The principal dieldrin metabolite in the rat is an oxidation product. A similar sex difference is found with barbiturates in the rat, the speed of elimination again being related to the microsomal oxidase activity (Remmer *et al.*, 1968). The connection between induction and excretion rate has also been demonstrated in the rat (Levine *et al.*, 1970) (Fig. 1). The greater persistence of dieldrin in the male pigeon than in the male rat is also of interest. With other substrates e.g. aldrin, HCE, chlordene epoxide, the pigeon shows

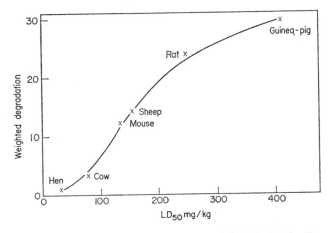

Fig. 16. Dimethoate: relationship between rate of degradation by liver preparations and acute toxicity. LD_{50}s are oral except for guinea-pig which was injected intravenously. Weighted degradation = liver weight as a percentage of body weight $\times$ μg dimethoate hydrolysed/g liver/30 min. (After O'Brien, 1967.)

similar or greater oxidase activity than the rat using liver microsomes (Walker and El Zorgani, 1974).

Malathion provides a good example of selective toxicity between species that is connected with differences in one type of enzyme (see Section II.C.). The fact that the carboxyesterase inhibitor EPN can make mammals as susceptible to malathion as insects strongly suggests that differences in the activity of this enzyme are the main reason for selectivity (O'Brien, 1967). A similar, but more complex, situation exists with the organophosphate insecticide dimethoate (Fig. 16). At first it was hoped that selectivity might be based upon amidase activity, which is high in the mouse but low in the cockroach. LD_{50} tests have shown, however, that there is a considerable range of sensitivity in both insects and vertebrates with no clear distinction between them (O'Brien, 1967). Furthermore, although most breakdown occurs in the liver in vertebrates, some species rely mainly on amidase activity, others mainly on phosphatase activity, and most species upon both. If the manner of degradation is disregarded, there is a good correlation between the weighted total degradation of dimethoate by vertebrate liver *in vitro* and the LD_{50} (O'Brien, 1967). This strongly suggests that metabolism is the most important factor determining dimethoate toxicity in vertebrates.

With insects the situation is different and degradation does not seem to be important in selectivity. The housefly for example is very susceptible to dimethoate and the reasons seem to be: a. very high sensitivity of cholinesterase to the insecticide, b. unusually rapid activation of dimethoate, c. relatively rapid cuticular absorption of dimethoate (O'Brien, 1967).

Investigation of the basis of resistance to insecticides has revealed differences in intake and/or elimination between strains. A well-documented example is the development of DDT resistance by the housefly. Comparing six resistant and four susceptible strains, Brown (1971) has noted that there is a close correlation between LD_{50} and DDT dehydrochlorinase activity *in vivo*. Conversion to the highly persistent but relatively non-toxic metabolite DDE appears to be the most important factor in DDT resistance. Nevertheless other factors such as difficulty of penetration of cuticle, lipid content of body, and insensitivity of nerves to the effects of the chemical are also associated with resistance in the housefly. Reduced susceptibility of nerves may be due to low permeability to DDT, high DDT dehydrochlorinase levels in the nerve, or a combination of the two. A further complication in the housefly is the existence of DDT-resistant strains with elevated microsomal oxidase activity (Oppenoorth, 1965), which is associated with an ability to convert DDT into hydrophilic metabolites. One strain in question lost its resistance after treatment with an inhibitor of mixed function oxidation and showed cross resistance to other insecticides (Oppenoorth and Houx, 1968). It should be added that DDT resistant larvae of *Drosophila melanogaster* and *D. virilis* metabolize DDT to dicofol (kelthane) and this appears to be a mixed function oxidation (Fig. 9). To summarize, the factors involved in the development of DDT resistance in the housefly are relatively complex but the most important single factor seems to be DDT dehydrochlorination.

The association of DDT resistance in *Heliothis virescens* with reduced cuticular penetration has already been discussed (Section II.A.). By contrast, resistance in another strain of the same insect was largely explained by enhanced DDT metabolism. Thus resistance mechanisms may be widely different even in different strains of the same species.

BHC resistance in one strain of housefly has been associated with a threefold decrease in cuticular absorption and a twofold increase in detoxication, but these factors alone are insufficient to account for the resistance found. They are reinforced by a reduced sensitivity of the nerve to γ-BHC in the resistant strain (see Brown, 1971). Interestingly a BHC-resistant strain of the mosquito *Anopheles gambiae* shows strong cross resistance to dieldrin, and this seems to be due to reduced sensitivity of the nerve to organochlorine insecticides and not to reduced absorption or enhanced detoxication (Brown, 1971).

Dieldrin resistance in houseflies does not seem to involve metabolism at all (Brooks and Harrison, 1964; Brown, 1971). The mechanism of resistance is still unclear although the nerves of resistant houseflies are relatively insensitive to the chemical in spite of the fact that the rates of intake and loss by nerves are no different from those in susceptible flies (see Brown, 1971). Dieldrin resistance in SKA flies was due to a major factor and a minor factor. The latter delayed penetration but only gave a twofold resistance (Sawicki and Farnham, 1968). The mechanism of the other factor was not identified.

Enhanced metabolism is the dominant resistance mechanism for organophosphates in the housefly and certain other insects on present evidence. Malathion-resistant strains of housefly and mosquito have shown relatively high carboxyesterase levels, and resistance is counteracted by EPN. In a study of two species of hide beetle it was shown that *Dermestes lardarius* was susceptible to malathion (LD_{50} 1·9 mg/kg) whereas *D. maculatus* was resistant (LD_{50} 19·1 mg/kg). Triphenyl phosphate reduced the LD_{50} for the latter species to 1·6 mg/kg, whereas it slightly increased the value for *D. lardarius* (Dyte, 1969).

Diazinon, like other thiophosphates, is activated by mixed function oxidation to give its $P = O$ analogue (diazoxon). Apart from this, Lewis and Lord (1969) have demonstrated four distinct degradative changes, two of which appear to be acquired resistance mechanisms since they are not found in normal houseflies (Fig. 7) (see Brooks, 1972). The latter two are a. a glutathione-dependent enzyme in the soluble fraction which is inhibited by SSS tributylphosphorotrithioate (TBTP) and removes an ethyl group from diazinon and b. a microsomal oxidase which transforms diazoxon into unknown metabolites and is inhibited by sesamex. The reversal of diazinon resistance by sesamex and TBTP supports the idea that these two systems provide the basis for resistance. The other two conversions occur in both susceptible and resistant houseflies. Diazinon resistance is not associated solely with enhanced metabolism: two resistant strains of housefly show reduced cuticular absorption (Brown, 1971).

In houseflies, carbamate resistance, like organophosphate resistance, is associated with enhanced metabolism (see Brown, 1971).

The development of resistance to persistent pesticides is not confined to invertebrates. A resistant strain of pine mice (*Microtus pinetorum*) had an LD_{50} of 18·97 mg/kg for endrin in contrast to a value of 2·56 mg/kg for normal mice (Petrella and Webb, 1973). The resistance was associated with an increased rate of excretion of hydrophilic metabolites. Whilst the rate of urinary excretion was similar in the two strains, excretion via the faeces was twice as rapid in the resistant strain as in the normal strain. The same faecal metabolites occurred in both strains. Two strains of mosquito fish (*Gambusia affinis*) from the river Mississippi showed resistance to DDT, aldrin and dieldrin. After exposure to 5 pp10^9 of aldrin both resistant strains showed higher levels of dieldrin and water-soluble metabolites in liver than were present in normal fish (Wells *et al.*, 1973), and this may have been due to more rapid metabolism in the resistant strains. The susceptible strain tended to have higher levels of aldrin and dieldrin in the brain than did the resistant strain.

In general, resistance tends to be correlated with reduced tissue levels of liposoluble pesticides, and reduced sensitivity at the site of action appears to be of minor importance. Factors such as intake, distribution, binding, and rates of excretion can all influence the levels established in tissues following exposure but the rate of metabolism tends to be the dominant factor. The development of insect resistance to a wide range of compounds including DDT, diazinon, malathion and carbaryl appears to have depended largely upon the enhancement of degradative enzymes. Such resistance can usually be counteracted by administering inhibitors for the enzyme systems in question. By the same principle synergists may be used to enhance the toxicity of insecticides to species which are non-susceptible due to high enzymic activity.

In this context it should be mentioned that induction occurs in insects as well as vertebrates when they are exposed to persistent liposoluble substances and here it is important to distinguish between induction and genetic change (Plapp and Casida, 1970). Both can involve an increase in enzymic activity but only with induction will the activity return to normal when the constraint is removed.

A few metabolic systems of the microsomal fraction (e.g. microsomal mixed function oxidases and microsomal glucuronyl transferases) are able to metabolize, and thereby promote the excretion of, a wide range of liposoluble foreign compounds (Section II.C.). The significance of this needs to be re-emphasized in the present context. If these systems develop as resistance mechanisms to one compound, then cross resistance to many other substances is bound to follow, even where the chemical structure is very different. In the same way, their induction by one compound can bring increased metabolism of many other substances. Usually induction leads to reduced toxicity but there are exceptions to this. Malathion and parathion for example are strongly activated by mixed function oxidation, their metabolites being potent anti-cholinesterases. Induction usually operates as a defence mechanism, which is reassuring for conservationists but raises problems for users of drugs and pesticides. However, the consequences of induction, like resistance itself, can be offset by the action of enzyme inhibitors.

IV. CONCLUSIONS

The environmental effects of a persistent pollutant can depend on its movement through the 'food web' (see Chapter 2), and it is desirable to identify those species that are likely to be efficient accumulators of it. The discussion in Section III centred upon the possible harmful effects to the organism actually accumulating a foreign compound. But a species may act as an important 'vector' of a pollutant even when unaffected by it.

The rate of metabolism is an important factor in determining the persistence of liposoluble compounds and there are good reasons for suspecting that enzymic differences between species are of key importance here. It is desirable to know which species or groups are deficient in important enzymes and furthermore, which chemical structures are difficult or impossible to metabolize. On the present very limited evidence the following points may be made.

Fish are deficient in certain enzymes which metabolize foreign compounds, e.g. mixed function oxidases, glucuronyl transferases. This may be because they can lose liposoluble compounds by passive diffusion into the surrounding water and they have not therefore developed an efficient system for producing water-soluble metabolites and conjugates which can be excreted in urine or bile. Whether this is true or not, excretion by passive diffusion does not serve them well against highly liposoluble pollutants such as DDT and dieldrin, which they accumulate very efficiently from water (see Section II.A.).

During organochlorine residue surveys of tissues and eggs of British birds in the early 1960s, correlations were noted between diet and the levels of dieldrin and pp'-DDE accumulated (Moore and Walker, 1964; Walker et al., 1967). Higher levels were usually found in predators than in herbivores or omnivores. With respect to the dieldrin residue levels that they contained, terrestrial birds fell into the following order: predators feeding upon birds > predators feeding upon mammals >

insectivores and herbivores. The reasons for this are by no means clear but two possibilities deserve consideration. Firstly, certain types of prey are likely to be more efficient vectors than others. The case of fish has already been discussed. It is also possible that birds are more efficient vectors than mammals. Secondly, species with different diets may differ in their capacity for metabolizing foreign compounds. It has been suggested that herbivores may have evolved more efficient enzyme systems than carnivores because they ingest a wider range of compounds in their diet (Wit and Snel, 1968). If this is correct, some omnivores may possess particularly efficient enzyme systems and it is therefore interesting to note that certain omnivorous members of the crow family showed higher hepatic microsomal epoxide hydrase activity than did other birds which were predominantly herbivorous or fish feeding (see Section II.C.).

In a study of the marine environment of the Farne Islands, the highest dieldrin and DDE concentrations were found in the highest trophic levels (Robinson et al., 1967). Once again fish appeared to be efficient accumulators of these residues. So too did certain fish-feeding birds and it is noteworthy that one of the fish-feeding species (the shag) showed relatively poor activity of microsomal enzymes towards HCE (Walker et al., 1973) (Section II.C.) in keeping with the fact that it contained dieldrin concentrations in the body that were some 50 times higher than the mean level in its prey (Robinson et al., 1967).

Apart from the question of comparative metabolism, insects are likely to be relatively poor vectors because of their sensitivity to dieldrin and this raises an important theoretical issue. The effectiveness of species as accumulators and vectors is limited by their own sensitivity to the toxic action of pollutants. One cannot, therefore, ignore toxic effects when analysing the distribution of pollutants in the living environment.

Turning now to the pollutants themselves, there is great variation in biodegradability between different liposoluble molecules. Certain structures are rather resistant to enzymic attack, e.g. the highly chlorinated ring structures found in cyclodiene insecticides and some polychlorinated biphenyls. With a better understanding of the relationship between molecular structure and resistance to metabolic breakdown, it may be possible to predict which liposoluble compounds will be strongly persistent in which living animals.

In conclusion, we have only limited knowledge of the basis for observed variations in intake and elimination. The situation could be improved by the development of comparative studies, which have been neglected in the past, and by a better understanding of the extent to which in vitro findings can be extrapolated to whole organisms. These two points are related since it is often much easier to do comparative studies (e.g. on metabolism) *in vitro* than *in vivo* and the value of such work increases if it can be used to interpret or predict events in the whole animal (Walker, 1974; Walker and El Zorgani, 1974). At the same time the attractiveness of this line of approach should not distract attention from its limitations and the care that is always needed when arguing from one experimental situation to another.

ACKNOWLEDGMENT

The author is grateful to Dr G. T. Brooks for valuable comments and criticisms.

REFERENCES

Abedi, Z. H. and Brown, A. W. A. (1961). *Ann. ent. Soc. Am.* **54**, 539–542.

Abou El Makarem, M. M., Millburn, P., Smith, R. L. and Williams, R. T. (1967). *Biochem. J.* **105**, 1280–1299.

Adamson, R. H., Bridges, J. W. and Williams, R. T. (1966). *Biochem. J.* **100**, 71.

Alabaster, J. S. (1969). *Proc. Br. Insectic. Fungic. Conf. 5th* 370–377.

Aldridge, W. N. (1953). *Biochem. J.* **53**, 117–124.

Augustinsson, K. B. (1961). *Ann. N.Y. Acad. Sci.* **94**, 844–860.

Baldwin, M. K. (1971). Ph.D. Thesis, University of Surrey.

Baldwin, M. K., Robinson, J. and Parke, D. V. (1972). *Fd Cosmet. Toxicol.* **10**, 333–351.

Benezet, H. J. and Forgash, A. J. (1972). *J. econ. Ent.* **65**, 895.

Benke, G. M. and Wilkinson, C. F. (1971). *J. econ. Ent.* **64**, 1032.

Boyland, E. (1971). *Handbk exptl. Pharmac.* **27**(2), 584–608.

Boyland, E. and Chasseaud, L. F. (1969). *Biochem. J.* **115**, 985–991.

Bradbury, F. R. and Standen, H. (1956). *J. Sci. Fd Agric.* **7**, 389–396.

Bradbury, F. R. and Sta den, H. (1959). *Nature, Lond.* **183**, 983–984.

Brodie, B. B. and Maickel, R. P. (1961). *Proc. 1st Int. Pharmacol. Meeting* **6**, 299.

Brooks, G. T. (1966). *Wld Rev. Pest Control* **5**, 62–84.

Brooks, G. T. (1969). *Proc. Br. Insectic. Fungic. Conf. 5th* 472–477.

Brooks, G. T. (1972). *Environ. Qual. Saf.* **1**, 106–164.

Brooks, G. T. (1973). *Nature, Lond.* **245**, 382–384.

Brooks, G. T. and Harrison, A. (1964). *Biochem. Pharmac.* **13**, 827–840.

Brooks, G. T., Harrison, A. and Lewis, S. E. (1970). *Biochem. Pharmac.* **19**, 255–273.

Brown, A. W. A. (1971). *In* 'Pesticides in the Environment', Vol. I, Part II. pp. 457–552, Marcel Dekker, New York.

Bühler, D. R. and Rasmusson, M. E. (1968). *Comp. Biochem. Physiol.* **25**, 223–239.

Bunyan, P. J., Davidson, J. and Shorthill, M. J. (1970). *Chem. Biol. Interactions* **2**, 175–182.

Bunyan, P. J., Townsend, M. G. and Taylor, A. (1972). *Chem. Biol. Interactions* **5**, 13–26.

Burns, J. J. (1970). The problems of species differences and statistics in toxicology. *Proc. Eur. Soc. Study Drug Toxicity* **XI**, 9–13.

Bush, F. M., Price, J. R. and Townsend, J. I. (1973). *Comp. Biochem. Physiol.* **44B**, 1137–1151.

Chasseaud, L. F. (1970). Foreign compound metabolism. *In* 'Mammals', Vol. 1. The Chemical Society 1.

Clark, A. G., Hitchcock, M. and Smith, J. N. (1966). *Nature, Lond.* **209**, 103.

Clark, A. G., Darby, F. J. and Smith, J. N. (1967). *Biochem. J.* **103**, 49–54.

Clark, A. G., Murphy, S. and Smith, J. N. (1969). *Biochem. J.* **113**, 89–96.

Clark, A. G., Hirom, P. C., Millburn, P. and Williams, R. T. (1971). *J. Pharm. Pharmac.* **23**, 150–152.

Cohen, A. J. and Smith, J. N. (1964). *Biochem. J.* **90**, 449–456.

Creaven, P. J., Parke, D. V. and Williams, R. T. (1965). *Biochem. J.* **96**, 390–398.

Creaven, P. J., Davies, W. and Williams, R. T. (1967). *Life Sci.* **6**, 105–111.

Cserr, H. F. (1967). *Fedn Proc. Fedn Am. Socs. exp. Biol.* **26(II)**, 1024–1026.

Darby, F. J. and Price-Evans, D. A. (1971). *Biochem. J.* **125**, 46–47.

DeWitt, J. B., Menzie, C. M., Adomaitis, V. A. and Reichel, W. L. (1960). *Trans. 25th N. Am. Wild. Conf.* 277–285.

Dinamarca, M. L., Saavedra, I. and Valdes, E. (1969). *Comp. Biochem. Physiol.* **31**, 269–282.

Dutton, G. J. (1971). *Handbk exptl. Pharmac.* **28(2)**, 378–400.

Dyte, C. E. (1969). *Proc. Br. Insectic. Fungic. Conf. 5th* 393–397.

Edwards, C. A. (1970). 'Persistent Pesticides in the Environment'. Butterworth, London.

El Zorgani, G. A., Walker, C. H. and Hassall, K. A. (1970). *Life Sci.* **9**, 415–420.

Estabrook, R. W., Baron, J., Peterson, J. and Ishimura, Y. (1971). *Biochem. J.* **125**, 3–4.

Forgash, A. J., Cook, B. J. and Riley, R. C. (1962). *J. econ. Ent.* **55**, 544–551.

Gilbert, D. and Golberg, L. (1965). *Fd Cosmet. Toxicol.* **3**, 417.

Grover, P. L. and Sims, P. (1965). *Biochem. J.* **96**, 521–525.

Gwiazda, N. and Lord, K. A. (1967). *Ann. appl. Biol.* **59**, 221.

Hirom, P. C., Millburn, P., Smith, R. L. and Williams, R. T. (1972a). *Biochem. J.* **129**, 1071–1077.

Hirom, P. C., Millburn, P., Smith, R. L. and Williams, R. T. (1972b). *Xenobiotica* **2**, 205–214.

Holden, A. V. (1962). *Ann. appl. Biol.* **50**, 467–477.

Hook, G. E. R., Jordan, T. W. and Smith, J. N. (1968). 'Enzymatic Oxidations of Toxicants.' pp. 27–47, N. Carolina State University.

Ishida, M. and Dahm, P. A. (1965a). *J. econ. Ent.* **58**, 383–392.

Ishida, M. and Dahm, P. A. (1965b). *J. econ. Ent.* **58**, 602–607.

Jefferies, D. J. (1971). *Meded. Fakult. Landbouwwetenschappen Gent* **36**, 34–42.

Junge, W. and Krisch, K. (1973). *Molec. cell. Biochem.* **1**, 41–52.

Korte, F. and Arent, H. (1965). *Life Sci.* **4**, 2017–2026.

Krieger, R. I. and Wilkinson, C. F. (1969). *Biochem. Pharmac.* **18**, 1404–1415.

La Du, B. N. and Snady, H. (1971). *Handbk exptl. Pharmac.* **28(2)**, 477–499.

Levine, W. G., Millburn, P., Smith, R. L. and Williams, R. T. (1970). *Biochem. Pharmac.* **19**, 235–244.

Lewis, J. B. and Lord, K. A. (1969). *Proc. Br. Insectic. Fungic. Conf. 5th* 465–471.

Lipke, H. and Kearns, C. W. (1960). *Adv. Pest Control Res.* **3**, 253–288.

Maddrell, J. H. P. (1971). *Adv. Insect Physiol.* **8**, 199–331.

Mason, H. S. (1957). *Science, N.Y.* **125,** 1185–1188.

Matsumura, F. (1971). 'Pesticide Chemistry,' Vol. II. pp. 95–116. Gordon and Breach.

Matthews, H. B. and Matsumura, F. (1969). *J. agric. Fd Chem.* **17,** 845–852.

Mehendale, H. H. and Dorough, H. W. (1972). 'Pesticide Chemistry', Vol. I. pp. 15–28. Gordon and Breach.

Mengle, D. C. and Casida, J. E. (1960). *J. agric. Fd Chem.* **8,** 431–437.

Moore, N. W. and Walker, C. H. (1964). *Nature, Lond.* **201,** 1072–1073.

Moriarty, F. (1968). *Ann. appl. Biol.* **62,** 371–393.

Moss, J. A. and Hathway, D. E. (1964). *Biochem. J.* **91,** 384–393.

O'Brien, R. D. (1967). 'Pesticides: Action and Metabolism.' Academic Press, London and New York.

Oda, J. and Muller, W. (1972). *Environ. Qual. Saf.* **1,** 248.

Oesch, F., Jerina, D. M., Creveling, C. R. and Daly, J. W. (1970). *Fedn Proc. Fedn Am. Socs exp. Biol.* **29,** 473 (Abst).

Oesch, F., Jerina, D. M. and Daly, J. W. (1971a). *Archs Biochem. Biophys.* **144,** 253–261.

Oesch, F., Kaubisch, N., Jerina, D. M. and Daly, J. W. (1971b). *Biochem.* **10,** 4858–4866.

Oesch, F., Jerina, D. M., Daly, J. W., Lu, A. Y. H., Kuntzmann, R. and Conney, A. (1972). *Archs Biochem. Biophys.* **153,** 62.

Dmura, T., Sato, R., Cooper, D. Y., Rosenthal, O. and Estabrook, R. W. (1965). *Fedn Proc. Fedn Am. Socs exp. Biol.* **24,** 1181–1189.

Dppenoorth, F. J. (1965). *Meded. Fakult. Landbouwwetenschappen Gent* **30,** 1390.

Dppenoorth, F. J. and Houx, N. W. H. (1968). *Entomologia exp. appl.* **11,** 81–93.

Os, G. A. J. van, Ariens, E. J. and Simonis, A. M. (1964). 'Molecular Pharmacology,' Vol. I, pp. 7–48. Academic Press, New York and London.

Parke, D. V. (1968). 'The Biochemistry of Foreign Compounds'. Pergamon Press, Oxford.

Petrella, V. J. and Webb, R. E. (1973). *Fedn Proc. Fedn Am. Socs exp. Biol.* **32** (3) (Abstract).

Plapp, F. W. Jr. and Casida, J. E. (1970). *J. econ. Ent.* **63,** 1091–1092.

Remmer, H. (1970). The problems of species differences and statistics in toxicology. *Proc. Eur. Soc. Study Drug Toxicity* **XI,** 14–18.

Remmer, N., Estabrook, R. W., Schenkman, J. and Greim, H. (1968). 'Enzymatic Oxidation of Toxicants.' pp. 65–88. University of N. Carolina.

Robinson, J., Richardson, A., Crabtree, A. N., Coulson, J. C. and Potts, G. R. (1967). *Nature, Lond.* **214,** 1307–1311.

Sanchez, F. F. and Sherman, N. (1966). *J. econ. Ent.* **59,** 272–277.

Sawicki, R. M. and Farnham, H. W. (1968). *Entomologia exp. appl.* **11,** 133–142.

Scheline, R. R. (1968). *J. Pharm. Sci.* **57,** 2021–2037.

Sims, P. (1973). *Biochem. J.* **131,** 405–413.

Smith, J. N. (1968). *Adv. Comp. Physiol. Biochem.* **3,** 173–221.

Smith, R. L. (1971). *Handbk exptl. Pharmac.* **28** (1), 354–389.

Stein, W. D. (1968). 'The Movement of Molecules across Membranes'. Academic Press, London and New York.

Street, J. C. (1968). 'Enzymatic Oxidations of Toxicants,' pp. 197–226. University of N. Carolina.

Sturkie, P. D. (1965). 'Avian Physiology', 2nd edition. Bailliere, Tindall and Cassell, London.

Terriere, L. C. (1968). 'Enzymatic Oxidations of Toxicants' pp. 113–150. University of N. Carolina.

Treherne, J. (1956). *J. Physiol., Lond.* **133,** 171–180.

Vinson, S. B. and Law, P. K. (1971). *J. econ. Ent.* **64,** 1387–1390.

Walker, C. H. (1974). *Environ. Qual. Saf.* **3,** 113–152.

Walker, C. H. and El Zorgani, G. A. (1972). *Environ. Qual. Saf.* **1,** 248.

Walker, C. H. and El Zorgani, G. A. (1974). *Archs environ. Contam. Toxicol.* **2,** 97–116.

Walker, C. H., Hamilton, G. and Harrison, G. (1967). *J. Sci. Fd Agric.* **18,** 123–129.

Walker, C. H., El Zorgani, G. A., Craven, A. C. C., Kenny, J. and Kurukgy, M. (1973). Proceedings FAO/IAEA/WHO Symposium on Nuclear Techniques in Comparative Studies of Food and Environmental Contamination, Otaniemi, Finland, pp. 529–540.

Wang, C. M., Narahashi, T. and Yamada, M. (1972). *Pestic. Biochem. Physiol.* **1,** 84.

Watts, W. S. (1969). *Nature, Lond.* **221,** 762–763.

Wells, M. R., Ludke, J. L. and Varborough, J. D. (1973). *J. agric. Fd Chem.* **21,** 428–429.

Whittam, R. (1964). 'Transport and Diffusion in the Red Cell Membrane.' Physiological Society Monograph.

Williams, R. T. (1959). 'Detoxication Mechanisms,' 2nd edition. Chapman and Hall, London.

Williams, R. T. (1971). *In* 'Fundamentals of Drug Metabolism and Drug Disposition,' pp. 187–205. Williams and Wilkins, Baltimore.

Wit, J. G. and Leeuwangh, P. (1969). *Biochim. biophys. Acta* **177,** 329–335.

Wit, J. G. and Snel, J. (1968). *Eur. J. Pharmac.* **3,** 370–373.

Zeidenberg, P., Orrenius, S. and Ernster, L. (1967). *J. Cell Biol.* **32,** 528–531.

4. The Role of the Thyroid in the Production of Sublethal Effects by Organochlorine Insecticides and Polychlorinated Biphenyls

D. J. JEFFERIES

Institute of Terrestrial Ecology,
Monks Wood Experimental Station,
Abbots Ripton,
Huntingdon, England

I. INTRODUCTION

The organochlorine insecticides have become world-wide environmental pollutants since their inception in the mid-1940s (Rudd, 1964; Moore, 1965; Woodwell et al., 1971). Agricultural, forestry, public health and industrial uses have resulted in considerable residues of these materials and their metabolites in wildlife, particularly birds (Prestt, 1967; Risebrough et al., 1967, 1968; Jensen et al., 1969; Jefferies, 1969b, 1972). Although intended to kill insects these compounds are also lethal to vertebrates if the doses are large enough (Negherbon, 1959; Heath et al., 1972). Lower doses can produce many sublethal effects on both invertebrate and vertebrate animals: those on insects have been reviewed by Moriarty (1969), and those on vertebrates by Stickel (1968), Peakall (1970a), Risebrough et al. (1970), Sprague (1971), Cooke (1973) and Jefferies (1973). Detection, and prediction, of these sublethal effects is important but difficult—the symptoms are diverse and vary with both species and insecticide. Much detailed research has been carried out on the effects of the organochlorines but so far this has been unrelated. We now have a hypothesis for linking these results together. This chapter will suggest that many of the sublethal effects found in vertebrates result from a very few initial lesions involving the thyroid gland. This hypothesis was first put forward by Jefferies (1969a) and expanded by Jefferies and French (1971) to explain the effects of DDT. Here it is further expanded to include the parallel effects found with the other organochlorine insecticides and the polychlorinated biphenyls (PCBs).

Initial sections (II and III) of this chapter describe the various isomers and derivatives of DDT used in experiments and also the normal structure and function of the thyroid to help in understanding the following discussion. Further sections (IV and V) discuss changes in morphology and activity of this organ and the subsequent effects on the metabolic rate of mammals and birds after exposure to organochlorine insecticides. The main part of the chapter takes the form of three reviews. First, reviews of those side effects known to be caused by experimentally altering thyroid activity (Section VI) and the accompanying changes in vitamin A status (Section VII) of the animal. Second, a review (Section VIII) of the known sublethal effects of the organochlorine insecticides on mammals and birds listed under similar headings. These two parallel series of effects are then compared in Section IX to show that most of the sublethal effects seen after dosing with these insecticides may well be due to a primary effect on the thyroid. A review of sublethal effects caused by PCBs (Section X) shows that these too may be due to changes in thyroid activity. Concluding Sections (XI and XII) discuss the various mechanisms which may be involved in producing such thyroid lesions and the importance of this information for understanding effects on wild vertebrates in the field.

II. DDT AND ITS DERIVATIVES

Most of the research on the sublethal effects of the organochlorine insecticides on vertebrates, and their effects on the thyroid, has been carried out using DDT and its derivatives. There are several isomers of the DDT molecule and these vary in the positions of the chlorine atoms on the two phenyl rings (Fig. 1). Technical DDT contains three principal isomers, *para–para'*, *ortho–para'* and *ortho–ortho'* DDT. *pp'*-DDT is the potent insecticide and forms 65–73 per cent of the technical mixture (Metcalf, 1955). The other main constituent is *op'*-DDT (19–21 per cent). Because of this mixture, most tests have been carried out using the

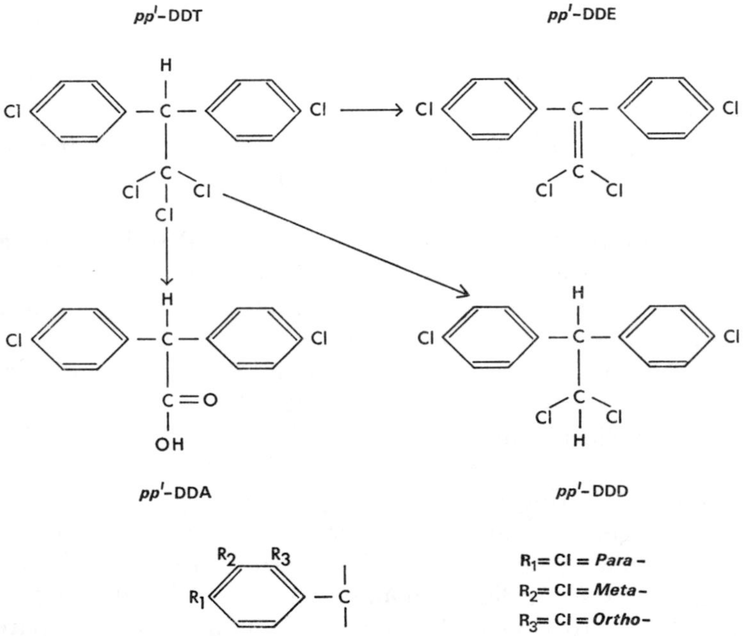

Fig. 1. The molecular configuration of the commonest isomer found in technical DDT, *para-para* DDT, and its three primary metabolites, *pp'*-DDE, *pp'*-DDD and *pp'*-DDA. The various positions of the chlorine atoms in different isomers of DDT and its metabolites are also shown.

pure *para–para'* isomer. The three primary metabolites of DDT which are found in animals dosed with DDT, i.e. DDE, DDD and DDA (Fig. 1), have *ortho*, *meta* and *para* isomers also. Isomers of all three derivatives have been used in experiments to detect sublethal effects. DDE, the main metabolite found on breakdown of DDT in living tissue (Jefferies and Walker, 1966; Fukuto and Metcalf, 1969) is very persistent and forms the most common organochlorine pollutant found in wildlife specimens.

III. THE THYROID GLAND : STRUCTURE, CONTROL AND FUNCTION

A. Form and Structure

Thyroid glands are present in all vertebrates, though their form and position varies greatly. In lower vertebrates, such as teleost fishes, the thyroid follicles may not be organized into a compact gland but may be dispersed in various parts of the organism. In birds the thyroid glands occur as two oval bodies situated separately on either side of the trachea at the base of the neck, and closely associated with the corresponding jugular vein and common carotid artery. In mammals, including man, on the other hand, the thyroid consists of two lobes lying on either side of and closely applied to the trachea and usually joined by a thin isthmus across its ventral surface.

The size of the gland varies relative to the total body weight in different species. In man, for example, the thyroid weighs some 25 to 40 g (Turner, 1966) whereas in the male rat it is only 22 mg (Johnson and LaRoche, 1968). These weights form 0·03–0·06 and 0·003 per cent of the body weight respectively. However, thyroid weights are not constant. The thyroid of both birds and mammals changes in weight with the physiological state of the animal, e.g. with reproductive condition, season of the year, environmental temperature and age. Weights can also vary between different strains of the same species, as in chickens (Sturkie, 1954; Falconer, 1971).

In birds and mammals the gland consists of an outer capsule of connective tissue surrounding a large number (about 100,000 in the rat; Turner, 1966) of approximately spherical follicles. Each follicle consists of a single layer of secretory epithelial cells, which enclose a gelatinous material, the colloid. Colloid is mainly an iodinated protein, thyroglobulin, formed by the secretory epithelium. The interfollicular region consists of a connective tissue stroma, which is highly vascularized. A quiescent thyroid has large follicles, full of colloid, the secretory epithelium is flattened, and the cells are cuboidal or squamous (Fig. 4a). When the activity of the thyroid increases, the volume of colloid decreases and the secretory cells become columnar.

B. Biosynthesis of Thyroid Hormones

There has been little work on the synthesis of the thyroid hormones in groups other than mammals but there is, at present, no evidence that the mechanism of synthesis differs in different classes of vertebrates.

Thyroglobulin is thought to be the storage form of the thyroid hormones. Biosynthesis of this large molecule in the follicular cells starts with formation of polypeptide sub-units containing normal un-iodinated amino acids (Thompson and Goldberg, 1968). These sub-units are then modified by the addition of substituted hexoses to form glycoproteins (Cheftel and Bouchilloux, 1968). Thyroglobulin is formed by aggregation and iodination of the glycoprotein sub-units. Iodination is thought to occur from the time of completion of the sub-units until after the final molecule of thyroglobulin has left the follicle cell and passed to the colloid (Falconer, 1971). The iodine for this process is obtained by concentration of iodide from the blood by the follicle cells (known as the 'iodide trap'). This is converted to iodine by a peroxidase system (Stanbury, 1967). Iodine reacts with the phenol ring of tyrosine in the protein to form first monoiodotyrosine and then diiodotyrosine (see Fig. 2). These iodinated tyrosyl groups are then combined to form triiodothyronine (probably a combination of mono- and diiodotyrosine) and thyroxine or tetraiodothyronine (probably a combination of two units of diiodotyrosine). The probable pathways for the formation of the thyroid hormones are discussed by Turner (1966), Blasi et al. (1969) and Falconer (1971). The completed molecules of thyroglobulin stored in the 'colloid 'of the intrafollicular space, thus contain thyroxine, triiodothyronine and also mono- and diiodotyrosine. Thyroxine and triiodothyronine are released into the circulatory system by hydrolysis of thyroglobulin by a protease secreted by the epithelial cells. This elaboration and breakdown of thyroglobulin in the follicle occurs continuously (Turner, 1966). The mono- and diiodotyrosines which are released do not leave the follicle but are deiodinated in the follicular cells and the iodine is recycled. The two thyronines possibly pass into the circulatory system as a consequence of a concentration gradient between the tissue fluids and the colloid (Turner, 1966).

C. Transport of Thyroid Hormones

In mammals and birds thyroxine and triiodothyronine are transported bound to serum proteins. The amount of thyroid hormone circulating in mammals is usually measured by analysis of the iodine in the blood that is bound to protein. This test for protein-bound iodine (PBI) is too insensitive for use with birds as the PBI levels are very low (Mellen and Hardy, 1957), due to a difference in their thyroxine-binding serum proteins. In mammals thyroxine is bound tightly to an α_2-globulin

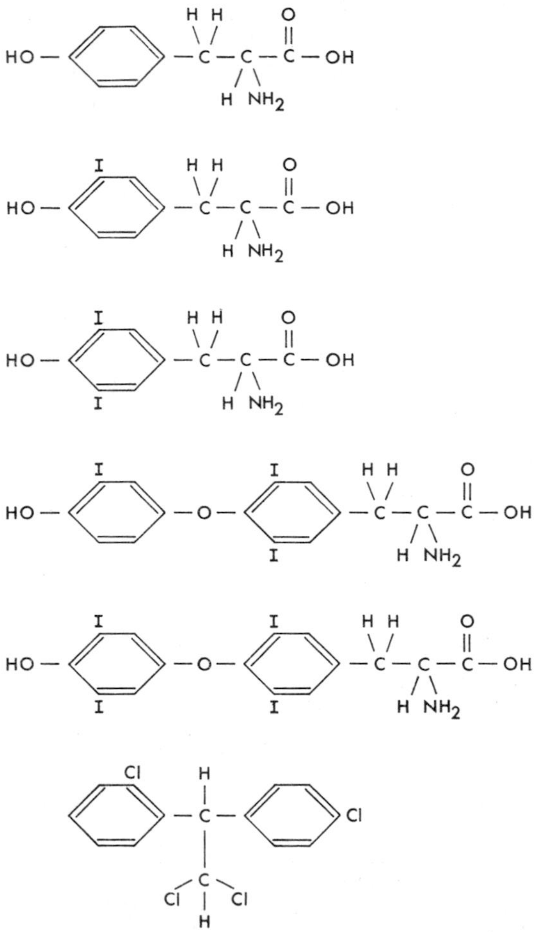

Tyrosine

Monoiodotyrosine

Diiodotyrosine

3,5,3′-Triiodothyronine

3,5,3′,5′-Tetraiodothyronine (Thyroxine)

ortho-para′-DDD

Fig. 2. Molecular configurations of tyrosine, the iodotyrosines and the two thyroid hormones, triiodothyronine and thyroxine, which are formed from them. Also shown is the molecular configuration of *op*′-DDD which is known to compete with thyroxine for binding sites on the thyroxine-binding serum proteins.

which selectively binds this compound. Only a small fraction of the thyroxine is bound to albumin (Robbins and Rall, 1967). Triiodothyronine is more loosely bound to both proteins. Mammalian plasma contains more thyroxine-binding protein than is necessary to bind normal concentrations of thyroxine and only about one-third of the thyroxine-binding capacity is usually in use (Turner, 1966). By contrast, although chickens, turkeys and pigeons are known to have thyroxine-binding prealbumins and albumins they have none of the important thyroxine-binding globulin (Farer *et al.*, 1962). Thus the thyroid hormones are thought to be loosely bound to albumin and prealbumin in avian blood and also transported in free solution (Falconer, 1971). The result is that the binding of thyroxine to duck and chicken thyroxine-binding proteins is much poorer than that in man and tests show that avian thyroxine binds rapidly with the human serum proteins when these are mixed with avian blood (Sturkie, 1965).

D. Action at Tissue Level

At the site of action the circulating hormones are freed from their carrying proteins, pass through the capillary walls and diffuse into the tissues. Some binding of thyroid hormones may then occur by tissue proteins (Turner, 1966). The actual form of the thyroid hormone acting upon peripheral tissues is unknown. Though thyroxine is the principal circulating thyroid hormone, many workers have thought that it may not be the active form and have suggested that a conversion to triiodo-thyronine or another form may occur before the tissues are affected. Within the cell the hormones may stimulate the synthesis or activation of oxidative enzymes and affect the metabolic rate by acting at one or more points in the Krebs cycle (Turner, 1966). The effect may be localized in the mitochondria.

The activity of the two thyroid hormones differs in birds and mammals. In the chicken, triiodothyronine and thyroxine have about the same potency, but in certain tests with mammals, the former has been found to have about seven times the potency of the latter (Heninger and Newcomer, 1964; Falconer, 1971). Again, this difference between birds and mammals is thought (Falconer, 1971) to be related to the variation in protein-binding of the two hormones in the two classes (see Section III.C.). Thus, in mammals, thyroxine is more strongly bound (to an α-globulin) than triiodothyronine and is therefore less able to diffuse into the tissues (Tata and Shellabarger, 1959). In birds, however, both are weakly bound to the same degree.

E. Catabolism of Thyroid Hormones

Catabolism of the thyroid hormones is largely carried out in the liver and to a lesser extent by the kidneys. Both thyroxine and triiodo-thyronine are conjugated as glucuronides in the liver or alternatively broken down by oxidative deamination. The conjugated hormones and deaminated metabolites then pass to the intestine in the bile (Turner, 1966). Small amounts of thyroxine, both free and in conjugated form, are excreted through the kidney.

The relatively short half-life (compared with that in mammals) of administered thyroid hormones in birds is thought (Falconer, 1971) to be one of the consequences of their loose binding with avian serum proteins (see Section III.C.). For instance, the half-lives of thyroxine and triiodothyronine in chicken plasma are 8·3 and 7·2 hr (Heninger and Newcomer, 1964), whereas in guinea-pigs and sheep the half-life of thyroxine is 31·3 and 37 hr respectively (Frienkel and Lewis, 1957; Ray and Premachandra, 1964).

F. Functions of the Thyroid

The thyroid has many functions, which have been studied in laboratory animals by surgery and with chemical agents that block or cause an apparent increase in thyroid activity. Thus hypothyroidism (the condition of the body associated with a diminished or apparently diminished secretion of the thyroid gland) may be produced by removing the thyroid (thyroidectomy) or the pituitary (hypophysectomy). Alternatively, the use of a chemical goitrogen such as thiouracil (see Section III.H.) produces a similar effect. Hyperthyroidism (the condition of the body associated with an abnormally high rate of secretion of thyroid hormones) may be brought about by oral administration or ingestion of thyroprotein (or iodocasein: prepared by iodinating casein), desiccated thyroid tissue or thyroxine itself. These studies have shown that one of the main functions of the thyroid is to control the metabolic rate and the response of the animal to the environmental temperature. The thyroid also plays a major role in the control of growth rate and normal thyroid activity is essential for successful reproduction in both birds and mammals. The moulting of birds is also under thyroid control.

In man, hyperthyroidism, in the form of Graves's disease, increases the metabolic rate. The patient loses weight rapidly as the result of increased catabolism of tissue protein and oxidation of stored fat. There is a marked nervous excitability, a fine involuntary tremor, breathlessness after exertion, a rapid heart beat, a warm flushed skin and an anxious, staring expression. The opposite condition, hypothyroidism, known as myxoedema in man, produces up to a 40 per cent decrease in the metabolic rate, subnormal temperature, slow pulse and respiration, slow speech and thinking, with a depression in sexual function. The hair becomes scanty and the skin is rough and coarse. There is a considerable increase in body weight and a puffiness, not due to oedema, but to a deposit of semifluid material containing 13 per cent protein. Hypothyroidism in the human infant is described as cretinism (Bell *et al.*, 1952).

G. Control of Thyroid Hormone Secretion

In homoiotherms thyroid activity is directly controlled by the thyroid stimulating hormone (TSH) secreted from the anterior lobe of the pituitary (Fig. 3). This hormone, which circulates in very low concentrations, produces a very rapid response in the thyroid gland. Within

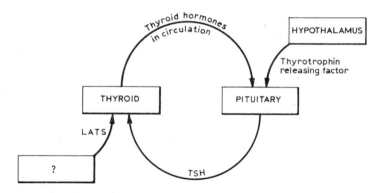

Fig. 3. Schematic representation of the feedback system which controls the release of thyroid hormones and the direct effects of the LATS system and the hypothalamus on the thyroid and pituitary respectively.

minutes of administration, the blood flow through the gland increases and there is an increased output of thyroid hormones by hydrolysis of the thyroglobulin in the storage colloid (Falconer, 1971). Later there is an increased iodide uptake and an increased thyroid hormone synthesis. The follicular epithelial cells become columnar, the quantity of stored colloid decreases and the gland increases in size. The relative amounts of TSH and thyroid hormone in the circulatory system are largely controlled by a negative feedback system, i.e. a low concentration of thyroid hormones in the blood acts on the pituitary causing it to release TSH which subsequently causes the thyroid gland to release thyroxine and triiodothyronine.

The central nervous system can also regulate TSH release directly by means of a neurosecretion (thyrotrophin releasing factor). This is liberated into the portal system within the hypothalamus and passes to the anterior pituitary where it causes a rapid release of TSH (Falconer, 1971). This second, nervous control of TSH and subsequent thyroid hormone secretion is of importance in the response of the animal to stresses such as pain and low temperatures and also during reproduction (Turner, 1966; Falconer, 1971; see Section VI.C.).

In recent years it has been found that pituitary TSH is not, at least in the pathological condition, the only hormone governing thyroid activity. A long-acting thyroid stimulator (LATS) may be involved in the pathogenesis of Graves's disease (McKenzie, 1965). When Harris and Woods (1958) showed that electrical stimulation of the rabbit's hypothalamus caused hyperthyroidism, presumably because of excessive release of TSH from the pituitary, it was thought that this might be the mechanism of this particular disease. However, repeated attempts to show increased thyrotrophin in the blood of affected patients gave inconclusive results. Later, another theory gained acceptance following experiments by Adams and Purves (Adams and Purves, 1956; Adams, 1958). The thyroid hormones of guinea-pigs were labelled with I^{131} and their endogenous TSH was suppressed by injecting thyroxine. Stimulation of the thyroid with exogenous TSH then increased the radioactivity of the blood which was at a maximum three hours after injection. However, if sera from hyperthyroid patients was injected instead, the I^{131} level in the guinea-pig's plasma was higher 16 hours after injection than it was three hours after. This demonstrated the presence of LATS in the abnormal sera. Adams showed also that TSH and LATS were both acting on the thyroid concurrently in such a situation. LATS is active on the thyroid of the mouse as well as of the guinea-pig, and this action is direct and not mediated by the pituitary. Thus LATS occurs in the blood of Graves's diseased subjects even after they have undergone pituitary-ablative surgery. There are major differences in the biological and physicochemical properties of LATS and TSH and it now seems certain that they are quite different compounds with different origins (McKenzie, 1965). However, the origin of LATS has yet to be established.

It is likely that other organs and hormone systems also play minor roles in thyroid control. Thus Turner (1966) suggests that since the liver is one of the major organs concerned with the destruction of excess thyroid hormone, it may play a secondary role in regulating the level of these materials circulating in the body. The links between thyroid secretion and levels of vitamin A (see Section VI.F.) suggest further complexity.

H. Changes in Thyroid Appearance and Function with Diet, Chemical Goitrogens and Surgery

The thyroid gland shows characteristic lesions after interference at various levels in the mechanisms of its control and thyroid hormone synthesis. The enlarged gland which usually results from such treatment is known as a goitre and chemical agents producing it are goitrogens.

1. Diet

Lack of sufficient iodine in the diet inhibits thyroid hormone synthesis. Therefore, the flow of thyroid stimulating hormone (TSH) from the pituitary continues unchecked and the thyroid attempts to restore thyroid hormone production to a satisfactory level. At first there is a compensatory hyperplasia (increase in number) and hypertrophy (increase in size) of the cells of the secretory epithelium with a decrease in follicle size. The amount of colloid also decreases. The gland becomes more vascular and increases in size and weight. This condition is known as simple hyperplastic goitre and indicates a highly active gland. If, after a period of time, the augmented pituitary stimulation does not succeed in restoring normal thyroxine output, the thyroid may become exhausted. The gland then decreases in size and atrophies. If, on the other hand, the supply of iodine is restored, the thyroid may recover. In man, large colloid goitres are endemic in certain geographical areas with low environmental iodine (Gillie, 1971). These goitres characteristically show follicles which are predominantly enlarged with flattened epithelia and distended with abnormally acidophilic colloid. However, small foci showing hyperplasia and others showing atrophy are present also (Ogilvie, 1962). Such goitres are thought to be the long term result of repeated cyles of regression and partial recovery with changes in available iodine and can be produced experimentally in mammals (Turner, 1966). Goitres due to iodine deficiency are known in birds also (Patton *et al.*, 1939). A marked and continuous deficiency of thyroid hormones in circulation may cause the production of tumours in the anterior pituitary (Turner, 1966).

2. Thiouracil and Sulphonamides

Goitres have been produced experimentally by the use of chemical agents, especially by the thiocarbamide derivatives (thiouracil, thiourea, propylthiouracil) and the sulphonamide drugs. Both produce hyperplastic goitres with loss of colloid and hyperplasia/hypertrophy of the secretory epithelium. These compounds act by blocking the iodination of tyrosine and so prevent the production of thyroxine and triiodothyronine. The enlarged thyroid can be reduced again by removal of the pituitary, the source of TSH (Turner, 1966).

3. Thiocyanates

Similar hyperplastic goitres are produced by thiocyanate, but by a different action. Here the chemical agent interferes with the 'trapping' of iodide ions within the thyroid (Turner, 1966).

4. Removal of the pituitary

The production of TSH can be eliminated or reduced by surgically removing the pituitary (hypophysectomy), or by isolating it from the hypothalamus by cutting the stalk or infundibulum (hypothalectomy). Hypothalectomized animals still possess the pars distalis but the output of TSH is subnormal without the thyrotrophin releasing factor from the hypothalamus. The thyroid enlarges, with large follicles containing abundant colloid and with flattened epithelia. This suggests minimal depletion of secretion. In hypophysectomized animals TSH is completely lacking and the thyroids atrophy. The capacity of the gland to trap iodide is then greatly reduced and only traces of thyroxine are produced (Turner, 1966).

IV. THYROID CHANGES AFTER FEEDING ORGANOCHLORINE INSECTICIDES

A. Thyroid Changes in Mammals

Nelson et al. (1944) were the first to report mild changes in the thyroids, of mice, rats, guinea-pigs, rabbits and dogs fed sublethal doses of DDT. Some of the rabbits and dogs showed moderate depletion of stainable colloid in the follicles but most showed no effect. Only four rats, two guinea-pigs and two mice were examined for thyroid changes. Three of the rats and both guinea-pigs showed moderate colloid depletion, but the mice showed no change. Such thyroid changes were thought to be of no significance at the time (Cameron and Burgess, 1945; Haag et al., 1948). No further work on this topic was published until 1968, by which time DDT and its metabolites had become world-wide pollutants and op'-DDD was in use as a drug for administration to patients suffering from adrenal carcinoma (Marshall and Tompkins,

1968). Fregly *et al.* (1968) then showed that *op'*-DDD (1,000 and 3,000 ppm), *mp'*-DDD (1,000 ppm) and *pp'*-DDD (1,000 and 3,000 ppm) fed to rats for 24 weeks increased their thyroid weights by 62, 81, 112, 94 and 113 per cent respectively. Later work by Wassermann *et al.* (1972) showed that dieldrin also produced a 'hyperfunctional morphologic appearance' (presumably increased size and decreased colloid) in the thyroids of treated rats.

B. Thyroid Changes in Birds

pp'-DDT and *pp'*-DDE are both known to produce marked effects on the reproductive success of the Bengalese finch, *Lonchura striata* (Jefferies, 1971). Many of the side effects found in these studies (e.g. delays in egg-laying and changes in egg weight—see Section VIII.B.) suggested a syndrome similar to that produced in domestic fowls by inducing hyperthyroidism (Jefferies, 1969a). As the thyroids of Bengalese finches are very small, further work to see if the avian thyroid is affected by organochlorine insecticides was carried out using the feral pigeon, *Columba livia*. Preliminary experiments feeding *pp'*-DDT to three groups of four pigeons at 9, 18 or 36 mg/kg/day for six weeks doubled the thyroid weight (Jefferies and French, 1969). A larger experiment, using 25 control and 54 DDT-dosed pigeons with five different dose rates, given for eight weeks, confirmed this increase in thyroid weight (Jefferies and French, 1971) and showed that the increase was similar at all dose rates (Table I). There were indications that pigeons dosed for 17 weeks had even larger thyroid weights.

The thyroids of all control birds had follicles with normal amounts of colloid, distributed evenly throughout the gland. The epithelial cells were squamous or cuboidal in shape (Fig. 4a). The thyroids from dosed birds, however, had smaller follicles, less colloid and hyperplastic epithelia. Some birds showed complete loss of colloid material. There was also evidence of vascular congestion with dilated capillaries (Fig. 4b). A quantitative estimate of the amount of colloid was made by measurement of the colloid areas within a standard microscope field. The decrease in colloid area was found to be similar over the whole range of exposures, 3–36 mg DDT/kg/day. As with thyroid weight and apparent morphological activity, there was no evidence of a graded response and, on average, sections from dosed birds had only 17 per cent of the colloid found in control sections (Table I).

Further work with *pp'*-DDE and dieldrin showed that dose rates of 18, 36 and 72 mg/kg/day DDE and 1, 2 and 4 mg/kg/day dieldrin also all produced hyperplastic goitres in the thyroids of pigeons. The

Table I

The total thyroid weight and the mean colloid area in thyroid sections from pigeons, *Columba livia*, dosed with dieldrin, *pp′*-DDE or *pp′*-DDT for eight weeks

Treatment	Dose rate in mg/kg/day	Concentration of insecticide in liver in ppm wet weight	Thyroid weight in mg (± S.E.)	Colloid area in μ^2 per field of 300,000 μ^2 (± S.E.)
Control	0	< 0·1 DDE	45 ± 3	49,580 ± 11,970
pp′-DDT	3	10·4 DDT + 16·4 DDE	89 ± 26	8,750 ± 8,210
	6	17·9 DDT + 26·1 DDE	70 ± 18	5,390 ± 3,870
	9	18·9 DDT + 25·0 DDE	78 ± 15	5,340 ± 3,400
	18	53·4 DDT + 166·3 DDE	95 ± 14	9,680 ± 5,870
	36	58·3 DDT + 293·7 DDE	85 ± 9	3,290 ± 1,860
pp′-DDE	18–72	235·9 to 500·1 DDE	81 ± 11	16,870 ± 15,150
Dieldrin	1–4	27·4 to 65·3 dieldrin	80 ± 20	10,050 ± 4,740

Data from Jefferies and French (1971, 1972).

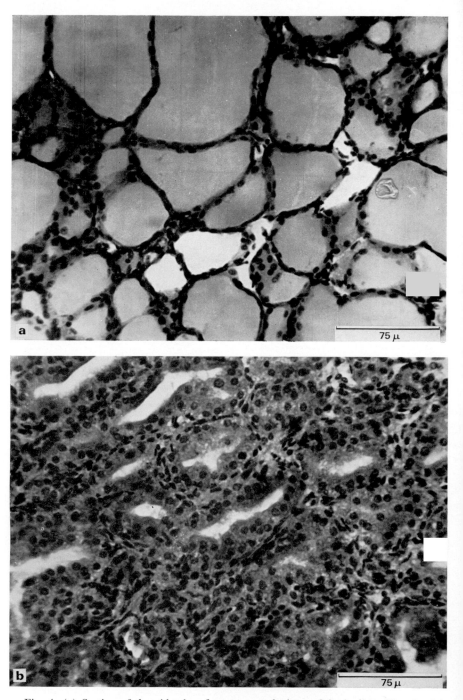

Fig. 4. (a) Section of thyroid taken from a control pigeon *Columba livia*. The gland is quiescent with follicles containing normal quantities of colloid. (b) Section of thyroid from pigeon dosed with *pp*′-DDT at the rate of 36 mg/kg/day for 42 days. This shows a reduction in follicular size and almost complete loss of colloid associated with hyperplasia.

thyroids were significantly enlarged, had less colloid (Table I), and visual examination showed small follicles, epithelial hyperplasia and vascular congestion (Jefferies and French, 1972).

Recent work by Richert and Prahlad (1972), carried out in a different way to the above experiments, showed different effects on the avian thyroid. Japanese quail *Coturnix coturnix* were fed DDA (200 ppm), DDT (100 ppm) or DDE (150 ppm) for 120 days and then returned to a normal diet for a further 85 days before the thyroids were examined. The thyroids of the birds originally fed DDE were significantly larger than those of controls (almost twice as large) even after this long period on normal diet. The thyroids of DDT-fed birds were larger than those of controls, but not significantly so, whilst those of DDA-fed birds were unaffected. Thyroid sections showed considerably enlarged follicles in both the DDT- and DDE-fed groups. This is just the opposite to that found by Jefferies and French (1969, 1971, 1972). Furthermore, the follicular epithelia of the thyroids from the DDE-fed group were frequently composed of simple squamous cells or low cuboidal cells. The DDT- and DDE-fed groups also had fewer resorption vacuoles in the peripheral follicles and none in the central follicles.

Work with chickens suggests that their thyroids are not affected like those of pigeons and quail. Thus, Davidson and Sell (1972) found that the thyroid size of white leghorn chickens was not significantly changed when dosed with either 100 or 200 ppm pp'-DDT or 10 or 20 ppm dieldrin in the diet. This lack of obvious effect is probably a valid result, but may have been duet to the environmental temperature, which can affect greatly the response of the thyroids. Thus mallard, *Anas platyrhynchos*, dosed with DDT during a very hot summer, when air temperatures even outside the pen reached 31°C, showed only a very minor effect on thyroid weight and colloid depletion (Jefferies, unpublished results). At this temperature the thyroid would be fairly inactive in any case and the effect of a goitrogen would be reduced. An investigation of the rate of thyroid secretion at various temperatures has been made by Dempsey and Astwood (1943). These authors treated rats with thiouracil and found that the rate of thyroid enlargement was low in a hot environment and high in cold temperatures.

C. Indications from these Changes

The thyroid morphology found after feeding organochlorine insecticides to both mammals and pigeons, i.e. increased size and weight, with hyperplasia and reduced colloid content of the follicles, indicates a highly active gland (see Sections III.G. and H.). This, at first sight, supports the original hypothesis that Bengalese finches were hyper-thyroid when fed DDT. However, these morphological changes are not specific and hyperplastic goitres can reflect either a hyper- or hypofunctioning gland (i.e. one producing much or very little thyroid hormone respectively—see Section III.H.). A hyperfunctioning gland may be the result of a. direct stimulation of the pituitary or thyroid to produce excess TSH or thyroid hormones respectively, b. stimulation of the LATS system, or c. a reduction in the concentration of circulating thyroid hormones which would stimulate the pituitary to produce TSH. This in turn would then stimulate the thyroid to accelerate the formation and secretion of thyroxine (see Section III.G.). A hypofunctioning gland may result if d. DDT acts as a goitrogen. Goitrogens, such as thiouracil, produce the same morphological picture of a highly active gland, as described above, but the gland is hypofunctioning as the formation of thyroid hormones is suppressed within it (see Section III.H.). With causes a. and b. the animal concerned would be in a state of hyperthyroidism, and with cause d. in a state of hypothyroidism. With cause c., as long as a sufficient supply of thyroid hormones remained available, symptoms of hypothyroidism would not develop. However, if the thyroid could not maintain a sufficiently high level of circulating hormone, hypothyroid symptoms would become apparent. With over-stimulation it is possible that hyperthyroidism could develop. Further investigations involving biochemical tests of levels of PBI in the serum or physiological tests of parameters of the metabolic rate are necessary to determine whether such hyperplastic goitrous thyroids are hyper- or hypofunctioning (see Section V).

No such doubts exist in the case of the quail experiment (Richert and Prahlad, 1972). The enlarged thyroids with increased colloid exhibited by this species show involution or inactivity with minimal depletion of colloid. The numbers of resorption vacuoles are low and these are known to decrease as thyroid activity decreases. Thus, these animals can only be in a state of hypothyroidism.

V. PRODUCTION OF HYPER- AND HYPOTHYROIDISM IN ANIMALS FED ORGANOCHLORINE INSECTICIDES AND THEIR DERIVATIVES

A. Hypothyroidism in Mammals

Fregly *et al.* (1968) noted indicators of metabolic rate, such as food intake and oxygen consumption, of the rats they dosed with *op'-*, *pp'-* and *mp'*-DDD (see Section IV.A.). At the 1,000 ppm dose rate, although there was an increase in thyroid weight, there were no overt symptoms of either hyper- or hypothyroidism. At 3,000 ppm, on the other hand, the increased thyroid weight was accompanied by a reduction in food intake, body weight gain and oxygen consumption, and an increased rate of cooling upon exposure to cold air. These symptoms are indicative of a hypometabolic state and the authors concluded that DDD resulted in hypothyroidism in the rat.

In man, op'-DDD is given as a drug to patients with adrenal carcinoma (Marshall and Tompkins, 1968). Early in the development of this treatment Danowski *et al.* (1964) reported that administration of op'-DDD could regularly be expected to decrease the amount of protein-bound iodine (PBI) in the serum (see Section III.C.). Further work carried out by Marshall and Tompkins (1968) on two patients with adrenal carcinoma, showed that although both had normal PBI levels before treatment, op'-DDD therapy reduced these by about 75 per cent. Neither patient had any thyroidal disorders before treatment and neither Danowski nor Marshall and Tompkins found any signs or symptoms of hypothyroidism during treatment, although slight lethargy was reported.

This effect on PBI level is not restricted to op'-DDD nor to people undergoing therapy for adrenal carcinoma. Wassermann *et al.* (1971) determined the PBI levels in the serum of 42 workers handling organochlorine pesticides and compared them with the levels from 51 people non-occupationally exposed to pesticides. Practically all the serum PBI values were within the range considered as normal, but the serum PBI was significantly lower in workers occupationally exposed to organochlorine insecticides ($5.42 \pm 0.49 \,\mu g/100$ ml) when compared to the mean value in non-occupationally exposed people ($6.93 \pm 1.12 \,\mu g/100$ ml). Wassermann *et al.* (1972) also carried out further work using specific insecticides and rabbits as test subjects. They found that both dieldrin and γ-BHC (given at 50 ppm in the drinking water) caused a significant decrease of serum PBI. This confirmed their original findings from the field and suggests that the reduction of PBI levels, and thus circulating thyroxine in mammals, is probably a common property of the organochlorine insecticides.

B. Hyper- and Hypothyroidism in Birds

The thyroids of pigeons fed DDT, DDE or dieldrin appeared highly active (see Section IV.B. and C.) but further tests were made (Jefferies and French, 1971; Jefferies *et al.*, 1971) to determine whether the final effect on the animals was hyperthyroidism or hypothyroidism. Four

Table II

The body temperature (after 11 weeks) and liver vitamin A stores (after 17 weeks) of pigeons, *Columba livia*, dosed with pp'-DDT

| Group | Dose rate in mg/kg/day DDT | | Body temperature after 11 weeks (in °C) | Vitamin A storage in liver after 17 weeks (in International units vitamin A/g of liver) | |
	During first regime of 11 weeks	During second regime of six weeks	Mean ± S.E.	Mean ± S.E.	Range
A	Control	Control	—	239 ± 19	199–309
B	Control	3	41·58 ± 0·13	389 ± 45	256–531
C	3	36	41·42 ± 0·09	324 ± 65	187–606
D	36	54	40·37 ± 0·21	63 ± 14	17–105

Data from Jefferies and French (1971).

groups (A, B, C, D) of six pigeons were fed pp'-DDT at dose rates of 0, 0, 3 or 36 mg/kg/day for 11 weeks, after which the rates were changed to 0, 3, 36 and 54 mg/kg/day respectively for a further six weeks (Table II). Two parameters of metabolic rate were measured in groups B, C and D during these dosing regimes. The body temperature was measured four times during the eleventh week of the first regime and twice weekly during each of the six weeks of the second regime. Oxygen consumption was also measured once weekly from the eleventh week onwards. At the end of the seventeenth week on dose, the surviving birds of all four groups were killed and the level of vitamin A in the liver was measured soon after death. This can be used as another indicator of metabolic rate because of its association with thyroid activity (see Section VI.F.).

After 11 weeks of dosing during the first regime the body temperatures were similar in the control Group B and low dose rate Group C but significantly lower in the high dose rate Group D (Table II). Two to three weeks after starting dosing Group B at 3 mg/kg/day during the second regime, the mean body temperature first increased to 41·85 ± 0·07°C but then decreased. At 36 and 54 mg/kg/day (Groups C and D) there was a significant rapid decrease in body temperature with time (Fig. 5a). During the six weeks Group D was fed 54 /mg/kg/day DDT, all six birds showed decreased appetite and trembling and were eventually killed when at the point of death. When trembling started the body temperature was 39·52 ± 0·35°C and this dropped to less than 38·0°C just before death.

Oxygen consumption in the control Group B was 1·004 ± 0·047 ml/hr/g body weight at the eleventh week of the first regime. Dosing this group at 3 mg/kg/day during the second regime caused a significant increase in consumption with time. Presumably this increase would have continued because Group C showed a mean consumption of 1·230 ± 0·160 ml/hr/g after 11 weeks on this dose rate during the first regime. Dosing at 36 and 54 mg/kg/day (Groups C and D; second regime), on the other hand, caused a significant decrease in oxygen consumption with time. After 11 weeks dosing at 36 mg/kg/day oxygen consumption was 0·760 ± 0·065 ml/hr/g (Group D; first regime) and 54 mg/kg/day DDT caused even further reduction (Fig. 5b).

The liver vitamin A storage in Group B was significantly higher than that of the control whilst that of Group D was significantly lower (Table II). In Group C the range of vitamin A values was very large. It is probable that the dose rate and timing was such that birds in this group were on the point of changing from high vitamin A storage as in Group B to low storage as in Group D.

Table III

Organ weights of pigeons Columba livia dosed with DDT, DDE or dieldrin for eight weeks

Treatment	Dose rate in mg/kg/day	% Mortality	Mean body weight of group in g	Mean organ weight ± standard error		
				Liver (g)	Paired adrenals (mg)	Heart (ventricles only) (g)
Control	0	0	401 ± 15	8·8 ± 0·7	39·7 ± 2·2	4·20 ± 0·16
pp′-DDT	3	0		9·1 ± 0·3	37·9 ± 3·8	4·63 ± 0·27
	6	0		10·5 ± 0·7	34·6 ± 6·8	
	9	0	418 ± 7	11·3 ± 0·7	45·0 ± 5·5	
	18	0		16·7 ± 1·1	47·5 ± 6·1	
	36	12		19·9 ± 0·8	46·7 ± 5·1	
	54	100		33·7 ± 3·6	59·9 ± 14·3	2·63 ± 0·15
pp′-DDE	18	0		19·8 ± 3·8	33·2 ± 3·9	4·22 ± 0·14
	36	33	414 ± 10	22·3 ± 1·4	63·9 ± 40·2	3·43 ± 0·57
	72	100		26·1 ± 0·7	77·6 ± 14·1	3·07 ± 0·12
Dieldrin	1	0		6·8 ± 1·2	26·8 ± 0·9	3·86 ± 0·33
	2	0	397 ± 15	7·9 ± 0·3	28·9 ± 3·7	4·50 ± 0·19
	4	67		10·4 ± 0·6	51·9 ± 5·4	3·81 ± 0·42

Data from Jefferies and French (1971, 1972); Jefferies et al. (1971).

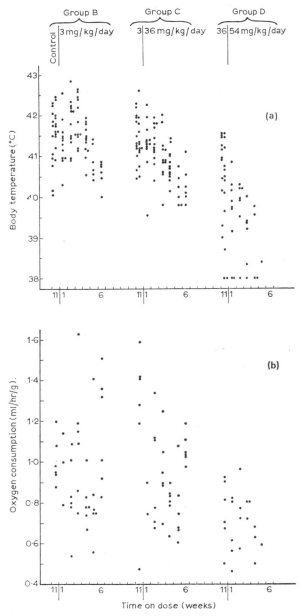

Fig. 5. Changes in (a) body temperature and (b) oxygen consumption of pigeons *Columba livia* dosed with *pp'*-DDT at various dose rates: Group B after control diet for 11 weeks and 3 mg/kg/day DDT for six weeks, Group C after 11 weeks on 3 mg/kg/day followed by six weeks on 36 mg/kg/day and Group D after 11 weeks on 36 mg/kg/day followed by six weeks on 54 mg/kg/day. (Reproduced with kind permission of the editor of *Environ. Pollut.*)

The effects of DDT on the above three indices of metabolic rate suggest therefore that metabolism increases as exposure increases until a critical level is reached, above which the metabolic rate decreases again. To confirm this suggestion, further work was undertaken on the pulse rate, amplitude of the ventricular beat and the heart weight of DDT-dosed pigeons (Jefferies et al., 1971). Thyroxine is known to accelerate the heart beat of domestic fowls (Höhn, 1961) and to increase the heart weight (Irwin et al., 1943). Forty-two pigeons were divided into five groups and given 3, 6, 9, 18 or 36 mg/kg/day DDT, whilst a further 12 birds were maintained as controls. Pulse rate and amplitude of the ventricular beat was then measured for each bird one day before dosing started and also after three weeks and six weeks of dosing.

The mean pulse rate before dosing was 269 $\pm$ 12 beats/min (range 133–518). The percentage changes in pulse rate after three weeks are shown in Fig. 6a. The pulse rate of the controls decreased by 17·0 per cent after three weeks and 19·8 per cent after six weeks. Such a decrease is common where daily handling causes a progressive increase in the confidence of the animal in the handler. Dosing with 3 mg/kg/day for three weeks increased the pulse rate 35·0 per cent relative to the controls. Higher dose rates produced progressively smaller increases of pulse rate. The pattern at six weeks was similar to that at three weeks.

The changes in amplitude of the ventricular beat after three weeks are shown in Fig. 6b. As with pulse rate, the amplitude in the controls had decreased (by 5·9 per cent) after three weeks. Dosing with 3 mg/kg/day DDT for three weeks increased the amplitude by 8·8 per cent when compared with that of the control. Increasing the dose rate then produced a significant decline in amplitude, until at 36 mg/kg/day this was lower than that of the controls with a mean decrease of 8·7 per cent taking the control decrease into account. A similar pattern was obtained at six weeks.

Such an effect on heart pulse rate and amplitude may be expected to change the weight of the heart if continued for a long enough period. To confirm the above pulse rate and amplitude changes, the hearts of 60 homing pigeons which had been fed 3, 6, 9, 18, 36 or 54 mg/kg/day of DDT for eight weeks were therefore weighed and compared with 19 controls of similar body weight (Fig. 7). The heart weight was increased by 10·3 per cent by feeding 3 mg/kg/day DDT but then decreased significantly with increasing dose rate until at 54 mg/kg/day they weighed only 62·7 per cent of those of the controls. At the highest dose rate the heart musculature had become thin and flaccid. Jefferies and French (1972) found that the hearts of pigeons dosed with DDE at 36 and 72 mg/kg/day were reduced in weight also (Table III).

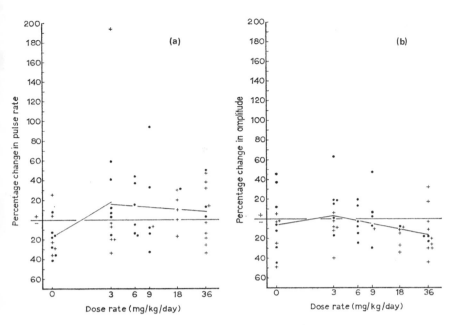

Fig. 6. The percentage change (● females; + males) in (a) pulse rate and (b) amplitude (as measured by total S + T deflection on the electro-cardiogram) in controls and dosed pigeons *Columba livia* after three weeks treatment with 3 to 36 mg *pp'*-DDT/kg body weight/ day. The starting point for each individual was the pulse rate and amplitude one day before dosing started. The dose rate + 1 is plotted on a log scale. The increase in pulse rate and amplitude between 0 and 3 mg/kg/day is shown by a line joining the means for these groups and the decrease with higher dose rates is shown by the calculated regression line. The horizontal line indicates the 'no-change' ordinate. (Reproduced with kind permission of the editor of *Br. Poult. Sci.*)

Any alteration in thyroid function alters metabolic rate. The changes in the metabolic rate of DDT-dosed pigeons follow an inverted 'V'-shaped pattern with increasing dose. This suggests that low dose rates of DDT (notably 3 mg/kg/day) produce hyperthyroidism (or a boost in the metabolic rate) which is then switched to hypothyroidism of increasing severity at all higher dose rates. This conclusion is supported by the changes in the vitamin A levels in the liver. The conversion of dietary carotene to vitamin A and its subsequent liver storage are greatly influenced by thyroid activity. Johnson and Baumann (1947) found that induction of hypothyroidism in rats lowered the total liver stores of vitamin A, whereas in hyperthyroid animals the liver stores of this vitamin were higher than those in controls. Thus, the vitamin A levels found in pigeons (Table II) fit the concept of production of both hyper- and hypothyroidism on dosing with DDT.

Further support is given by the results for pulse rate, amplitude (Fig. 6) and heart weight (Fig. 7). Although the presence of a boost in the metabolic rate at 3 mg/kg/day DDT is more difficult to substantiate than the steady decline with increasing dose rate, the sum product of six indications of such a boost leaves little doubt as to its presence. Apart from this initial boost, the presence of hypothyroidism after dosing of pigeons with DDT presents a similar picture to that found in dosed mammals. There is as yet no indication that such an initial boost in metabolic rate occurs in mammals.

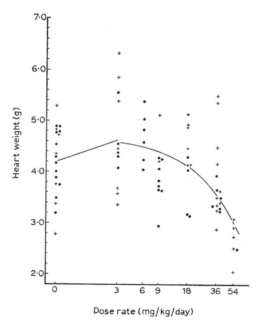

Fig. 7. The ventricular weights of pigeons *Columba livia* dosed with *pp'*-DDT at 0–54 mg/kg/day for eight weeks (● females; + males). The dose rate + 1 is plotted on a log scale. The increase in heart weight between 0 and 3 mg/kg/day is shown by a line joining the means for these groups and the decrease with higher dose rates is shown by the calculated regression line. (Reproduced with kind permission of the editor of *Br. Poult. Sci.*)

A second avian species in which hypothyroidism has been proved is the Japanese quail. It has been noted already that this bird showed large involuted thyroids after being fed DDT or DDE (see Sections IV.B. and C.). Further work by Richert and Prahlad (1972) showed that the uptake of I^{125} by the thyroids of the DDE group was significantly reduced. It was approximately half that of the control group and confirms that both formation and depletion of colloid was minimal.

In contrast to pigeons and quail, *pp'*-DDT appears to induce only hyperthyroidism in Bengalese finches (see Section IV.B.). Further measurements were therefore made on pulse rate, amplitude of the ventricular beat and heart weight of DDT-dosed Bengalese finches in order to confirm this suggestion. Four Bengalese finches were dosed with DDT at four different dose rates ranging from 3·8 to 11·7 mg/kg/day for six weeks (some mortality occurs at dose rates between 12 and 19 mg/kg/day DDT and 19 mg/kg/day is the limiting dose rate for survival in this species—see Table IV), whilst a further four birds were maintained as controls. The mean pulse rate for the eight birds was 954 ± 16 beats/min before dosing started. The controls showed a slight gain of 2·3 per cent after three weeks and of 3·7 per cent after six weeks. Although the mean increase in pulse rate of the dosed birds was only 7·9 per cent at three weeks, at six weeks their pulse rate had increased by a mean of 16·9 per cent to an average of 1,101 beats/min. The four dosed birds at 3·8, 7·5, 8·7 and 11·7 mg/kg/day showed pulse rate increases of 6, 18, 21 and 23 per cent respectively (Jefferies et al., 1971). The amplitude of the ventricular beat was greatly increased (17·8 per cent) in the controls after three weeks but the increase shown by dosed birds was very much greater (30·0 per cent) (Jefferies et al., 1971). Unlike the pigeons these birds were not handled daily for dosing and so lacked the confidence which comes with habituation.

Such considerable changes in pulse rate and amplitude, if sustained, could be expected to alter heart size and weight. Weighing the ventricles of 104 finches from DDT experiments (Table IV) showed that there was indeed an increase over the controls even at the lowest dose rate of 2·3 mg/kg/day. Increasing the dose rate up to and including lethal doses then progressively increased the heart weight. The maximum ventricular weight in dosed birds (0·477 g) was over twice that of controls (0·230 g). The positive correlation between heart weight and dose rate was significant for both males and females (Jefferies, 1969a).

Thus, it appears that Bengalese finches dosed with DDT are indeed in a state of hyperthyroidism. Also, the steady increase in heart weight with increasing dose rate suggests that they remain in a state of hyperthyroidism even up to lethal dose rates, i.e. there is no phase of hypothyroidism in this species as there is in the pigeon.

It is possible that the domestic chicken reacts in a similar way to the Bengalese finch. Many of the reactions of the chicken to doses of organochlorine insecticides are those usually following hyperthyroidism (see Section IX.A.3.). The lack of change in thyroid size found by Davidson and Sell (1972) in this species supports rather than detracts from this theory. An increase in circulating thyroid hormones need not

Table IV

The heart and liver weights of Bengalese finches *Lonchura striata* fed *pp'*-DDT in the diet for over 100 days

| Dose rate of DDT (mg/kg/day) | | No. of birds in group | % Mortality | Liver weight (g) Mean ± standard error | | Heart weight (g) | |
Range	Mean for group			Male	Female	Mean ± S.E.	Range
Control	0	28	4	0·569 ± 0·021	0·682 ± 0·031	0·185 ± 0·003	0·150–0·230
0– 5	2·32	37	3	0·556 ± 0·017	0·668 ± 0·019	0·193 ± 0·003	0·162–0·235
5–12	7·74	20	5	0·569 ± 0·023	0·671 ± 0·032	0·204 ± 0·016	0·143–0·477
12–19	15·79	12	17	0·569 ± 0·019	0·695 ± 0·027	0·212 ± 0·014	0·168–0·313
over 19	33·64	7	100	0·497 ± 0·024	0·652 ± 0·209	0·215 ± 0·016	0·182–0·308

Data from Jefferies, previously unpublished results.

There was no significant difference in body weight between treated and control birds or between males and females. All birds died within 46 days at any dose rates above 19 mg DDT/kg body weight/day.

be accompanied by a greatly increased thyroid size whereas hypothyroidism following goitrogenic activity or a reduction in circulating
thyroxine is likely to be accompanied by thyroid weight changes.

VI. THE EFFECTS OF HYPER- AND HYPOTHYROIDISM ON MAMMALS AND BIRDS

The effects of both hyper- and hypothyroidism on the animal and its
capacity for reproduction are considerable and the degree of effect can
vary with the severity of the disorder. This section lists most of the
functions of the thyroid together with the known effects of increasing
or decreasing its activity. The next section covers those effects likely to
follow the attendant changes in vitamin A status. These are the effects
which one would expect to follow the changes in thyroid activity
brought about by organochlorine insecticides.

A. Metabolic Rate, Growth Rate, Body Weight and Food Consumption

The most characteristic effect of the thyroid hormones in homoiotherms
is to increase oxygen consumption and energy production in the tissues
affected. In mammals, the pituitary-controlled increase in thyroxine
output as environmental temperature decreases (and the corresponding
decrease as temperature increases) is important in regulating the body
temperature and basal metabolic rate to ensure survival (Collins and
Weiner, 1968). A similar change in thyroxine output with environmental temperature has been observed in birds (Chaudhuri and Sadhu,
1961; Hendrich and Turner, 1965; Falconer, 1971). In the experimental situation, as would be expected, administration of thyroid
hormones increases the basal metabolic rate whereas thyroidectomy
or hypophysectomy decrease the rate below normal. Mcyer and
Ranson (1945) found that thyroidectomy or 0·5 per cent of the goitrogen thiouracil in the diet of rats reduced the basal metabolic rate by
59 per cent. As little as 0·1 per cent thiouracil in the drinking water of
young rats depressed this rate by 23·7 per cent (Reineke et al., 1945).
   Thyroidectomy, or the administration of goitrogens, decreases the
growth rate of birds and mammals. Thus, the growth rate of chickens
and turkeys was retarded when they were fed thiouracil (Kempster and
Turner, 1945; Andrews and Schnetzler, 1946; Blakely and Anderson,
1949). In mammals, thyroidectomy in immature sheep, goats, rabbits

and rats has long been known to retard both growth and maturation (Goldsmith *et al.*, 1945). Inducing hypothyroidism in the adult animal also decreases the body weight. Leathem (1945) found a loss in body weight in adult rats fed 1 per cent thiourea, and Blivaiss and Domm (1942) noted that the body weights of cockerels thyroidectomized for moulting experiments were 40 to 45 per cent below those of the controls. Several authors have reported a reduction in food intake of birds (Blakely and Anderson, 1949; Snedecor, 1971) and mammals (Leathem, 1945) after thyroidectomy or treatment with goitrogens. However, the depression in body weight or growth rate was greater than could be accounted for by the slight reduction in food intake alone (Leathem, 1945) and in some cases the efficiency of food utilization has been significantly lower in hypothyroid goitrogen-fed chickens and turkeys (Kempster and Turner, 1945; Blakely and Anderson, 1949).

Treatment of animals with thyroproteins and the production of mild hyperthyroidism produces the opposite effect. Koger *et al.* (1942) reported an improvement of growth and appetite in mice receiving subcutaneous injections of crystalline thyroxine and Wheeler *et al.* (1948), feeding thyroproteins to young chickens, found that they grew more rapidly during the first six weeks. If too high a level of thyroxine is given to the animal, however, severe hyperthyroidism results in toxic symptoms and a reversal in effect. Thus, Irwin *et al.* (1943) found that the production of hyperthyroidism in young chicks fed thyroactive iodocasein caused them to be heavier than the controls at 12 weeks of age. On the other hand, when fed at higher rates (about double) the growth rate was depressed. Severe hyperthyroidism in adults may decrease body weight due to oxidation of body fat (see Section III.F.).

B. Behavioural Changes

There are several outward changes in the movements and behaviour of human patients suffering from hyper- and hypothyroidism. Thus, one of the diagnostic symptoms of hyperthyroidism in man is a fine muscular tremor which may be seen most easily by the magnified movements of the tip of the extended index finger. Subtotal thyroidectomy eliminates this tremor (Bell *et al.*, 1952). Also, it has been known for some time that the excess of thyroid hormones in circulation in subjects with Graves's disease (see Section III.F.) may react upon the nervous system, possibly through the feedback system (see Section III.G.), thus modifying the patient's behaviour. There may be emotional instability, nervousness, muscular tremors and even dementia

(Turner, 1966). Another form of dementia, known as myxoedema dementia, occurs in men suffering from very severe hypothyroidism (Adams and Rosman, 1971). This may be due to very slow cerebration (see Section III.F.).

C. Reproduction of Mammals

Berliner and Warbritton reported, as early as 1937, that semen quality in rams was at its lowest during the summer months. They suggested that this poor sperm production may be associated with the decline in thyroid hormone secretion following the high temperatures during this period. Indeed, treating rams with thyroxine during August improved semen characteristics. Later research confirmed that reduced thyroid activity was a major factor in the production of summer sterility in stock animals. Thus, Bogart and Mayer (1946) and Reineke (1946) confirmed that thyroxine or thyroproteins alleviated this symptom in rams and bulls respectively.

Hypothyroidism can also affect reproduction in the rat. Thus, Leathem (1946) reported that thiourea decreased seminal vesicle size. However, Jones et al. (1946), who administered thiouracil to both male and female rats, found that there was no effect upon the males' ability to sire litters (out of 11 males, ten sired litters). On the other hand, the resulting reproductive success was very low. Out of 27 matings of 15 females, 22 resulted in conception followed by absorption of all the foetuses. The overall results were therefore somewhat similar to those reported after DDT administration to mice (Bernard and Gaertner, 1964; see Section VIII.A.7.).

D. Reproduction of Birds

Normal production of thyroid hormones is very important in the development of the gonads and the secondary sexual characters of birds as well as for successful reproduction (Taylor and Burmester, 1940; Blivaiss, 1947). Egg weight, egg production, shell weight, yolk weight, time of ovulation and male fertility may all be altered by changes in thyroid activity. Usually hypothyroidism reduces reproductive success whilst mild hyperthyroidism improves it. Excessive hyperthyroidism again produces an effect similar to that of hypothyroidism, so there is a 'U'-shaped relationship of effect to thyroid activity as found in growth rate studies (see Section VI.A.). The various effects are detailed below.

1. Delayed Ovulation

Moderate hyperthyroidism in hens fed desiccated thyroid reduced both the growth rate of the ovum and the weight of yolk in the egg laid (Asmundson and Pinsky, 1935).

2. Egg Production

Reineke and Turner (1945) were the first to investigate the annual cycle in thyroid hormone output from the thyroid gland of the chicken. They found that the lowest activity occurred during the period from April to August with maximum secretion during October and November. This cycle of low avian thyroid activity during the summer followed by elevation in the winter is now well documented and is almost certainly regulated by environmental temperature. High environmental temperatures depress thyroid secretion (Falconer, 1971) whilst low temperatures increase TSH release (Hendrich and Turner, 1965).

It has been suggested that this seasonal slight hypothyroidism is the possible cause of the decline in egg production which usually occurs in chickens during the summer months (Thornton and Moreng, 1959; Tyler and Geake, 1960; Sturkie, 1965). Indeed, when tested, extremes of hypothyroidism brought about by thyroidectomy and thiouracil have been found to reduce egg production drastically (by about 70 per cent in one case) (Taylor and Burmester, 1940; Berg and Bearse, 1951). A tendency to hyperthyroidism, on the other hand, appears to produce the opposite effect (Crew, 1925). Thus, studies of the correlation between the laying ability of individual chickens and their natural level of thyroid activity have shown that hens laying four-egg sequences have a higher thyroxine secretion rate than similar hens laying two-egg sequences (Booker and Sturkie, 1950). Also, feeding optimum amounts of thyroproteins helps to prevent the above seasonal fall in egg production (Turner et al., 1945a,b). However, higher rates of thyroprotein intake decreased egg production. Thus, whilst both extremes of thyroid activity reduce laying drastically, moderate degrees of hyper- and hypothyroidism cause slight increases and decreases in egg production respectively.

3. Egg Weight

The weights of eggs laid by experimental chickens are decreased by both extremes of thyroid malfunction. Thus, hypothyroidism produced by thyroidectomy (Taylor and Burmester, 1940) or thiouracil (Berg and Bearse, 1951) and hyperthyroidism, produced by the use of thyro-proteins or iodized casein (Asmundson and Pinsky, 1935; Wilson, 1949), both reduced the weights of eggs laid.

4. Shell Weight and Thickness

Chicken eggshells are thinner in summer and it is thought that this may be due to the reduced thyroid activity during this season (see Section VI.D.2.). Experimental tests of this theory have provided some positive results. Thus, thiouracil in the diet of chickens was found to reduce their shell thickness (Gabuten and Shaffner, 1954). Also, in earlier work, Taylor and Burmester (1940) had noted a 9 per cent reduction in percentage shell weight after thyroidectomy of this species. Conversely, hyperthyroidism, produced by adding iodinated casein or thyroproteins to the diet, caused chickens to lay eggs with thicker shells (Berg and Bearse, 1951; Gabuten and Shaffner, 1954). Also Wilson (1949) reported that thicker shells were sometimes laid by hens made hyperthyroid in his experiments. However, it is known that, during the latter work, the egg weight also decreased, so it is possible that the shell weight itself may not have been affected—the same weight of shell material over a smaller egg would result in a thicker shell. On the other hand, Asmundson and Pinsky (1935) found that hyperthyroidism increased the shell weight of their experimental hens slightly, so shell weight and thickness may both be increased. It is feasible, though as far as I know unproven, that, following the usual relationship of effect with thyroid activity, more extreme hyperthyroidism would again result in thin-shelled eggs. There is some support for this possibility: both hyper- and hypothyroidism will inhibit the oestrogen-induced rise in plasma calcium (see next section).

5. Changes in Calcium Metabolism

Deposition of medullary bone (a source of calcium for eggshells in the female—see Section VIII.B.20.) can be induced in drakes by treatment with oestrogen. Thyroidectomy of such treated birds retards this bone formation (Benoit and Clavert, 1947). The increase in oestrogen occurring in laying hens causes an increase in the amount of calcium in the plasma. This rise can be inhibited by both thyroxine and thiouracil (Höhn, 1961).

6. Fertility of Males

Wheeler and Andrews (1943) found that semen production in cockerels increased significantly in winter. The volume of semen, the total number of spermatozoa per ejaculate and the average sperm survival time were all at their highest during the period November to March. Later research showed that this cycle, like that for egg production and eggshell thickness, was linked with that of the thyroid.

Hypothyroidism, induced by thiouracil in the diet, decreased development of seminiferous tubules, reduced the volume of semen produced and decreased the motility and survival time of the spermatozoa of chickens (Shaffner and Andrews, 1948). There was a significant reduction in actual male fertility (controls 35–45 per cent; treated 0–10 per cent fertility). Shaffner and Andrews concluded that thiouracil and the consequent hypothyroidism decreased the ability of the spermatozoa to survive within the oviduct of the hen. On the other hand, moderate hyperthyroidism produced by low doses of thyroid hormone increases the sperm concentration in the semen (Wilwerth et al., 1954). Also, Hays (1948) found that he could prevent the seasonal decline in the fertility of cockerels, as occurred in his controls, by administration of low doses of thyroxine. Again as in other parameters, high doses of thyroxine depress spermatogenesis (Sturkie, 1965) and impair fertility (Wilwerth et al., 1954). Both hyperthyroidism (Irwin et al., 1943; Wheeler et al., 1948) and hypothyroidism (Blivaiss and Domm, 1942; Andrews and Schnetzler, 1946) reduce the testes weight of growing chickens.

7. Secondary Sexual Characters

Several authors have reported that hypothyroidism in young cockerels retards the development of comb, wattles and spurs (Blivaiss and Domm, 1942; Andrews and Schnetzler, 1946; Shaffner and Andrews, 1948). The comb weight of goitrogen-fed (hypothyroid) cockerels was only one-third that of the control group (Snedecor, 1971). Tests of the effects of hyperthyroidism, produced by feeding thyroproteins to young chickens, showed that here too there was a significant decrease in the weight of the comb when compared with controls (Wheeler et al., 1948). It is likely that these reductions in comb size and weight are caused by the depression in androgen secretion from the smaller testes, which are known to result from both hypo- and hyperthyroidism. It is possible that mild hyperthyroidism may produce combs as large as or larger than those of controls, because this treatment is known to increase male fertility (see previous section).

8. Ageing

Crew (1925) fed desiccated thyroid gland to cocks and hens, five to eight years old, for a period of six months. After moulting, their plumage was characteristic of younger fowl. The head furnishings too were red and turgid, and egg production was increased. Thus, mild hyperthyroidism had in some way 'rejuvenated' the test animals.

E. Induced Changes in the Thyroid Activity of the Embryo

As early as 1945 Goldsmith *et al.* reported that when pregnant rats were fed a diet containing thiourea, the offspring showed hyperplasia in the thyroid gland. Also, it has been known for some time that the use of propylthiouracil therapy, to treat human hyperthyroidism during pregnancy, resulted in goitre in the newborn child (Burrow, 1965). The thiourea group of drugs can cross the placental barrier, and it is thought that the goitres are caused by indirect stimulation of the production of foetal TSH. Animal experiments have shown that treatment with thyroxine inhibits this development of goitre in the foetus as thyroxine is also able to cross the placental barrier (Burrow, 1965).

A parallel situation exists in birds. Thiouracil in the diet of hens caused the development of goitrous thyroid glands in the chicks hatching from their eggs (Andrews and Schnetzler, 1945). Again the evidence suggested that the thiouracil was included in the egg at laying and then affected the embryo during development. Goitrous thyroid glands are also produced in the offspring of hens fed diets containing thyroproteins (Wheeler and Hoffman, 1948; McCartney and Shaffner, 1949a). Eggs from these hens fed either thyroproteins or thiouracil showed a small but obvious prolongation of the incubation period. Injecting eggs with the goitrogen thiourea produced a similar prolongation of incubation time (Brandstetter *et al.*, 1962).

Wheeler and Hoffman (1948) concluded from further work on the chicks hatching from the eggs laid by hens fed thyroproteins, that since they had a prolonged incubation period, a greater thyroid size and a decreased heart rate they were hypothyroid. This unexpected and surprising observation was later confirmed by McCartney and Shaffner (1949b), who measured the thyroid activity and metabolic rate of chicks hatched from eggs laid by both thyroprotein- and thiouracil-fed hens. As might be expected, the hens themselves showed by their rate of oxygen consumption that the former treatment produced hyperthyroidism (12 per cent higher oxygen consumption) and the latter produced hypothyroidism (30 per cent decrease in resting metabolism). However, both treatments of the dam produced chicks with an oxygen requirement 16 per cent less than that of controls and with a lower thyroidal activity.

The production of hypothyroid chicks from hens fed the goitrogen thiouracil would be expected with this material being passed to the egg as suggested. Further evidence for this reasoning was provided by McCartney and Shaffner (1949b) who found that the thyroid glands of the chicks from thiouracil-fed dams continued to enlarge during the first week after hatching, presumably due to the thiouracil stored in the yolk sac. However, this continued enlargement after hatching did not occur in chicks from thyroprotein-fed dams and the reason for their hypothyroidism is as yet unclear. McCartney and Shaffner injected thyroxine into the eggs laid by the thyroprotein-fed females and found that this consistently reduced the thyroid size of the hatching chicks. This indicated that there was an actual deficiency of thyroxine in these eggs, and they deduced that the exogenous thyroxine given to the parent in the thyroproteins was not accumulating within their eggs. McCartney and Shaffner postulated that, as the exogenous thyroxine is not passed to the egg, the reduction in the amount of maternal thyroxine passing to the egg may be of greater importance. A high level of exogenous thyroxine circulating in the female would reduce its TSH production and hence its thyroid activity. Huston and Wheeler (1961), however, proposed that the embryonic goitrogenicity of the thyroprotein was due to one of its major components, diiodotyrosine. Metabolism of this material by the embryo and the liberation of iodide could indirectly lead to goitrous thyroids through inhibition of embryonic thyroxine production.

Injection of thyroxine into the egg is said to shorten the incubation period (Beyer, 1952) but Rogler et al. (1959) could not confirm this. Booker and Sturkie (1949) showed that, as might be expected, the embryonic thyroid is involuted when the egg's thyroxine content is increased in this way.

F. Storage and Circulation of Vitamin A

The link between thyroid activity and vitamin A metabolism has been studied intensively. The evidence for an inter-relationship between the two is based on claims that thyroxine influences the storage of vitamin A and the rate at which this vitamin is used up. Also, that thyroxine is concerned in the absorption and conversion of carotene to vitamin A. Moore (1957) reviewed this research and concluded that there was little doubt of the ability of the thyroid to influence the metabolism of vitamin A but that probably many instances of presumed interaction could be explained by the influence of the thyroid gland on the basal metabolic rate, which in turn influences vitamin A metabolism. There is, however, other evidence to suggest a more direct link between the two, and some authors suggest an 'antagonistic' effect of one on the other. Thus, it has been found that experimentally induced severe excess of vitamin A in an animal may have an antithyroid effect and suppress thyroid activity (Sadhu and Brody, 1947; Frape *et al.*, 1959) as well as vice versa. One of the results of changes in thyroid activity is a change in vitamin A storage in the liver. Thus, Johnson and Baumann (1947) found that hypothyroid rats store very little vitamin A in the liver whereas hyperthyroid animals store more vitamin A than control rats. The reverse result has been reported for vitamin A in the blood of human patients: it is low in hyperthyroid patients and high in those with hypothyroidism (Moore, 1957). Such a reversal between levels in liver stores and blood is to be expected (see Section VIII.A.8.).

G. Other Effects

1. Feather Structure and Moulting

The thyroid hormones are important in the moulting process of birds. Thyroid activity normally increases prior to moulting and any interference with this activity may produce an abnormal moult. Thus, thyroidectomy prevents the moult occurring in some species, whilst in young birds it may delay the appearance of the adult plumage. Feathers in thyroidectomized cockerels show a loss of melanin and a change in structure: they have a fluffy appearance due to a decrease in the numbers of barbs and barbules (Blivaiss and Domm, 1942). Injection of thyroxine reverses this effect and restores feather structure to normal (Falconer, 1971). On the other hand, feeding thyroproteins to chicks improves the rate of feather growth (Irwin *et al.*, 1943; Parker, 1943; Wheeler *et al.*, 1948). Induction of severe hyperthyroidism by large doses of thyroid hormones brings on a sudden moult within seven or eight days (Sturkie, 1965).

2. Circulatory System

Feeding thyroactive iodocasein to growing chicks increases the heart weight of both sexes, presumably because of an increased pulse rate (Irwin *et al.*, 1943). The heart weight increases progressively with the dose rate of thyroxine. In man, hyperthyroidism is associated with a rapid pulse rate and hypothyroidism with a slow one (Bell *et al.*, 1952).

Another of the symptoms accompanying myxoedema (hypothyroidism in adult man) is that of anaemia (Bell *et al.*, 1952). This has been verified in rats too as feeding them thiourea reduces their erythrocyte counts (Leathem, 1945). Leathem also found that thiourea increased plasma globulin. Plasma albumin was unchanged. He reported other work showing that hypophysectomy and thyroidectomy also increased serum globulin concentration. Administration of thyroxine to hypophysectomized rats prevented the rise in serum globulin.

3. Water Balance

The blood volume is much reduced in hypothyroid animals, with extra-cellular retention of water, sodium and chloride. Administration of thyroid hormones to such an animal causes diuresis and a urinary loss of sodium. Treatment of normal individuals with thyroid hormones causes excessive water and potassium loss through the kidneys (Turner, 1966).

4. Organ Weights

One of the most important organs to show weight changes with changes in thyroid activity is the liver. Shaffner and Andrews (1948) induced hypothyroidism in cockerels with thiouracil and found that the liver weight was approximately doubled. Snedecor (1968; 1971) confirmed this result with chicks. Shaffner and Andrews noted that these enlarged livers showed increased fat deposition and congested liver sinuses. The liver weight remains unchanged in chicks made hyperthyroid by feeding them thyroactive iodocasein (Irwin *et al.*, 1943). The above increase in liver weight with induced hypothyroidism may occur only in birds, as Leathem (1945) found that there was no change in the liver weight of hypothyroid rats.

Growing chicks made hyperthyroid by ingesting thyroproteins, showed a significant decrease in the weight of the pituitary (Irwin *et al.*,

1943; Wheeler *et al.*, 1948). A reduction in spleen size has been noted in hypothyroid chickens (Shaffner and Andrews, 1948).

Hypertrophy of the adrenal appears to follow induced hypothyroidism in mammals. Thus, the adrenal weights of rats increased by 50 per cent after treatment with the goitrogen, thiourea (Leathem, 1945). Adrenal hypertrophy also occurs after treatment of rats with another goitrogen, Amphenone 'B' (Hertz *et al.*, 1950; Hogness *et al.*, 1953). Sturkie (1965) records that enlargement of the adrenals follows induced hypothyroidism in birds and that hyperthyroidism may produce a similar effect.

5. Fat and Carbohydrate Metabolism

Experimental alteration of thyroid activity can change both fat and carbohydrate metabolism. Thus, fat deposition increased significantly in chickens made hypothyroid with thiouracil (Andrews and Schnetzler, 1946). Also, feeding 0·1 per cent thiouracil to turkeys increased the fat deposition and improved carcase grades. The percentage skin fat of the thiouracil-fed birds was, on average, more than double that of controls (Blakely and Anderson, 1949). The liver glycogen concentration in hypothyroid chickens is much higher than that in controls (Snedecor, 1971).

6. Incidence of Disease and Limb Disorders

Shaffner and Andrews (1948) noted that cockerels made hypothyroid with thiouracil were much more susceptible to common poultry diseases such as respiratory disturbances and Newcastle disease. Also, Blivaiss and Domm (1942) found that thyroidectomized chickens commonly developed respiratory disturbances which were often fatal. This connection between hypothyroidism and respiratory disturbances is most probably linked to the levels of vitamin A in the affected animals (see Section VII.A.1. and 2.).

There also appears to be a correlation between hypothyroidism and the incidence of perosis or slipped tendon. In perosis, the leg bones of the developing bird are well calcified and hard but become bowed or badly twisted during growth and the Achilles' tendon slips out of its normal position (Barger *et al.*, 1958). This disorder was one of the symptoms observed in young chicks fed thiouracil for five weeks (Briggs and Lillie, 1946). The authors suggested that thyroxine may aid in preventing perosis under normal conditions.

VII. THE EFFECTS OF A DEFICIENCY OR EXCESS OF VITAMIN A

Adequate levels of vitamin A are important to both developing and adult mammals and birds. This vitamin is required for the regeneration of the visual pigments, rhodopsin and iodopsin, to maintain the normal regeneration of the secretory cells of the internal and external epithelia of the body and to maintain normal bone growth. It is also essential for normal embryonic development. Both a deficiency and an excess of vitamin A produce characteristic lesions in the animals concerned. These have been reviewed for both mammals and birds by Moore (1967a and b) and for birds by Coates (1971). The effects are of relevance because of the close relationship between vitamin A metabolism and storage and thyroid activity (see Section VI.F.). Thus, some of the effects found after administration of thyroproteins or thiouracil may be due to changes in vitamin A levels, e.g. the absorption of the foetus (see Sections VI.C. and VII.A.1.) and the increased incidence of infection (see Sections VI.G.6. and VII.A.1. and 2.).

A. Avitaminosis A

1. Effect on Mammals

The earliest signs of vitamin A deficiency in mammals are a decrease in appetite, changes in the eye, loss in weight and a cessation of growth (Moore, 1967a; Doxey, 1971). Papilloedema (a swelling of the optic disc associated with raised intracranial pressure) precedes 'night blindness' in calves, and may be present whilst the animal's vision is still normal (Doxey, 1971). 'Night blindness' follows if the retina is unable to obtain sufficient vitamin A aldehyde for the formation of rhodopsin and iodopsin. This may lead to permanent blindness with secondary changes in the retina. Some blindness and deafness in pigs, dogs and cattle with vitamin A deficiency is caused by destructive changes in the nerves. These nerve lesions are associated with hypertrophy of the bones, which narrows the foramina in the skull and pinches the optic and auditory nerves (Moore, 1967a).

Xerophthalmia (keratinization of the corneal epithelium) is common in vitamin A-deficient mammals and xerosis, in which the columnar epithelia of the mucous membranes are replaced by thick layers of horny stratified epithelia, is widespread throughout the body (involving urinogenital, respiratory and alimentary systems) forming a prolific source of secondary lesions such as infections. A high incidence of diarrhoea, pneumonia and conjunctivitis is associated with these epithelial changes (Doxey, 1971).

Reduced availability of vitamin A can decrease breeding success. Failure to produce young may be due to infertility of the male: the testes of vitamin A-deficient rats, mice and guinea-pigs are undersized, and those of bulls have degenerate seminiferous tubules. Reproductive failure in the female rat may occur through refusal to copulate, an abnormal oestrous cycle, and resorption or abortion of the foetuses. It is likely that many of these difficulties are due to epithelial changes. Thus, xerosis could prevent normal copulation and zygote implantation. Numerous anatomical deformities, including hydrocephaly and defective modelling of the bones, can occur in the foetus following a lack of vitamin A in the maternal diet (Moore, 1967a; Doxey, 1971).

Nockels and Phillips (1971) noted that there is an interference with gluconeogenesis in intact vitamin A-deficient rats, as there is in birds, and that this leads to an absence of liver glycogen.

2. Effects on Birds

In young chicks deprived of vitamin A growth is retarded or ceases altogether. In adults there is a general unthriftiness with ruffled plumage and reduced body weight. Also, lethargy, incoordination and a staggering gait or ataxia are apparent. The eyelids are dry, though frank xerophthalmia is not as common as in mammals. A white deposit of urates occurs in the kidneys and ureters, often clogging the latter (Barger et al., 1958; Moore, 1967a).

The photochemistry of vision in birds, or at least in the chicken, is similar to that in mammals (Coates, 1971) and defective vision and blindness may be expected if rhodopsin and iodopsin cannot be formed due to insufficiency of vitamin A aldehyde.

Changes in the mucous secretory epithelia are among the first symptoms shown by vitamin A-deficient birds as in mammals. The mucous secretory cells of the conjunctiva, alimentary canal and trachea are gradually replaced by a stratified keratinizing epithelium (Aydelotte, 1963; Coats, 1971). Destruction of the mucous membrane of the respiratory tract renders the birds very susceptible to secondary infections (Barger et al., 1958). Resistance to intestinal parasitic infestation is also reduced, possibly through changes in the epithelial membranes of the alimentary canal (Moore, 1967a; Coates, 1971). Coates reported that poultry flocks on a low intake of vitamin A were much more severely affected by common poultry diseases than controls with adequate supplies of this vitamin. It is possible, however, that an effect on antibody production may be as important in this increased susceptibility as are the changes in the mucous membranes. It has been suggested (Leutskaja, 1963, 1964) that vitamin A is a requirement for antibody formation, and chickens fed low vitamin A diets responded to *Salmonella pullorum* antigen with lower agglutinin levels than did the controls (Panda and Combs, 1963).

The development of bone in young birds is as sensitive to circulatory vitamin A levels as that in mammals. Vitamin A deficiency reduces bone resorption, but because bone deposition continues the skeleton becomes thickened and deformed (Coates, 1971). It is thought that the nerve lesions that cause incoordination and ataxia in chicks are due to the compression of the central nervous system by deformation of the vertebrae and foramen of the skull by this bone hypertrophy (Wolbach and Hegsted, 1952).

Another feature of vitamin A deficiency in birds, as in mammals, is that it leads to a decrease in liver glycogen levels. This may indicate an abnormal turnover of these stores (Nockels and Phillips, 1971). Barger *et al.* (1958) report that low levels of dietary vitamin A reduce egg production and hatchability in poultry flocks and that if the deficiency is great, mortality may reach 100 per cent in a very short time.

B. Hypervitaminosis A

1. Effects on Mammals

These include resorption of the foetus and congenital abnormalities (Moore, 1967b). Teratogenic effects have been observed in both the rat (Cohlan, 1954) and the hamster (Ferm, 1967). A typical lesion in the growing animal is the attenuation of the shafts of the long bones. Other effects on mammals are exophthalmia, haemorrhages associated with a greatly increased clotting time and a temporary thickening of the skin (Moore, 1967b).

2. Effects on Birds

Chickens fed excess vitamin A have a low rate of egg production and lay small eggs with poor hatchability and a prolonged incubation period (March *et al.*, 1972). The last two effects may be due to high vitamin A levels in the egg itself. Tests showed that feeding high levels of vitamin A to laying hens resulted in abnormally high levels of this vitamin in the egg. Also, injecting vitamin A into eggs reduced hatchability and prolonged incubation time. The dead, unhatched embryos showed a number of developmental abnormalities and haemorrhages appeared to be a frequent cause of mortality. The experiments of Thompson *et al.* (1965) suggested that the early chick embryo is very sensitive to both hyper- and hypovitaminosis A.

Blood samples from young chickens given excess vitamin A showed a marked reduction in packed cell volume. Taylor *et al.* (1968) suggested that this may be due to the increased fragility of the erythrocytes, which had already been reported in other chicks given an excess of this vitamin (March *et al.*, 1966). The latter authors thought that the high level of vitamin A may have had an indirect effect on thyroid activity. An 'antagonistic' action of high levels of circulating vitamin A on thyroid activity has been reported (see Section VI.F.) and suppression of the thyroid could lead to a greater number of old fragile cells circulating in the blood. It is likely that the prolonged incubation time for eggs containing high vitamin A levels (March *et al.*, 1972) is also due to a suppression of thyroid activity, this time in the embryo.

VIII. KNOWN SUBLETHAL EFFECTS OF ORGANOCHLORINE INSECTICIDES

A very large amount of research has been carried out on the sublethal effects of the organochlorine insecticides on animals, mostly with DDT. Much of the earlier work was carried out with mammals to determine the safety of their intended uses on man. Later, when people became aware that these materials had become environmental pollutants, and wild birds showed particularly high residues and apparent effects, birds featured more commonly than mammals in these toxicological tests. This section lists most of the important effects found so far on both mammals and birds. How little we know about these compounds, even now after intensive research for nearly thirty years, may be gauged by the fact that papers reporting new effects of DDT and its metabolites are still being published every month.

A. Effects on Mammals

1. Metabolic Rate

Riker *et al.* (1946) fed rats on a diet containing 1,000 ppm DDT and found that the mean basal metabolic rate increased rapidly, reached a maximum of 23 per cent above the control value by the third day and then remained just below this level for the next five days. They also tested the metabolic rate by examining the oxygen consumption of liver slices taken from DDT-poisoned rats. Liver slices from rats fed for eight days on a diet containing 1,000 ppm DDT consumed 22 per cent more oxygen than the controls. After a longer period on dose, however, this was reduced to 11 per cent above control level and if slices were taken from livers which appeared greatly altered in chronically poisoned rats, the oxygen consumption was less than that of the controls. This relationship of their results with time was observed by Hayes (1959). Hayes also noted that in some experiments there was a transitional period during which this oxygen consumption of liver slices from DDT-poisoned animals was not significantly different from the control level.

2. Body Temperature

DDT appears to lower the body temperature of affected mammals. Thus, Cameron and Burgess (1945) found that one of the first signs of DDT poisoning in rabbits, guinea-pigs and rats was that the animal became 'cold to the touch'. Also, Hayes (1959) noted that in the published case history of one man, who received a large single dose of DDT in the course of his work, the body temperature was subnormal ten days after the accident.

3. Respiration Rate

Hayes (1959; reporting some work by Deichmann in 1950) noted that in DDT-poisoned rabbits there was a marked increase in the frequency and amplitude of respiratory movements which started with the onset of hyperirritability. Later, the depth of respiration frequently returned to normal though the rate remained high. In some animals both rate and amplitude decreased progressively before death. Also, Hayes listed rapid respiration among the symptoms shown by men accidentally exposed to large doses of DDT and Koster (1947) reported dyspnoea (laboured breathing) in cats receiving injections of large doses of DDT.

4. Growth Rate, Body Weight and Food Consumption

Growth was retarded in fox cubs poisoned with dieldrin (Blackmore, 1963) and in rats fed 700 ppm DDT (Sarett and Jandorf, 1946, 1947) or 600 ppm γ-BHC (Negherbon, 1959). Cameron and Burgess (1945) reported a loss in body weight of DDT-dosed adult rabbits, guinea-pigs and rats. This could be due to a reduced BMR (see Section VI.A.). However, Laug and Fitzhugh (1946) observed that rats receiving high concentrations of DDT in the diet grew more slowly than control litters although they ate more food. Also, rats which received 1,000 ppm DDT in the diet were found to lose weight whilst consuming more food than controls (Riker et al., 1946). These results support the conclusion (Hayes, 1959) that the BMR increases, at least in these animals (see Section VIII.A.1.).

5. Behavioural Changes

The typical symptoms of DDT poisoning in mammals include fine and coarse muscular twitchings, and tremors with signs of extensor rigidity (Cameron and Burgess, 1945). It was noted that the extensor rigidity was shown to a particular degree in poisoned cats and stiffness of the distal parts of the limbs was often observed even before the onset of tremors (Smith and Stohlman, 1944; Hayes, 1959). Hyperexcitability and hypersensitivity to stimuli such as noise are commonly listed among the symptoms of mammals poisoned with DDT (Cameron and Burgess, 1945), γ-BHC (Negherbon, 1959) or dieldrin (Negherbon, 1959; Blackmore, 1963). Weanling rats fed 600 ppm γ-BHC were found to be hyperactive (Negherbon, 1959).

Peterle and Peterle (1971) studied the effects of feeding a low dose rate of 7 ppm technical DDT on the aggressive behaviour of male mice. Treated mice 'lost' more bouts (as determined by posturing and avoidance behaviour) and controls made more biting attacks. Thus, the DDT-fed mice were significantly less aggressive than control mice and were more likely to submit in territorial fights. Hayes (1959) noted that in the case histories of men exposed to DDT, apprehension and mental anxiety are mentioned several times. Blackmore (1963) reported a change in the behavioural characteristics of foxes, Vulpes vulpes, dosed with dieldrin. Wild foxes became tame whilst previously semi-tame foxes became aggressive. Jefferies (1969b) noted apparent tameness in badgers, Meles meles, poisoned by dieldrin.

A number of authors have mentioned inappetence or anorexia (the inability to take food) as a characteristic of severe poisoning with DDT, γ-BHC and dieldrin in rats, rabbits, guinea-pigs, dogs and foxes (Cameron and Burgess, 1945; Negherbon, 1959; Blackmore, 1963). This failure to take food may only properly be ascribed to lack of appetite if the animal received the organochlorine, not by inclusion in the diet, but by stomach tube or capsule or some other route. Otherwise the cause may be an alteration in the taste of the food.

6. Effects on Reproduction of Rats

Fitzhugh (1948) reported that there was no effect on fecundity (i.e. total number of young per producing pair), but that rats fed diets containing 50, 100 or 600 ppm DDT showed a progressive decline in the percentage of young successfully weaned, as compared with rats fed diets containing 0 or 10 ppm DDT. However, Hayes (1959) suggested that this mortality of suckling rats of dams fed 50 or 100 ppm, although greater than mortality in controls, was no greater than the normal mortality in this age group in many laboratories. Also, as 600 ppm is a toxic level for female rats and DDT would be secreted in the milk at a high level, the reported results at this dose rate may indicate solely a general systemic toxicity rather than an effect on reproduction. This suggestion was supported by some work by Deichmann, Witherup and Kitzmiller in 1950 (reported by Hayes, 1959), which showed that the reproductive ability of surviving male and female rats was not affected by a single LD_{50} dose of DDT.

Results of the long-term study of Ottoboni (1969) also support the conclusion that DDT has little effect on the success of breeding rats. Dose rates of 0, 20 and 200 ppm technical grade DDT in the diet were begun with a weanling parent generation and terminated with the weaning of the third litters by the F_1 generation. DDT had no apparent effect on fecundity of dams, litter size, weight at birth or viability of the young. Comparison of total numbers of pregnancies indicated that DDT had no effect on fertility either. Growth rate was similar at all dose rates and DDT may actually increase reproductive performance in 52-week-old rats by exerting some protective effect against the normal age decrement in reproduction.

7. Effects on Reproduction of Mice

The mouse appears to be more sensitive than the rat and shows some detrimental effects on reproductive success. Bernard and Gaertner (1964) fed dietary levels of 200 and 300 ppm technical DDT to groups of mice and found that the fertility of the mice declined progressively with increasing dose rate of DDT. Thus, the percentage of dams producing litters in control, 200 and 300 ppm groups was 80, 40 and 17 per cent respectively. The number of young born per litter in the two dosed groups, however, was not significantly different from that in the controls. The authors concluded that reproductive capacity was completely destroyed in some mice whilst in others it was unaffected. However, both dose rates used were rather high for mice and both produced some mortality (600 ppm kills all mice within 35 days).

Deichmann and Keplinger (1966) fed 250 ppm DDT to breeding mice and observed effects over five generations. They concluded that DDT decreased viability of the suckling young. However, again the dose rate was rather high for sublethal dosing. Ware and Good (1967) used a much lower dose rate, 7 ppm, and carried out separate tests on two strains. The first strain showed some reduction in fertility (55·4 per cent compared to 67 per cent in control) but no effect on fecundity or litter size. However, a repeat of this test did not confirm this reduction in fertility. Another test, with another strain, showed little difference in fertility, fecundity or litter size of controls and dosed animals. Examination of the number of days to produce the first litter showed a delay in both tests with the first strain but not with the second. Tarján and Kemény (1969) used an even lower dose rate (2·8–3·0 ppm DDT, corresponding to a daily intake of 0·4–0·7 mg/kg body weight) which was fed for five generations. At this level there were no differences in fertility, fecundity, litter size or numbers of surviving weanlings.

Örberg et al. (1972) examined the effect of DDT on another aspect of the breeding cycle of mice, the length of the oestrous cycle, and found that injection of 40 mg/kg DDT significantly prolonged this cycle by about a day. This implies less frequent periods of sexual receptivity in the female mice and could cause a decline in reproductive capacity. The effect was attributed to the increased catabolism of steroid hormones (see Section VIII.A.12.). Research by Lundberg and Kihlström (1973) has shown that dosing breeding mice with 50 or 100 mg/kg pp'-DDT significantly decreases the number of implanted ova.

Some studies have been made with organochlorines other than DDT. Deichmann and Keplinger (1966), again using high dose rates, found that 25 ppm of aldrin or dieldrin caused some mortality before mating or delivery and there were fewer young per litter in those which bred. None of the young survived more than four days. Ten ppm dieldrin or 100 ppm chlordane caused some effects on the viability of the young. Good and Ware (1969) used a lower dose rate (5 ppm) of dieldrin and endrin. The endrin caused considerable mortality but neither compound affected fertility (percent of surviving pairs producing young), fecundity or the number of young produced per day. However, both materials caused a slight decrease in litter size. This did not reduce fecundity as the mean number of litters per surviving pair was increased above the control figure.

8. Vitamin A Storage and Circulation

Phillips (1963) demonstrated that feeding rats with more than 10 ppm DDT in the diet for up to 72 days decreased the utilization of orally administered carotene and vitamin A and reduced storage of vitamin A in the liver. Cattle fed on forage treated with DDT also had significantly less vitamin A in the liver (Phillips and Hidiroglou, 1965). Whereas the net gain of vitamin A in the control livers during the 83-day feeding period was 13·4 μg vitamin A/g liver, there was a net loss of 1·9 μg/g in the dosed animals. Conversely, the level of vitamin A in serum increased rapidly in dosed cattle and from 62 days onwards it was significantly higher than in the controls. Keil *et al.* (1972) demonstrated that human volunteers occupationally exposed to DDT had significantly higher serum vitamin A levels than control subjects. However, the possibility that decreased liver vitamin A stores may accompany this elevation could not be tested. Lee *et al.* (1964) observed decreased vitamin A stores in livers of rats after feeding them dieldrin.

9. Circulatory System

Hayes (1959) reported several cases in which men who had been accidentally or experimentally exposed to high levels of DDT showed irregularities of the circulatory system. Thus, the pulse rate was described as weak and slow or irregular with low blood pressure, though respiration was rapid. Cardiac arrhythmias including ventricular fibrillation have been reported before death in dogs and rabbits poisoned with DDT (Philips and Gilman, 1946; Judah, 1949). Hayes (1959) believes that the high (almost trebled) blood potassium found in rabbits receiving acute lethal doses of this material may explain these cardiac irregularities. Negherbon (1959) noted that dieldrin produced brachycardia (rapid pulse rate) and γ-BHC increased blood pressure in mammals generally.

Cameron and Burgess (1945) reported that large skin applications of DDT appear to induce anaemia. The haemoglobin percentage tended to decrease, but the red cell count remained unchanged in rabbits dosed in this way. Smith and Stohlman (1944) confirmed this finding of anaemia in DDT-dosed rabbits (50 mg/kg). Similar results have been reported for rats (Draize *et al.*, 1944), guinea-pigs (Tarsitano, 1948), cats (Velbinger, 1947a) and dogs (McNamara *et al.*, 1946) dosed with DDT. In man also, after an oral dose of 500–1,500 mg DDT, there was a decrease in both erythrocyte count and haemoglobin level. The latter decreased 15–18 per cent in one day (Velbinger, 1947b). Haemosiderosis of the spleen was reported after feeding DDT to mice (Neal et al., 1944), rats and rabbits (Lillie and Smith, 1944). Haemosiderin is a brown pigment, formed during the breakdown of haemoglobin. In man the amount of haemosiderin in the spleen is often much increased in certain diseases associated with blood destruction (Bell et al., 1952). It is possible that DDT may decrease haemoglobin by increased breakdown.

Smith and Stohlman (1944) found that white cell counts were normal after dosing rabbits with 50 mg/kg DDT. Cameron and Burgess (1945), however, reported that large skin applications of DDT to rabbits increased the number of leucocytes and increased white cell production in the bone marrow. Leucocytes usually increase after stresses such as violent exercise, fever or tissue damage (Bell et al., 1952).

Hayes (1959) noted that one dog receiving a high dose rate (100 mg/kg/day) of DDT via the respiratory route developed an increase in prothrombin time, and that blood pH dropped in chronically poisoned animals.

Wassermann et al. (1972) reported that both dieldrin and γ-BHC inhibited the usual increase in serum gamma globulin after Salmonella typhi administration to rabbits. Earlier work by these authors had shown that pp'-DDT decreased the gamma globulin level in the sera of rats.

10. Water Balance

Three of the organochlorine insecticides are thought to upset water balance in mammals. Thus, γ-BHC is known to cause frequent urination in experimental animals (Negherbon, 1959). Also, dosing of dogs with DDT, either orally or via the respiratory route (100 mg/kg/day) produced a small but consistent increase in the volume of urine excreted in 24 hours (Hayes, 1959). Information from field situations suggests that dieldrin produces increased thirst in such mammals as ground squirrels Citellus sp., foxes and badgers. Many such poisoned animals have been found to have drowned whilst drinking (Scott et al., 1959; Taylor and Blackmore, 1961; Jefferies, 1969b).

The opposite effect, water retention in the tissues, has been reported by Cameron and Burgess (1945). Rats, guinea-pigs and rabbits given repeated skin applications of DDT in kerosene had obvious oedema in the subcutaneous tissues.

11. Organ Weights

A significant increase in liver weight has been reported in rats fed dieldrin at 20 ppm (Phillips, 1965), γ-BHC at 100 ppm (Negherbon, 1959) and DDT at both 700 ppm (Sarett and Jandorf, 1946, 1947) and 100–2,500 ppm in the diet (Ortega, 1966). Dieldrin also causes liver enlargement in the dog and mouse (Wright *et al.*, 1972). The hypertrophied liver has a higher lipid content than normal in the rat (Sarett and Jandorf, 1946, 1947) and this has been reported as amounting to fatty degeneration in the livers of DDT-dosed cattle (Nelson *et al.*, 1944), cats and rabbits (Lillie and Smith, 1944).

12. Induction of Hepatic Enzymes

Organochlorine insecticides will induce the production of mixed function oxidase systems in the livers of mammals which are also capable of bringing about hydroxylation of the steroid hormones (Conney *et al.*, 1967; Welch *et al.*, 1967) (see Chapter 3).

13. Lipid Metabolism

Petrásek and Placer (1965) starved rats for six days and then gave them a high fat diet containing 50 or 500 ppm DDT for a further 27 days. They found that both groups of DDT-fed rats had considerably lower fat reserves than the controls, although the food intake was similar. This may have been caused by either a reduction in fat formation or an increase in mobilization. The finding of increased esterase activity in the adipose tissue of the DDT-fed group (*in vivo*) may support the latter. The authors suggested that DDT had reduced the general metabolic rate and energy output of the experimental animals. However, it is possible to interpret their results as showing the opposite, i.e. an increased BMR.

14. Carbohydrate Metabolism

Acute poisoning with DDT causes a quick mobilization of liver glycogen, which is later exhausted. Thus, there is an early hyperglycaemia (elevated blood sugar level) followed by hypoglycaemia (reduced blood sugar level) (Läuger *et al.*, 1945a and b; Hayes, 1959). In dogs given doses of 1,000 and 2,000 mg/kg DDT the blood sugar increased from a normal concentration of 100 mg per cent to over 200 mg per cent in seven to eight hours and then down to 50 mg per cent before death. The liver of rats given 1,000 mg/kg DDT was found to be free of glycogen two to six hours after dosing. Some poisoned animals may be saved by glucose injection. Thus, Koster (1947) found that glucose given before or after a dose of DDT in the lethal range reduced both convulsions and mortality. Also, when given before the DDT it reduced the tremors and dyspnoea he found in dosed cats. The effects of chronic or low doses of DDT on carbohydrate metabolism, on the other hand, are less well documented. Sarett and Jandorf (1946, 1947) were able to find no significant decrease in the liver glycogen of rats receiving 700 ppm in the diet for 40 days.

15. Calcium Metabolism

Cameron and Burgess (1945) found that DDT changed blood calcium levels in rabbits. These increased during the first two or three days after dosing, and then fell below normal levels in most cases. Judah (1949) also reported abnormally high blood calcium levels in DDT-dosed mammals. Blood calcium in a man accidentally exposed to DDT rose from 11·2 mg/100 cc before exposure to 18 mg/100 cc after 15 days. This level decreased when he was removed from work with DDT (Cameron and Burgess, 1945).

16. Oestrogenic Effects

Burlington and Lindeman (1950) were the first to suggest that DDT might produce oestrogenic effects. Their hypothesis was that since the molecular configuration of the DDT molecule was similar to that of the synthetic oestrogen diethylstilboestrol (Fig. 8) it might elicit the same response in the animal. Further interest in this subject was shown by Levin et al. (1968) who tested the op'- and pp'-isomers of DDT separately on ovariectomized rats. They found that whereas op'-DDT exerted an oestrogen-like effect by increasing the wet weight of the uterus, pp'-DDT was only weakly active. Bitman et al. (1968) confirmed these results by showing an increase in weight, water content, glycogen and RNA in the rat uterus after administration of op'-DDT while pp'-DDT exhibited only slight activity. Further support was given by Wrenn et al. (1970), who demonstrated that large single doses of op'-DDT exerted a clear oestrogenic effect on immature rats by causing early vaginal opening. A similar but much less marked effect was obtained with *pp'*-DDT also. However, Welch *et al.* (1969) showed that single intraperitoneal injections of either pure *op'*- or *pp'*-DDT as well as technical grade DDT or pure methoxychlor would significantly increase the uterine weight of rats.

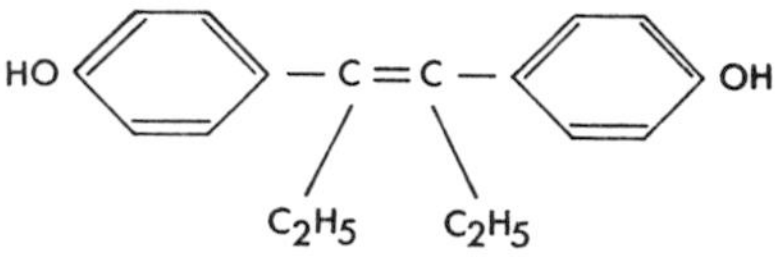

Diethylstilboestrol

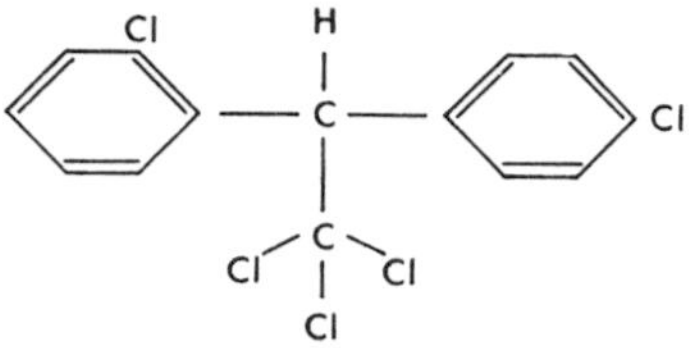

ortho-para'- DDT

Fig. 8. Molecular configuration of the isomer of DDT, *op'*-DDT, known to produce oestrogenic effects in birds and mammals, and the molecule of synthetic oestrogen, diethylstilboestrol, which it is thought to mimic.

Several workers have since shown that a considerable amount of *op'*-DDT is required to produce an oestrogenic action and that *op'*-DDT does not possess all the properties of oestrogen. Thus, Wrenn *et al.* (1970) found that chronic low level feeding of *op'*-DDT to rats produced no significant effect on uterine weight, water content and glycogen, the parameters most sensitive to oestrogen stimulation. Similarly, chronic doses of *op'*-DDT in the diet were found to have no oestrogenic action on the ewe (Wrenn *et al.*, 1971). Also, unlike oestrone, when given to rats, *op'*-DDT does not inhibit pregnancy (Duby *et al.*, 1971).

17. Skin Defects

Nelson *et al.* (1944) tested DDT on several species of mammals and found that one of the main macroscopic features was a scaliness or hyperkeratosis of the skin.

18. Defects in Vision

Naevested (1947) reported that after accidentally consuming DDT, three young men had wide, non-reacting, pupils and impaired vision.

In another, similar, case vision was affected by slight accommodation paralysis of the eyes (Hayes, 1959). Blackmore (1963) and Jefferies (1969b) both reported apparent blindness in dieldrin-poisoned foxes and badgers.

19. Incidence of Disease

Nelson *et al.* (1944) reported pulmonary infection in guinea-pigs dosed with DDT. Presumably the infection was noticeably greater than in control animals. Also, Ottoboni (1969) found that a group of breeding rats given a diet containing 200 ppm technical grade DDT had an increased incidence of 'ringtail'.

B. Effects on Birds

1. Metabolic Rate and Body Temperature

The metabolic rate and body temperature of pigeons increase with low doses of DDT, but there is a progressive decrease at higher dose rates (see Section V.B.).

2. Body Weights

Lillie *et al.* (1972) found that feeding low levels (5, 25 and 50 ppm) of *pp'*-DDT, *op'*-DDT or *pp'*-DDE to chickens increased body weights significantly. Also, the 5 and 25 ppm levels of DDE increased body weight gains more than the 50 ppm level.

3. Behavioural Changes

The fine muscular tremors seen in mammals poisoned with DDT are also one of the characteristic symptoms in birds. In experiments to determine the effect of DDT on the reproductive success of the Bengalese finch I have noted cycles in these tremors. At 0900 hours one could see various degrees of tremoring in many of the birds given high doses of DDT. By early afternoon this tremoring was hardly observable and by evening the birds appeared normal. This cycle was repeated daily, and was probably due to the normal diurnal cycle of use of the stored fat, which has high levels of the DDT. It may be observable only in small birds in which the overnight use of storage fat may be more than 50 per cent of that available (Newton, 1972). Feeding next morning would replenish most of the stores used up and would bring about a decrease in circulating DDT by enabling it to be re-absorbed into the fat. If the morning tremoring and fluttering are so severe that feeding is mechanically impossible, the bird is unlikely to survive the next night.

Several authors have recorded behavioural changes in birds contaminated in the field or receiving experimental doses of organochlorine insecticides. There may be increased aggression, decreased alertness or reduced territorial drive. Thus, Jefferies (1967, 1971) reported occasional extremely aggressive behaviour in DDT- and DDE-dosed Bengalese finches. This was directed towards the mate and young chicks and included killing and dismembering the latter. Egg disappearance from nests of captive American sparrowhawks *Falco sparverius* fed DDT plus dieldrin was thought to be due to egg breakage and eating of eggs by parent birds (Porter and Wiemeyer, 1969). Direct aggression against the egg has been observed in the field in grey herons *Ardea cinerea* containing high dieldrin residues (Prestt, 1970). On the other hand, Dahlgren *et al.* (1970) reported that young hatched from the eggs of pheasants *Phasianus colchicus* dosed with dieldrin were more easily caught than those of controls. Also, the results of McEwen and Brown (1966) suggested that sharp-tailed grouse *Pedioecetes phasianellus* dosed with dieldrin and released were more vulnerable to predators than were the controls. Field observations showed that when these dosed males were returned to their territories they stopped displaying and were evicted by more vigorous males.

Some inappetence has been noted in pigeons dosed with pp'-DDE, pp'- or op'-DDT (French and Jefferies, 1969; Jefferies and French, 1971, 1972). As these birds were dosed by gelatin capsule, this inappetence must be due to internal action of the insecticide and not to aversion to treated food.

4. Delayed Egg Laying

Jefferies (1967, 1971), using Bengalese finches, found that the interval between pairing and laying the first egg increased progressively and significantly with the dose rate of DDT or DDE. Controls normally lay within eight to 28 days after pairing. Delays of up to 99 days occurred after dosing. Sublethal doses of DDT, DDE or dieldrin caused a similar lag in ovulation in ring doves *Streptopelia risoria* (Peakall, 1970b).

Delayed breeding has been well documented for one species in the field. Gonad development in woodpigeons *Columba palumbus* was retarded in March and April 1961, despite particularly favourable environmental conditions (Lofts and Murton, 1966). Most factors that cause late breeding were ruled out and the only other known factor involved was a large-scale use of dieldrin on cereal seeds, which caused exceptional mortality in this species.

5. Egg Production

This aspect of avian reproduction appears to be one of the least affected. Work with American sparrowhawks (Porter and Wiemeyer, 1969), mallard (Heath *et al.*, 1969), North American black duck *Anas rufipes* (Longcore *et al.*, 1971b) and Japanese quail (DeWitt, 1956) given dieldrin, DDT, DDE, DDD, aldrin or endrin showed no demonstrable effect on egg production. There was a tendency for Bengalese finches to lay larger clutches as the amount of DDT in the diet increased. Thus, six or seven eggs (instead of the usual five) were produced by 21 per cent of the control pairs, 32 per cent fed at 34 μg/day and 44 per cent fed at 139 μg DDT/day/bird. However, the mean clutch size of dosed and control pairs was not significantly different, as many of the pairs fed dose rates of DDT approaching lethal levels produced no eggs, or small clutches of two eggs (Jefferies, 1971).

6. Egg Weight

The weights of individual eggs laid by Bengalese finches given DDT were significantly reduced and the degree of reduction was correlated with the dose rate. The mean egg weights in controls and in birds fed 1 to 50, 51 to 100 and 101 to 300 μg DDT/day were 1·198, 1·162, 1·154 and 1·146 g respectively (Jefferies, 1969a). Similar reductions in egg weight were caused by DDE (Jefferies, 1971). Also, the eggs of Japanese quail given 100 ppm of *op'*-DDT or *pp'*-DDT were significantly lighter than those of the controls (Bitman *et al.*, 1969).

7. Shell Weight and Thickness

The recent great interest in the effects of organochlorine insecticides on eggshell thickness followed Ratcliffe's (1967) finding of thin egg-shells in British predatory birds in the field. Since then several species have been tested with a range of insecticides and their metabolites. The now large literature on the production of thin eggshells in the laboratory has been reviewed by Cooke (1973). Briefly, mallard (Heath *et al.*, 1969), black duck (Longcore *et al.*, 1971b), ring doves (Peakall, 1970b), Japanese quail (Bitman *et al.*, 1969) and American sparrowhawks (Porter and Wiemeyer, 1969; Wiemeyer and Porter, 1970) have all been found to produce thinner (up to 38 per cent) eggshells when dosed with *pp'*-DDE, *pp'*-DDT, *pp'*-DDD or *op'*-DDT. Dieldrin does not appear to be as active as the DDT compounds in producing thin-shelled eggs. Thus, even with dose rates as high as 10 ppm in the diet, the thickness of mallard eggshells was only reduced by a maximum of 4 per cent (Lehner and Egbert, 1969). Again, Peakall (1970b) found that injection of ring doves wtih 150 mg/kg DDE within a day of laying, reduced the shell weight of the following egg, whereas 30 mg/kg dieldrin had no effect.

Tests of the composition of organochlorine insecticide thinned shells showed that they contained a significantly smaller percentage of shell calcium (Bitman *et al.*, 1969; Longcore *et al.*, 1971a). In the field many species show a significant negative correlation between shell thickness and DDE concentration in the egg (Enderson and Berger, 1970; Keith *et al.*, 1970). Also, there is a correlation between the degree of decline in eggshell thickness of various species and their mean organochlorine insecticide load (Ratcliffe, 1970). This laboratory and field information, together with the dating of the onset of shell thinning and its geographical distribution in certain species, leaves little doubt that the organochlorines were and are the causative agents of this phenomenon in wild birds (Ratcliffe, 1970).

However, both laboratory and field tests show that organochlorine insecticides do not cause shell thinning in all species. Stephen *et al.* (1970) reported that feeding *pp'*-DDT + *pp'*-DDE to chickens did not significantly alter the percentage of eggshell calcium. This was later confirmed by three other series of experiments. Thus, Davidson and Sell (1972), Cecil *et al.* (1972) and Balasubramanian (1972) could find no change in the eggshell thickness or shell calcium of chickens given up to 50 ppm *op'*-DDT, up to 100 ppm *pp'*-DDE, up to 200 ppm *pp'*-DDT, up to 20 ppm dieldrin or DDT + dieldrin together in the diet. Also, the opposite of eggshell thinning was found in some eggs laid by Bengalese finches fed sublethal dose rates of DDT during reproduction. The overall percentage shell weight (shell weight as a percentage of egg weight) increased significantly from 6·11 in the controls to 6·53 in the dosed birds. However, only the largest eggs (those laid at low dose rates) had heavier shells for their weight than those laid by controls. The smallest eggs (those laid at the highest dose rates—see Section VIII.B.6.) had lighter and presumably thinner shells than controls (Jefferies, 1969a). In this respect the relationship of shell weight to dose rate is similar to that of clutch size in this species (see Section VIII.B.5.). Thicker shells have been reported from at least one species in the field. The eggshell thickness of moorhens *Gallinula chloropus* contaminated with organochlorine insecticides showed a significant positive rather than negative correlation with the DDE content of the eggs (Fowler *et al.*, 1971).

8. Egg Breakage

Porter and Wiemeyer (1969), Bitman *et al.* (1969) and Heath *et al.* (1969) all noticed an increased frequency of cracking and breakage of the eggs of organochlorine-dosed birds. This has been noted in the field also in species which were later found to be highly contaminated (Ratcliffe, 1958, 1960, 1970). Increased breakage could be brought about by both aberrant behaviour (see Section VIII.B.3.) and/or a greater incidence of mechanical damage due to thinner shells. The eggshells of mallard dosed with DDE (10, 40 ppm) and DDT (2·5, 10, 25 ppm) cracked more readily than those of controls and the percentage cracked reached 25 per cent and 18 per cent respectively of the total laid compared with 5 per cent among controls (Heath *et al.*, 1969). Those eggs with hairline cracks hatched at about half the rate of whole eggs whilst those with definite fractures did not hatch at all.

9. Infertility

Infertility does not appear to be a major contributor to reduced breeding success in birds dosed with organochlorines. A measurable reduction in fertility is present in some species or at some dose rates with some insecticides but not in all. Reduced fertility when dosed with pp'-DDT, pp'-DDD, pp'-DDE or dieldrin has been found in mallard (Heath *et al.*, 1969), quail (DeWitt, 1956), pheasants (Genelly and Rudd, 1956) and Bengalese finches (Jefferies, 1971). DeWitt (1956), Azevedo *et al.* (1965), Brown *et al.* (1965), Porter and Wiemeyer (1969), Neill *et al.* (1971) and Longcore *et al.* (1971b) all reported that there was no change in the number of embryonated eggs in the species they tested and at the dose rates used.

The possibility of infertility in dosed males through a. failure of spermatogenesis or b. production of abnormal or c. insufficient spermatozoa has been examined by several workers. Locke *et al.* (1966) found that DDT did not interfere with spermatogenesis in adult bald eagles *Haliaëtus leucocephalus* until the dose rate was nearly lethal, when the testes showed degenerative changes. Similar results were obtained by Albert (1962) using domestic cockerels. However, the work of Burlington and Lindeman (1950) shows that an organochlorine given during development may produce a much greater effect than when administered to adults. Thus, growing cockerels injected with DDT had testes which were only one-fifth of the control weight. These reduced testes had decreased tubular development and more intertubular tissue. With regard to the second and third factors, sperm from DDT-dosed adult mallard and pheasants was morphologically normal and motile (Locke *et al.*, 1966) but DDT drastically reduced sperm production in cockerels (Albert, 1962). This effect on the quantity of sperm produced could be important as it has been suggested that a minimum of 100 million spermatozoa must be inseminated for optimum fertility (Sturkie, 1965).

10. Hatchability

Many workers have reported increased embryonic mortality after feeding organochlorine insecticides to breeding birds. These included some who had reported no effect on the number of embryonated eggs in the species they tested. Mallard (Heath *et al.*, 1969), grey partridge *Perdix perdix* (Neill *et al.*, 1971), quail (DeWitt, 1955, 1956; Shellenberger and Newell, 1965), pheasants (DeWitt, 1956; Genelly and Rudd, 1956), Bengalese finches (Jefferies, 1971), black ducks (Longcore *et al.*, 1971b) and American sparrowhawks (Porter and Wiemeyer, 1969) all showed a considerable decrease in hatchability of the eggs when fed *pp'*-DDT *pp'*-DDE, *pp'*-DDD, aldrin, dieldrin or endrin during reproduction.

Only three authors reported no effect on hatchability with quail, pheasants and chickens at certain sublethal dose rates of DDT, aldrin, dieldrin and endrin (DeWitt, 1956; Azevedo *et al.*, 1965; Brown *et al.*, 1965).

11. Post-hatching Mortality

An increase in post-hatching mortality has been found by most workers studying the effects of organochlorine insecticides on avian reproduction. Bengalese finches (Jefferies, 1971), mallard (Heath *et al.*,

1969), pheasants (DeWitt, 1956; Genelly and Rudd, 1956; Azevedo *et al.*, 1965), quail (DeWitt, 1956), American sparrowhawks (Porter and Wiemeyer, 1969) and black ducks (Longcore *et al.*, 1971b) fed pp'-DDT, pp'-DDE, endrin, aldrin or dieldrin all showed increased chick mortality just after hatching. In DDT-fed Bengalese finches this mortality appeared to be the major factor contributing to the reduced breeding success. At high dose rates, 52 per cent of the chick mortality occurred within one day of hatching. This increased post-hatching mortality is almost certainly due to the sudden increase in the organochlorine content of the blood when there is a rapid absorption of the remaining contents of the yolk sac during the early period before the chick feeds (demonstrated by Koeman *et al.*, 1967). Also, the process of hatching and entering a new environment presumably involves some additional stress on the young animal. Again only three authors could find no demonstrable effect on post-hatching survival at the dose rates of pp'-DDT, pp'-DDD, aldrin or dieldrin they fed to grey partridges, mallard, quail and pheasant (DeWitt, 1956; Heath *et al.*, 1969; Neill *et al.*, 1971).

12. Post-hatching Weight

The weight of the newly-hatched chick is correlated with the weight of the egg in Bengalese finches. Although the chicks of DDT- and DDE-fed pairs show this same correlation, the chick weights are significantly smaller for a given egg weight. In control pairs and pairs fed DDT (1–50 and 51–250 μg/day) or DDE (1–320 μg/day) the chicks from a 1·0 g egg weighed 0·799, 0·753, 0·699 and 0·709 g respectively (Jefferies, 1971). Thus, not only are chicks from DDT- and DDE-fed pairs smaller because of their lighter eggs (see Section VIII.B.6.), they are smaller at corresponding egg weights also. The reduced chick weight suggests that the yolks of eggs laid by dosed finches may be smaller than those of control eggs of similar size. This may contribute to the high chick mortality noted in organochlorine feeding tests using this species (Jefferies, 1971).

13. Incubation and Fledging Periods

Jefferies (1971) measured the time taken to complete incubation and rearing the young, in DDT-dosed Bengalese finches. Incubation time varies with clutch size and position of the egg in the clutch. Thus, with four, five and six egg clutches the mean incubation time for the first egg was 16·8, 17·3 and 18·0 days respectively in the control and 18·0, 18·1 and 18·3 days in DDT-fed pairs. This difference occurs with the second egg too. Thus, incubation times for at least the first two eggs are longer in DDT-fed pairs than in controls. DDT also caused a significant increase in the rearing time (control 19–29; DDT 22–34 days).

14. Secondary Sexual Characters

Burlington and Lindeman (1950) administered DDT subcutaneously to growing cockerels. There was a striking inhibition of the growth of the secondary sexual characters such as the comb. As the testes weights of these dosed birds were only one fifth those of controls (see Section VIII.B.9.) this inhibition is most likely to be due to decreased production of androgens.

15. Vitamin A Storage

Pigeons given low dose rates of DDT had high liver vitamin A stores whilst those given higher dose rates had low stores (see Section V.B.). Nelson et al. (1972) found no obvious changes in the levels of vitamin A stores in the livers of mallard fed low dose rates (1 mg/kg/day) of dieldrin for 12 weeks.

16. Circulatory System

The heart weight of pigeons dosed with pp'-DDT increases at 3 mg/kg/day and then decreases significantly with increasing dose rate (see Section V.B.). Jefferies and French (1972) found a similar significant dose-related decrease in the heart weight of pigeons dosed with pp'-DDE (Table III). As with pp'-DDT, the hearts of pigeons fed high dose rates of DDE were flaccid and showed thin musculature. There was no obvious corresponding change in the heart weights of pigeons dosed with dieldrin (Jefferies and French, 1972; Table III). In contrast to pigeons, the heart weight of Bengalese finches increased progressively with the dose rate of DDT (Jefferies, 1969a; Table IV and Section V.B.). These changes in heart weight reflect changes in pulse rate and amplitude.

The erythrocyte count and haemoglobin content of the blood

of chickens was significantly reduced by the administration of BHC (25 ppm), dieldrin (1·25 ppm) or DDT (35 ppm) in their diet (Srivastava *et al.*, 1960).

17. Organ Weights

As in mammals, dosing pigeons with *pp'*-DDT or *pp'*-DDE at a range of dose rates from low sublethal to lethal produced a large progressive increase in liver weight (Table III). In contrast to pigeons, Bengalese finches dosed with *pp'*-DDT showed no alteration in the weight of the liver at any sublethal dose rate (Table IV) though lethal levels reduce the weight of this organ slightly because of lost fat (see Section VIII.B.19.). The effect of DDT on chicken liver is similar to that on Bengalese finches. Thus, Davidson and Sell (1972) found that the liver size of white leghorn chickens was not significantly affected by dosing them with either 100 or 200 ppm *pp'*-DDT. Also although Nelson *et al.* (1944) found moderately severe liver damage in guinea-pigs, dogs and rabbits poisoned with DDT they could find little or no liver damage in poisoned chicks.

Unlike DDT, administration of dieldrin to pigeons does not produce any obvious changes in the liver weight (Table III). Similarly song thrushes *Turdus philomelos* showed no obvious increase in liver weight after six weeks on diets containing sublethal dose rates of dieldrin (0·15–5·69 ppm). A lethal dose rate of 12·38 ppm decreased liver weight by reducing the fat content (Jefferies and Davis, 1968). Also, Davidson and Sell (1972) and Nelson *et al.* (1972) found that the liver sizes of chickens and ducks were not significantly altered by dosing these birds with dieldrin.

The weights of paired adrenals of pigeons dosed with *pp'*-DDT decreased from 39·7 mg in controls to 34·6 mg at 6 mg/kg/day DDT and then increased progressively and significantly with the dose rate to weigh 59·9 mg at 54 mg/kg/day. This is the opposite pattern to that shown by heart weight (Table III). The same pattern of decreased and increased adrenal weights was seen with increasing dose rate of DDE but was less obvious in the few pigeons dosed with dieldrin (Table III).

18. Induction of Hepatic Enzymes

In vitro experiments with livers of dosed pigeons and ring doves have shown that relatively small quantities of DDT, DDE and dieldrin will induce hepatic enzyme systems which in turn will increase metabolism of the steroid hormones, progesterone, testosterone and oestradiol (Peakall, 1967, 1969; Risebrough *et al.*, 1968). It was thought likely that feedback mechanisms would maintain normal concentrations of these hormones in the face of increased metabolism (Peakall, 1967). Later experiments (Peakall, 1970b) showed that when ring doves were fed DDT, the level of oestradiol in the blood of birds killed between mating and laying was in fact lower than that in controls. However, this may not be due to an induced hepatic enzyme system; it could be due to reduced production of gonadotrophins (see Section XI.B.).

19. Lipid Metabolism

Song thrushes fed sublethal doses of dieldrin by Jefferies and Davis (1968) showed very little change in body weight during the experiment. However, the bird which died whilst being fed the highest dose rate (12·38 ppm) showed a rapid loss in body weight (15 per cent) during its seven days on test. This loss in weight was not due to reduced food consumption as the weight eaten was significantly higher than that of the birds which survived. The reduction in weight was due to the loss of all storage fat. Bengalese finches fed lethal dose rates of DDT also show a loss of all storage fat at death.

20. Calcium Metabolism

The finding that the degree of thinning of birds' eggshells correlated with their organochlorine insecticide content (Keith *et al.*, 1970; Ratcliffe, 1970) stimulated research on the effects of these materials on avian calcium metabolism to discover the mechanism of action. First, Peakall (1969) found that the intake of calcium from the gut was not reduced. It was then thought that if oestrogens are hydroxylated by organochlorine induced hepatic enzymes (see Section VIII.B.18.), it was feasible that medullary bone formation could be affected. Oestrogen produced by the ovary before egg laying mediates the deposition of calcium in the medullary bone, which then serves as a labile source of calcium for shell formation. Thus, Peakall (1970b) fed female ring doves 10 ppm DDT and then gave doses of Ca^{45} one day before mating. He found that there was indeed a significant reduction in the amount of Ca^{45} in the tibia and femur in birds killed eight days after mating. Oestreicher *et al.* (1971) injected male pigeons with oestrogen to induce medullary bone formation and then fed them DDE. Again, there was a 48 per cent reduction in the weight of bone produced.

However, only slight changes have been found in the blood calcium levels of Japanese quail which were laying thin-shelled eggs after being fed *op'*- or *pp'*-DDT (control 20·7; *op'*-DDT 20·5; *pp'*-DDT 19·7 mg per cent) (Bitman *et al.*, 1969). This argues against reduced medullary bone formation being the major factor and suggests another possible site of effect. An effect on the carbonic anhydrase system within the shell gland itself would explain the apparent lack of change in blood calcium levels. The major function of this enzyme system in this particular organ is apparently to ensure an adequate supply of carbonate ions in the process of calcium carbonate deposition in the eggshell. Experimental work by both Bitman *et al.* (1970) using Japanese quail and Peakall (1970b) using ring doves, did indeed show marked inhibition with DDE and DDT (but not with dieldrin). Both of these species show eggshell thinning when dosed with DDT and DDE (see Section VIII.B.7.). No carbonic anhydrase inhibition occurs in chickens given *pp'*-DDE (100 ppm) or *pp'*-DDT plus dieldrin (50 + 5 ppm) in the diet (Balasubramanian, 1972). This species does not show eggshell thinning with these materials (see Section VIII.B.7.).

One other site has been tested, that of possible DDT interference with calcitonin (the hormone of the ultimobranchial body which regulates blood calcium). However, no obvious changes were seen (Kenny *et al.*, 1972).

21. Oestrogenic Effects

Burlington and Lindeman (1950) first suggested that DDT may be acting in an oestrogen-like manner because of its inhibition of male characters in developing cockerels. However, after further experiments they decided that this was not so as they did not find the expected change in plasma calcium (Burlington and Lindeman, 1952). Later, Bitman *et al.* (1968) showed that, as for mammals (see Section VIII.A.16.), it was the *op'*-DDT isomer of DDT which produced definite oestrogenic effects on the oviducts of chickens and Japanese quail (increased weight and glycogen content) whilst the *pp'*-DDT isomer produced little effect. Again, as with mammals, it was found that *op'*-DDT did not reproduce all the effects of oestrogen. Both Bitman *et al.* (1969) and Cooke (1970) measured the serum calcium levels in quail dosed with *op'*-DDT but neither could find any marked changes. This led Cooke to suggest that *op'*-DDT may exert an effect on the endocrine system in some way without displaying all the properties of a potent oestrogen.

22. Skin Defects and Limb Disorders

Mallard fed a low dose rate of dieldrin (1 mg/kg/day) for five weeks showed marked keratinization of the foot pads (Nelson *et al.*, 1972). Also, Srivastava *et al.* (1960) noted that chickens fed BHC (25 ppm), dieldrin (1·25 ppm) or DDT (35 ppm) showed a hock disorder very similar to perosis. The incidence of perosis is influenced by a deficiency of manganese and biotin in the diet and also by the activity of the thyroid (see Section VI.G.6.).

23. Defects in Vision

Revzin (1966) injected pigeons with endrin (0·5 to 3·0 mg/kg) and found changes in the telencephalic neuronal function which suggested that this treatment would cause visual impairment. Such an impairment could reduce a bird's ability to avoid predators and compete for food (see Section VIII.B.3.).

24. Effect on the Salt Gland

The salt or nasal glands are paired glands situated at the base of the bill which form the main route of sodium chloride excretion in birds. They are particularly large in marine species. Friend *et al.* (1973) noted that suppression of the salt gland function could be detrimental to survival in habitats of high salinity and examined the effects of DDE on this function in the mallard. They found that sublethal levels (10, 100 and 1000 ppm) of DDE had no effect on extra-renal elimination of salt in mallards whose salt glands had been previously stimulated by low level (1 per cent) salt exposure but that DDE can suppress salt gland secretion in mature birds not previously exposed to salt.

IX. THE HYPOTHESIS THAT THE SUBLETHAL EFFECTS CAUSED BY ORGANOCHLORINE INSECTICIDES ARE LARGELY DUE TO ABERRANT THYROID ACTIVITY AND CHANGES IN VITAMIN A STORAGE

Sections VI and VII list those effects which can be brought about by experimentally altering the activity of the thyroid, i.e. the levels of circulating thyroid hormones and the levels of stored and circulating vitamin A. Section VIII lists the effects which are exhibited by mammals and birds dosed with organochlorine insecticides. These two sets of data are compared in the present section by grouping the effects produced by organochlorine insecticides into those which could have been equally well observed by subjecting the experimental animals to hyper- or hypothyroidism and the consequent hypervitaminosis or avitaminosis A. The similarity of the two sets of effects in this more detailed survey are so striking that they provide strong support for the hypothesis (Jefferies, 1969a; Jefferies and French, 1971) that most of the sublethal effects due to organochlorines could be caused by this one lesion on the thyroid. In the comparison below, the first reference in the brackets is that to the work with organochlorine insecticides whilst the second is to the work on the thyroid activity or vitamin A levels.

A. Effects which could have been Produced by Hyperthyroidism

1. In Organochlorine-dosed Mammals

a. The initial increase of metabolic rate in rats dosed with DDT (VIII.A.1./VI.A.).

b. The increase in frequency and amplitude of respiration in DDT-dosed rabbits (VIII.A.3./III.F.).

c. The reduced growth rates and body weights, with increased food consumption, seen in rats receiving DDT which suggest an increased BMR (VIII.A.4./VI.A., see also III.F.).

d. The fine muscular tremor observed in DDT-poisoned mammals (VIII.A.5./VI.B., see also III.F.).

e. The hyperactivity, hyperexcitability and hypersensitivity to stimuli seen in mammals dosed with DDT, BHC or dieldrin (VIII.A.5./VI.B., see also III.F.).

f. The apprehension and mental anxiety of men dosed with DDT (VIII.A.5./VI.B., see also III.F.).

g. The sudden aggressiveness seen in dieldrin-dosed foxes may be due to the 'emotional' instability and dementia known to accompany hyperthyroidism (VIII.A.5./VI.B.).

h. The protective effect against the normal reduction in breeding success with age in old rats fed DDT, appears similar to the 'rejuvenation' apparent in old chickens made hyperthyroid (VIII.A.6./VI.D.8.).

i. The delay in production of the first litter and increase in the number of litters per parent in DDT- and dieldrin-dosed mice may be effects of hyperthyroidism as in birds (VIII.A.7./VI.D.1. and D.2.).

j. Brachycardia seen in mammals fed dieldrin or BHC (VIII.A.9./ VI.G.2.).

k. A high blood potassium is thought to be causing cardiac irregularities in DDT-fed rabbits. This occurs in hyperthyroid mammals also (VIII.A.9./VI.G.3.).

l. The inhibition of increases in serum gamma globulin levels caused by dieldrin and BHC in rabbits may also occur in hyperthyroid mammals (VIII.A.9./VI.G.2.).

m. Increased urine production and thirst caused by DDT, BHC and dieldrin is seen in hyperthyroid mammals which show excessive water loss as urine (VIII.A.10./VI.G.3.).

n. Reduced ability to store lipid in DDT-dosed rats may be due to increased mobilization as in hyperthyroidism (VIII.A.13./III.F.).

2. In DDT- and DDE-dosed Bengalese Finches

a. Tremors observed after dosing with DDT (VIII.B.3./VI.B.).

b. Sudden extremely aggressive behaviour in dosed finches may follow 'emotional' instability and dementia as occurs in hyperthyroidism (VIII.B.3./VI.B.).

c. The progressive increase in the interval between pairing and laying the first egg after dosing with DDT or DDE (VIII.B.4./VI.D.1).

d. The tendency for large clutches to be more common among pairs fed low dose rates of DDT (VIII.B.5.) and the production of clutches of two or no eggs at all at very high dose rates of DDT (VIII.B.5.) are also found with moderate and severe hyperthyroidism (VI.D.2.).

e. The progressive decrease in egg weight with increasing dose rate of DDT and DDE (VIII.B.6./VI.D.3.).

f. An increase in shell thickness at low dose rates of DDT followed by a decrease in shell thickness at high dose rates of DDT may follow mild and severe hyperthyroidism respectively (VIII.B.7./VI.D.4.).

g. The reduction of hatching weight of chicks by DDT and DDE may be due to a reduction in the weight of yolk in the eggs laid, caused by hyperthyroidism in the female parent (VIII.B.12./VI.D.1.).

h. The increased incubation and fledging periods in finches dosed with DDT may be due to changes in parental behaviour due to hyperthyroidism, i.e. hyperactivity, nervousness and instability may affect incubation and feeding (VIII.B.13./VI.B.). On the other hand, one would expect high vitamin A stores in hyperthyroid Bengalese finches and these would be passed on to the egg. High vitamin A levels in the egg are known to prolong incubation, probably due to suppression of embryonic thyroid activity (VII.B.2.).

i. The progressive increase in heart weight and pulse rate with increasing dose rate of DDT (VIII.B.16./VI.G.2.).

j. The absence of increased liver weights (VIII.B.17./VI.G.4.).

3. In Organochlorine-dosed Chickens

a. Improved growth rate and body weight when fed DDT or DDE (VIII.B.2./VI.A.).

b. The absence of eggshell thinning when fed DDT, DDE or dieldrin (VIII.B.7./VI.D.4.).

c. The reduction in the weight of the testes and a decrease in spermatogenesis could be produced by severe hyperthyroidism (VIII.B.9./VI.D.6.).

d. The inhibition of the growth of the secondary sexual characters, such as the comb of growing cockerels dosed with DDT, may be produced by severe hyperthyroidism (VIII.B.14./VI.D.7.).

e. No increase in liver weight with DDT (VIII.B.17./VI.G.4.).

4. In Other Species of Birds Dosed with Organochlorines

a. An initial increase in metabolic rate and body temperature in DDT-dosed pigeons (VIII.B.1./VI.A.).

b. Tremors seen in DDT-dosed birds (VIII.B.3./VI.B.).

c. Egg breakage by direct aggression observed in the field and noted in the laboratory with DDT- and dieldrin-dosed birds may follow 'emotional' instability and dementia as occurs in hyperthyroidism (VIII.B.3. and B.8./VI.B.).

d. The delay in egg laying in DDT-, DDE- and dieldrin-dosed ring doves and wood pigeons (VIII.B.4./VI.D.1.).

e. High stores of vitamin A in livers of pigeons dosed with low dose rates of DDT (VIII.B.15./VI.F.).

f. The increase in pulse rate, amplitude and heart weight in pigeons dosed with low dose rates of DDT (VIII.B.16./VI.G.2.).

g. The absence of liver weight increases in dieldrin-dosed pigeons and song thrushes (VIII.B.17./VI.G.4.).

h. The rapid loss of lipid, with normal food consumption, in dieldrin-poisoned song thrushes (VIII.B.19./III.F.).

B. Effects which could have been Produced by Hypothyroidism

1. In Organochlorine-dosed Mammals

a. The secondary reduction in metabolic rate seen in rats dosed with DDT (VIII.A.1./VI.A.).

b. The lower body temperature of mammals dosed with DDT (VIII.A.2./III.F.).

c. The progressive decrease in the rate and amplitude of respiration in DDT-dosed mammals (VIII.A.3./III.F.).

d. Reduced fertility of mice dosed with DDT may be due to reduced sperm production as found in hypothyroid mammals (VIII.A.7./VI.C.).

e. The absence of litters from some DDT-dosed mice may be due to resorption of the foetuses as occurs in hypothyroid rats (VIII.A.7./VI.C.).

f. Low liver vitamin A stores found in DDT- and dieldrin-dosed rats and DDT-dosed cattle, associated with high serum vitamin A (VIII.A.8./VI.F.).

g. The slow pulse rate and low blood pressure occurring in DDT-dosed men (VIII.A.9 /VI.G.2.).

h. The anaemia with reduced erythrocyte counts which is found in DDT-dosed mammals (VIII.A.9./VI.G.2.).

i. Water retention in the tissues of DDT-dosed mammals (VIII.A.10./VI.G.3.).

j. The increase in liver weight and lipid content in mammals dosed with DDT and dieldrin is parallel to that found in birds made hypothyroid (VIII.A.11./VI.G.4.).

k. Oestrogenic effects seen in DDT-dosed mammals may follow hypothyroidism as they are known to be produced similarly by goitrogens (VIII.A.16./XI.C.).

l. Increased pulmonary infection and increased incidence of diseases (such as 'ringtail') in DDT-dosed mammals also occurs with hypothyroidism and xerosis following avitaminosis A (VIII.A.19./VI.G.6.).

2. In Organochlorine-dosed Birds

a. The secondary progressive decrease in metabolic rate and body temperature seen in DDT-dosed pigeons (VIII.B.1./VI.A.).

b. The decrease in eggshell thickness found in birds fed DDT, DDE, DDD or dieldrin (VIII.B.7./VI.D.4.).

c. Reduced fertility of birds dosed chronically with DDT, DDD, DDE or dieldrin (VIII.B.9./VI.D.6.).

d. Low liver vitamin A stores in pigeons given high dose rates of DDT (VIII.B.15./VI.F.).

e. The progressive decrease in pulse rate, amplitude and heart weight in pigeons given high dose rates of DDT (VIII.B.16./VI.G.2.).

f. The increased liver weight of pigeons dosed with DDT or DDE (VIII.B.17./VI.G.4.).

g. Oestrogenic effects seen in DDT-dosed birds may follow hypo-thyroidism as they are known to be produced by goitrogens other than DDT (VIII.B.21./XI.C.).

h. Perosis in chickens dosed with BHC, dieldrin or DDT (VIII.B.22./VI.G.6.).

i. The reduced erythrocyte count and haemoglobin reported in chickens dosed with BHC, dieldrin or DDT (VIII.B.16./VI.G.2.).

j. The adrenal hypertrophy in DDT-dosed pigeons (VIII.B.17./VI.G.4.).

C. Effects which could have been Produced by Hypervitaminosis A

a. The increased clotting time found in a dog dosed with DDT (VIII.A.9./VII.B.1.).

b. Absence of litters from some DDT-dosed mice may be due to foetus resorption which also occurs with high vitamin A (VIII.A.7./VII.B.1.).

c. The reduced egg weight and prolonged incubation time seen in Bengalese finches dosed with DDT or DDE (VIII.B.6. and B.13./VII.B.2.).

D. Effects which could have been Produced by Avitaminosis A

a. The inappetence found in mammals severely poisoned with DDT, BHC or dieldrin, and pigeons dosed with DDE or DDT (VIII.A.5. and B.3./VII.A.1.).

b. Reduced fertility of mice dosed with DDT (VIII.A.7./VII.A.1.).

c. Absence of litters from some DDT-dosed mice may be due to non-copulation and foetus resorption or abortion due to xerosis after vitamin A deficiency (VIII.A.7./VII.A.1.).

d. The abnormal oestrous cycle in DDT-dosed mice is also seen after vitamin A deficiency (VIII.A.7./VII.A.1.).

e. The reduction in implanted ova shown by DDT-dosed mice could occur with xerosis of the uterus membranes following avitaminosis A (VIII.A.7./VII.A.1.).

f. Scaliness and hyperkeratosis of the skin in DDT-dosed mammals and the marked foot pad keratinization seen in dieldrin-dosed mallard may both be due to xerosis (VIII.A.17. and B.22./VII.A.1. and A.2.).

g. The defective vision and apparent blindness in DDT- and dieldrin-dosed mammals could be due to papilloedema and failure to produce rhodopsin and iodopsin (VIII.A.18./VII.A.1.).

h. Increased pulmonary infection and incidence of diseases such as 'ringtail' in DDT-dosed mammals (VIII.A.19./VII.A.1.).

E. Effects which could have been Produced by Several of the above Factors

a. The reduced aggressiveness of male mice dosed with DDT (VIII.A.5.), and the inability of sharp-tailed grouse dosed with dieldrin to display and defend territory (VIII.B.3.), could be due to lethargy following hypothyroidism (III.F. and VII.A.2.), reduced androgen production (VI.D.7.), reduced vision (VIII.A.18. and B.23./VII.A.1.) or the 'emotional' instability, apprehension and nervousness known to accompany hyperthyroidism (III.F./VI.B.). The apparent tameness of badgers and foxes (VIII.A.5.) dosed with dieldrin may be due to some of these factors also.

b. The increased ease of catching of young from pheasants dosed with dieldrin (VIII.B.3.) may be due to lethargy (III.F. and VII.A.2.) owing to inbred hypothyroidism (VI.E.) or avitaminosis A (VII.A.2.), or another effect such as reduced vision (VIII.B.23./VII.A.1.). The increased vulnerability to predators of dieldrin-dosed sharp-tailed grouse (VIII.B.3.) may be due to some of these factors also.

c. The reduction in egg weight of quail fed DDT (VIII.B.6.) could be caused by either hyper- or hypothyroidism (VI.D.3.).

d. Reduced hatchability of birds' eggs (VIII.B.10.) could follow avitaminosis A (VII.A.2.), hypervitaminosis A (VII.B.2.) or an effect on the embryonic thyroid (VI.E.).

e. Some of the post-hatching mortality found in birds dosed with organochlorine insecticides (VIII.B.11.) could be due to thyroid changes in the embryo (VI.E.) or to reduced chick size (VIII.B.12.) following reduction in egg weight (VIII.B.6.) and egg yolk (VI.D.1.).

f. The reported suppression of salt gland secretion in DDE-dosed mallard (VIII.B.24.) could be due to an effect on the adrenal, which is known to control this gland (Sturkie, 1965), or to an effect on internal water balance as the gland is osmoregulatory in function (both adrenal and water balance are affected by hyper- and hypothyroidism, VI.G.4., VI.G.3.).

Other possible causes are induced blood acidosis (XI.E.) and carbonic anhydrase inhibition (VIII.B.20.) as this system is required for correct functioning of the gland (Maren, 1967).

X. THYROID EFFECTS OF THE POLYCHLORINATED BIPHENYLS

The reactions of animals dosed with the polychlorinated biphenyls (PCBs) are similar in many ways to those of animals dosed with DDT and other organochlorine insecticides, i.e. they appear to show hyper- and hypothyroidism. Thus, the published literature lists the following points.

a. An increase in liver weights and liver lipid in PCB (Aroclor 1242)-dosed rats and Japanese quail (Cecil et al., 1973). Also increased liver weights in Japanese quail and pigeons dosed with Aroclor 1254 (D. J. Jefferies, work in progress) and chickens fed Aroclor 1242 (McCune et al., 1962) (see Sections IX.B.1.k. and IX.B.2.f.).

b. A decrease in liver vitamin A stores in dosed (Aroclor 1242) rats and quail (Cecil et al., 1973) (see Sections IX.B.1.f. and IX.B.2.d.).

c. A reduction in egg production by PCB-dosed quail (Aroclor 1242; Cecil et al., 1973), pheasants (Aroclor 1254; Dahlgren and Linder, 1971) and chickens (Aroclor 1242 and 1254; reported by Dustman et al., 1971) (see Section VI.D.2.).

d. An increased heart weight indicating increased pulse rate in Aroclor 1254-dosed Bengalese finches (Prestt et al., 1970) and a decreased heart weight indicating a decreased pulse rate in Aroclor 1254-dosed lesser black-backed gulls Larus fuscus (Jefferies and Parslow, 1972) (see Section IX.A.2.i. and IX.B.2.e.).

e. An increase above normal in the nocturnal activity of robins Erithacus rubecula given PCB (Clophen A50) during the migratory period (Ulfstrand et al., 1971) (see Section IX.A.1.e. and III.F.).

f. An increase in the length of the oestrous cycle in PCB (Clophen A60)-dosed mice (Örberg et al., 1972) (see Section IX.D.d.).

g. The presence of oestrogenic activity in PCB mixtures with relatively little chlorine (21 to 48 per cent) when given to rats. The mixtures with higher chlorination, between 54 and 68 per cent, did not show this activity (Bitman and Cecil, 1970) (see Section IX.B.1.k.).

h. The finding of increased susceptibility to hepatitis virus in ducklings dosed with Aroclor 1254 may parallel the findings of increased susceptibility to diseases in organochlorine insecticide dosed mammals (Friend and Trainer, 1970) (see Section IX.D.h.).

i. A decrease in hatchability in PCB-dosed pheasants (Aroclor 1254; Dahlgren and Linder, 1971) and chickens (Aroclor 1242 and 1254; reported by Dustman *et al.*, 1971) (see Section IX.E.d.).

j. A reduction in chick weight and post-hatching survival in Aroclor 1254-dosed pheasants (Dahlgren and Linder, 1971) (see Section IX.A.2.g. and IX.E.e.).

k. In behavioural tests, the offspring of Aroclor 1254-dosed pheasants made the undesirable choice of jumping to the deep side of a 'visual cliff' more often than the controls or made no choice at all within the test period (Dahlgren and Linder, 1971). This may indicate reduced vision (see Section IX.D.g.).

l. Hydropericardia, the presence of considerable amounts of fluid in the pericardial sac were mentioned by both Flick *et al.* (1965) and Koeman *et al.* (1969) in chickens and quail poisoned with PCBs. This may be due to hypothyroidism, which has been found to increase the extracellular retention of water (see Section VI.G.3.).

An examination of the thyroids of lesser black-backed gulls dosed with Aroclor 1254 for eight weeks confirmed the above suggestion that PCBs were affecting the functions of this gland. Thus, Jefferies and Parslow (1972) found increased gland weights with larger follicles and more colloid. This histological picture of a thyroid in involution with minimal thyroid hormone secretion is similar to that found by Richert and Prahlad (1972) after long-term dosing with DDT (see Section IV.B. and XI.B.). So it could indicate pituitary exhaustion after over-production of TSH (as in the case of organochlorine insecticides, see Section XI.B.). However, the involuted thyroid found after PCB administration is also similar to that seen after hypothalectomy (see Section III.H.). Recent work, still in progress at Monks Wood, shows that in some species thyroid weight decreases and atrophy occurs in PCB-dosed birds within eight weeks of the initial dose. This information and the speed at which involution occurs, argues against the mechanism being similar to that causing hypothyroidism in DDT-dosed animals and suggests a direct action of PCB on the pituitary, with inhibition amounting to hypothalectomy (see Section III.H.). Either way, the overt effect on the animal would be hypothyroidism and a lowered metabolic rate. The results described above for PCB-dosed

Bengalese finches d. and robins e. suggest that, as with the organo-chlorine insecticides, in some species there can also be a hyperthyroid phase.

One sublethal effect shown by DDT and its metabolites but not apparently shown by birds dosed with various PCBs, is that of eggshell thinning. Thus, mallard fed Aroclor 1268 (Tucker and Haegele, 1970) and ring doves fed Aroclor 1254 and injected with this material (Peakall, 1971) all laid eggs with normal shells. Pheasants did not show eggshell thinning with Aroclor 1254 even at dose rates large enough to decrease egg production and hatchability (Dahlgren and Linder, 1971). Although some early experiments carried out by Monsanto Chemical Co. (reported by Cooke, 1973) showed eggshell thinning in chickens fed Aroclor 1242, 1254 and 1260, their food consumption was considerably decreased (by up to 37 per cent). Cooke thought that this decreased food consumption could account for the level of shell thinning found. A later experiment by the Monsanto Chemical Co. using Aroclor 1242 showed no effect on either food consumption or eggshell thickness. Balasubramanian (1972) confirmed the latter observation as he could find no significant differences in egghell thickness in the eggs laid by chickens dosed with PCB (Aroclor 1221). He also noted that he could find no effect of this material on carbonic anhydrase activity.

XI. POSSIBLE MECHANISMS OF ACTION

A. Production of Hypo- and Hyperthyroidism

Enough research has been carried out now to enable one to suggest, with some experimental basis, how organochlorine insecticides may cause hypothyroidism. Suggestions for hyperthyroidism, however, are much more tentative.

One suggestion of a possible mechanism for hypothyroidism was put forward by Fregly et al. (1968). Although the rats they dosed with op'-, pp'- and mp'-DDD showed symptoms of hypothyroidism (see Section V.A.), they also showed increases in the rates of release of radio-active iodide (I^{131}) from the thyroid gland. Thus, in this species at least, the organochlorine is not acting as a goitrogen like thiouracil (see Section III.H.) and blocking thyroxine output. The gland is, in fact, hyperfunctioning with a high output of thyroxine. Further research showed that, after administration of thyroxine-I^{131}, there was a significantly greater faecal and reduced urinary excretion of radioactivity in all DDD- treated groups, compared to the controls. They suggested then that this showed a greater hepatic metabolism of the thyroid hormones (see Section III.E.) in the DDD-fed rats. This would lower the amounts of thyroid hormones circulating in the blood and the pituitary would then secrete more TSH in an attempt to compensate by increasing thyroid activity, hence the increase in thyroid weight. As long as a sufficient supply of thyroid hormones remained available, overt signs of hypothyroidism would not appear. If thyroxine metabolism increased at a greater rate than production, then DDD would cause hypothyroidism (as it did at the highest dose rate tested—see Section V.A.).

There is some support for this hypothesis as both DDT and dieldrin cause enlargement of the liver in a number of mammalian species (see Section VIII.A.11.). This increase in liver weight is associated with a proliferation of the smooth endoplasmic reticulum (SER) (Ortega, 1966; Wright *et al.*, 1972). Liver microsomes isolated from these SER membranes contain a mixed function oxidase system which can catalyse the hydroxylation of several endogenous molecules. Thus, the organochlorine insecticides can induce enzyme systems in the livers of birds and mammals which, in addition, will bring about increased metabolism of the steroid hormones (see Sections VIII.A.12. and VIII.B.18.), other organochlorine insecticides (Gillett *et al.*, 1966) and drugs such as phenobarbitone (Straw *et al.*, 1965). This liver enlargement with cell hypertrophy associated with proliferation of the SER and increased activity of its oxidase systems has been called 'hyperfunctional liver enlargement' (Golberg, 1966) and was thought to be an adaptive response to increased functional demand in the presence of a toxin. It is feasible then, that such 'hyperfunctional liver enlargement' could increase catabolism of thyroid hormones. Then one might expect the thyroid to enlarge when it compensated by increased release of hormones. However, not all birds dosed with organochlorines develop these enlarged livers. Also, the presence or absence of liver enlargement in such dosed birds is correlated with the symptoms of hypo- and hyperthyroidism respectively (see Sections VIII.B.17., IX.A.2. and A.3.). As these changes in thyroid activity alone will determine any changes in liver weight (hypothyroidism increases it whilst hyperthyroidism does not—see Section VI.G.4.), it therefore seems likely that dosed birds often have enlarged livers because of the insecticide's effect on the thyroid rather than being the cause of it. This also means that the idea that the liver weight increases as an adaptive response to the toxin, may be incorrect in this case.

The best current suggestion of a possible mechanism for hypothyroidism arose from the medical use of *op'*-DDD for the treatment of patients with adrenal carcinoma. Danowski *et al.* (1964) found that use of this compound decreased the serum protein-bound iodine (PBI) level in treated patients, although there were no overt signs of hypothyroidism. They speculated that *op'*-DDD reduced the thyroid's synthesis of thyroid hormones, in a similar way to thiouracil (see Section III.H.), or alternatively that it decreased the transport of thyroxine by the thyroxine-binding serum proteins (see Section III.C.). Tests showed that *op'*-DDD did not block the intrathyroidal binding of iodine and tyrosine (see Section III.B.), neither was there any reduction in thyroidal intake of iodine, i.e. thyroid hormone production appeared to be normal. Regarding the second possibility, Oppenheimer and Tavernetti (1962) had suggested earlier that the binding of diphenylhydantoin to thyroxine-binding globulin (TBG) may be due to the steric similarity between the molecules of that compound and thyroxine (Figs 2 and 9). Thus, Danowski suggested that *op'*-DDD, another diphenyl compound, might also compete with thyroxine for binding sites on the TBG and so produce a lowered PBI. Marshall and Tompkins (1968) later tested this hypothesis by measuring the resin sponge intake of triiodothyronine in the sera of their patients receiving *op'*-DDD. This was found to be considerably elevated, indicating a tendency towards a hyperfunctioning thyroid. They concluded that the combination of a reduced PBI with increased output and circulation of triiodothyronine, could only occur either as the result of competition by the *op'*-DDD for thyroxine-binding sites on the transporting proteins (see Section III.C.) or with a decrease in TBG. They knew there was no decrease in the amount of TBG and so they established that the thyroxine-binding capacity of the TBG in sera taken from patients treated with *op'*-DDD was significantly reduced compared to that of pretreatment sera. This confirmed the original hypothesis of Danowski *et al.*

After their discovery that 5,5-diphenylhydantoin (DPH) could displace thyroxine from its serum alpha globulin carrier, thyroxine-binding globulin (TBG), Oppenheimer and Tavernetti (1962) tested 22 other analogues of hydantoin for this particular capacity. Of ten analogues of hydantoin capable of thyroxine displacement, all but one possessed a diphenyl substituent at the 5-C position (i.e. had phenyl groups at R_1 and R_2—see diphenylhydantoin in Fig. 9). The one exception had one phenyl and one cyclohexene group. Of 13 analogues of hydantoin which failed to displace thyroxine, none had a diphenyl substituent at this point. As the relative specificity of the binding capacity of TBG is well established, the demonstration that thyroxine and DPH bind competitively for this serum protein suggested a strong structural similarity in their molecules. Oppenheimer and Tavernetti then postulated that an analogy existed between DPH and thyroxine by virtue of the diphenyl linkage of DPH at 5-C (i.e. with both phenyl groups linked to the same carbon atom—see Fig. 9) and the diphenyl ether linkage of thyroxine (i.e. with both phenyl groups linked to one oxygen atom—see Fig. 2). This analogy is much more clear when viewed as a three-dimensional representation. Thus, the angle between the two valence bonds of oxygen at the ether linkage of thyroxine is approximately 110°, and corresponds closely to the angle of 109°28′ between the two valence bonds of carbon connecting the phenyl rings of DPH. Also, the distance between the ether oxygen of thyroxine and the phenyl ring is 1·36 Å, and the corresponding distance from the phenyl ring to the 5-C carbon atom in DPH is 1·46 Å.

Both Danowski *et al.* (1964) and Marshall and Tompkins (1968) recognized that *op'*-DDD fulfills the criteria put forward by Oppenheimer and Tavernetti as necessary for a molecule to be a competitor to thyroxine for binding sites on TBG. Also, Marshall and Tompkins tested Metyrapone, the molecular structure of which does not fulfil these criteria (Fig. 9), and confirmed that it does not compete with thyroxine. Furthermore, they noted that Amphenone B, which does fulfil these requirements (Fig. 9), is also known to be goitrogenic (Hertz *et al.*, 1950; Hogness *et al.*, 1953).

Examination of the molecular configurations of the various isomers of DDT, DDE, DDD and DDA (Fig. 1) shows that these also fulfil these criteria. It seems reasonable then to suppose, as a working hypothesis, that the competitive binding of these organochlorine compounds with thyroxine-binding serum proteins produces hypothyroidism in dosed animals. Men dosed with DDD are not hypothyroid, perhaps because of the low dose rates used, the relatively large amounts of triiodo-thyronine still circulating at these dose rates and man's very efficient thyroid hormone transport system (discussed below). The increased excretion of products from thyroxine breakdown noted in DDD-dosed rats by Fregly *et al.* (1968) could be due to hepatic catabolism of the increased quantities of free thyroxine in circulation (see Section III.E.).

The way by which hyperthyroidism could be brought about in an organochlorine-dosed animal has not been studied to the same extent as has hypothyroidism. There must be a separate mechanism as the degree of hyperthyroidism in the Bengalese finch increases in severity with the dose rate of DDT (see Sections V.B. and IX.A.2.). This suggests that it is unlikely that hyperthyroidism is produced simply by an abnormal extension of the normal feedback system i.e. the stimulation

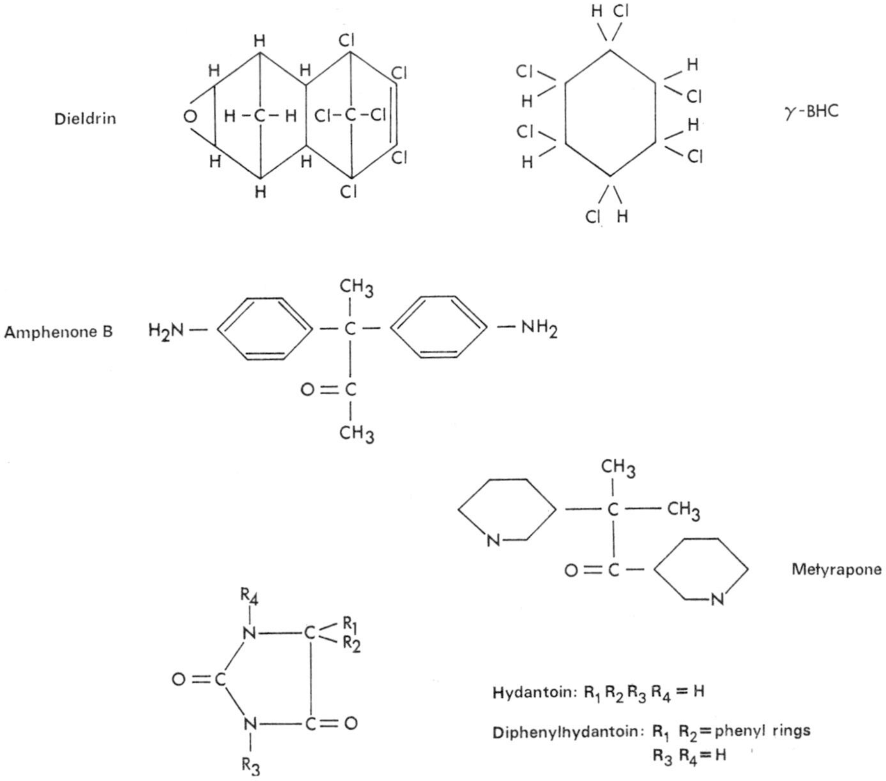

Fig. 9. The molecular configuration of diphenylhydantoin which is known to compete with thyroxine for binding sites on the thyroxine-binding serum proteins, thus reducing serum PBI. Also shown are the molecules of amphenone B which is goitrogenic and metyrapone which has no effect on PBI. The structural requirements for sufficient molecular similarity to the thyroxine molecule (see Fig. 2) to cause competition for binding sites are discussed in Section XI.A. The molecular configurations of two commonly used organochlorine insecticides, dieldrin and γ-BHC, are given for purposes of comparison. These too are known to reduce serum PBI, possibly by a different mechanism as their molecules are apparently structurally very different from that of thyroxine.

of the pituitary by reduction in circulating thyroxine to over-produce TSH and over-correct the situation. Only three known pathways for direct action exist. a. DDT could act as a thyroxine through a molecular similarity. This would appear to be impossible as Frieden and Winzler (1948) have tested many molecules for thyroxine-like activity and found that the major structural prerequisites for this function are: i. an orthodihalogenophenolic diphenyl ether configuration; ii. a hydroxy group either *ortho* or *para* to the ether oxygen; and

iii. a side chain which must include a functional group such as a carboxyl or an amino group or both. None of the molecules of the organochlorine insecticides conform to these requirements (Figs 1 and 8). Thus, although they are similar enough to link to the thyroxine-binding serum proteins they are not similar enough to act as thyroxine itself. b. The second alternative is by direct stimulation of the anterior pituitary by increased secretion of the thyrotrophin releasing factor (see Section III.G.), brought about by action of the insecticide on the central nervous system. This seems unlikely: i. because hyperthyroidism by stimulation of the pituitary would involve increased secretion of gonadotrophins as well, and eventually of oestrogens (see Sections XI.B. and C.), which would make symptoms such as delayed ovulation unlikely (see Section VIII.B.4.); and ii. because of the apparent inactivation of the pituitary by chronic dosing (see Section XI.B.). c. The third possible pathway is through stimulation of the production of LATS (see Section III.G.). This appears to be the most likely mechanism as the LATS system is thought to be of prime importance in the pathogenesis of the aberrant situation of hyperthyroidism in man (see Section III.G.). Also, it is known that Graves's disease can be caused by a sudden emotional shock (Turner, 1966). If a sudden shock can cause a development of the LATS system, it is conceivable that the sudden entry of a large amount of an organochlorine with its attendant effects on the nervous system (e.g. membrane destabilization, O'Brien and Matsumura, 1964; O'Brien, 1967) could provide another such shock.

It would appear then, that the two mechanisms described above both operate within the dosed animal, i.e. with increasing dose rate there is an increasing stimulation of the thyroid, either by LATS or the pituitary, and there is also an increasing competition for binding sites with a consequent reduction in levels of circulating thyroid hormones. The effects shown by the animal would depend on which of these mechanisms is dominant at that time. It seems likely from the literature, that most animals react like the DDT-dosed pigeons (see Section V.B.), i.e. with chronic dosing, hyperthyroidism develops first, and this is then replaced by hypothyroidism. Thus, the reason for DDT-dosed pigeons showing hyperthyroidism at low dose rates and hypothyroidism at high dose rates in the experiments described in Section V.B. is that their reactions were examined at one point in time. Presumably, even at high dose rates, a pigeon passes through a period of hyperthyroidism, as DDT accumulates, before hypothyroidism develops. Similarly, pigeons on some low dose rates may eventually become hypothyroid also (though if the rate is low enough they may never do so). With acute dosing the phase of hyperthyroidism may be very short. There is some evidence for this 'switch-over' in the literature: a. The oxygen consumption of liver slices (an indicator of BMR) taken from rats fed DDT showed an increase above normal after a short period on dose, followed by a reduction below normal after a longer period at the same dose rate. At an intermediate point in time there was no difference between dosed and control animals (see Section VIII.A.1.). b. Rabbits given DDT showed an elevated blood calcium for three days after dosing, followed by a fall below the normal level (see Section VIII.A.15.). c. The range of liver vitamin A levels in DDT-dosed pigeons is very great at medium dose rates and some birds showed very high and some very low concentrations. This suggests that the birds concerned were at the point of changeover from the high vitamin A stores of low dose rates to the low vitamin A stores of high dose rates (see Section V.B.).

In at least one species, the Bengalese finch, the phase of hypo-thyroidism does not occur (see Sections V.B. and IX.A.2.). The reason for this difference between finches and pigeons in their reaction, may well lie in differences in the protein fraction of their sera and the import-ance of solution in the normal transport of their thyroid hormones(see Section III.C.). The serum protein make-up of avian blood varies considerably from species to species (Sturkie, 1965). Also, differences in serum protein make-up between birds and mammals may account for the much more marked sublethal reaction of birds to DDT than that shown by mammals (Jefferies et al., 1971) (cf. effects on breeding birds, Section VIII.B.4. to B.14. and rats, Section VIII.A.6.). The thyroid hormone transport system in birds is relatively inefficient com-pared to that in man (see Section III.C.). As only one-third of the thyroxine-binding capacity of mammalian blood is usually in use, one would expect that considerable doses of organochlorine insecticides would be required before overt signs of hypothyroidism would appear. However, with the inefficient system in avian blood, an effect on the thyroxine-binding capacity, and hence hypothyroidism, is likely to develop much more quickly in birds, and at lower dose rates, than in mammals.

Although the above hypothesis for the production of hypothyroidism in organochlorine-dosed animals fits the data for analogues of DDT very well, dieldrin and γ-BHC are anomalous. Both molecules are apparently very different from that of thyroxine (compare Figs 2 and 9). On the other hand, most of the reactions induced by these materials are those of hyperthyroidism (see Sections IX.A.1.e, g, i, j, l, m; IX.A.3.b; IX.A.4.c, d, g, h) and no molecular similarity may be necessary to produce this condition. Again, dieldrin does not produce any effect on the liver weight of pigeons (an indication of hyperthyroidism), even at chronic lethal dose rates, whereas both DDT and DDE fed in parallel experiments produced marked liver weight increases and signs of hypothyroidism in this species (Table III). In addition, there were no liver weight changes in song thrushes, chickens and ducks dosed with dieldrin (see Section VIII.B.17.). However, a few symptoms remain which are typical of hypothyroidism, i.e. low liver vitamin A stores in dosed mammals (see Section IX.B.1.f.), perosis (see Section IX.B.2.h.) and reduced haemoglobin levels (see Section IX.B.2.i.) in birds. Also, dieldrin caused slight eggshell thinning in ducks (an effect correlates with hypothyroidism—See Sections VI.D.4. and XI.D.), though this was not repeated in ring doves. It is known that the symptoms of severe hyperthyroidism are similar to those of hypothyroidism (i.e. with growth rate, egg production, etc. see Sections VI.A. and VI.D.2.) but it is unlikely that all of these effects are really symptoms of severe hyperthyroidism. Finally, the finding that both dieldrin and γ-BHC cause a significant decrease in the protein bound iodine content in the sera of rabbits (see Section V.A.) can only indicate a tendency towards hypothyroidism. Thus, one must conclude that, although the reactions produced by dieldrin and γ-BHC are mostly those of hyperthyroidism, these materials are capable of producing some degree of hypothyroidism under some conditions. The possibility that dieldrin and γ-BHC produce a phase of hypothyroidism does not necessarily invalidate or even necessitate some revision of the hypothesis that the mechanism of action of DDT/DDE is by competition for binding sites. The former materials could act like other goitrogens by interference with the 'iodide trap' or by blocking the iodination of tyrosine (see Section III.H.), i.e. by acting intrathyroidally. More research is required to settle this point.

There is no doubt that hypothyroidism develops in animals dosed with PCBs although, like dieldrin and γ-BHC, the molecular structure of their components is very different from that of thyroxine. Again, however, this does not invalidate the proposed mechanism for production of hypothyroidism put forward in this section. If the primary effect of PCBs is on the pituitary (see Section X), then molecular similarity between PCB and thyroxine is unnecessary. Dieldrin, on the other hand, cannot act by pituitary inhibition: the thyroids of dieldrin-dosed birds appear to show hyperplastic goitres (Jefferies and French, 1972) and are hyperfunctioning as with DDT. They do not show involution or atrophy.

B. Changes in Pituitary Activity and their Effects on Thyroid Appearance

In the rat, the pars distalis of the pituitary contains two kinds of acidophilic and four kinds of basophilic cells. The two types of acidophils secrete the growth hormone (STH) and prolactin. The basophils can be divided into gonadotrophic cells secreting follicle stimulating hormone (FSH) and luteinizing hormone (LH), the thyrotrophic cells secreting TSH and the corticotrophic cells secreting adrenocorticotrophic hormone (ACTH). The cytology of the pars distalis in birds is generally similar to that of mammals but the functions of the various cells have not been worked out with the same certainty (Turner, 1966).

Treatment of an animal with a goitrogen such as thiouracil or DDT reduces the quantity of circulating thyroid hormones and the pituitary therefore increases the flow of TSH. The thyroid becomes very active and its appearance changes to that of a hyperplastic goitre. As the level of circulating thyroid hormones would show little increase, the feedback mechanism ensures that the pituitary remains hyperactive and the thyrotrophic cells undergo degranulation and increase in size. If, after a time, the augmented pituitary stimulation and the hyperactivity of the thyroid are unable to restore normal levels of circulating thyroid hormones (as would be the case with these two materials) the thyroid may become exhausted and atrophy (see Section III.H.). Alternatively, the activity of the pituitary may increase. The thyrotrophic cells then increase in numbers, form focal hyperplasias and finally give rise to adenomatous nodules or tumours. At this point the pituitary too becomes exhausted and shows a reduction in overall activity (Turner, 1966). There is some experimental evidence for these stages in pituitary change following introduction of organochlorine insecticides or other chemical goitrogens.

The existence of the first phase, hyperactivity of the pituitary, is demonstrated by research showing that production of a. the gonadotrophins and b. adrenocorticotrophic hormone is increased on administration of a goitrogen. Firstly Leathem (1945) noted that an increase in basophils and a decrease in acidophils had been reported in the pituitaries of rats fed goitrogenic drugs. He concluded that this suggested that an increase in the gonadotrophins such as follicle stimulating hormone may accompany the increased TSH and tested his theory by assaying the pituitaries of thiourea-fed rats. The ovarian weights of the recipients indicated that the gonadotrophic hormone content of the goitrogen-affected pituitaries was indeed somewhat greater than that of pituitaries from normal rats. Secondly Hertz *et al.*

(1950) found that, besides thyroid hypertrophy, adrenal hypertrophy occurred after administering the goitrogen Amphenone B to rats. This adrenal enlargement did not occur in hypophysectomized animals, thus showing that the goitrogen was stimulating adrenotrophic activity as well as thyrotrophic activity in the anterior pituitary. Furthermore, the size and weight of the avian pituitary is known to be increased following thyroidectomy (Sturkie, 1965). This would be expected with increased pituitary activity and an increase in the size and number of thyrotrophic cells.

The concluding phase of pituitary exhaustion is demonstrated by the work of Richert and Prahlad (1972) (see Section IV.B.). They found that 85 days after finishing long-term dosing with DDT and DDE, the thyroids of quail did not show the usual hyperfunctioning hyperplastic goitres seen with short-term dosing of pigeons, but were enlarged and involuted showing minimal colloid depletion. Thus, the hypothyroidism observed in these birds would be due to thyroid inactivity. Such a condition would only follow pituitary inactivity and atrophy (see Section III.H.). Summarizing, short-term dosing with goitrogens like DDT and thiourea may result in hyperactivity of the pituitary with increased gonadotrophin production, although the thyroid is physiologically inoperative. A long exposure, on the other hand, may inactivate both the thyroid and the pituitary, with consequent reduction in gonadotrophin production. The fact that the latter condition is still apparent 85 days after ceasing dosing suggests that such an effect may be permanent. This is disturbing from the point of view of wildlife contamination.

As a corollary, the induction of hyperthyroidism in experimental animals by feeding thyroproteins would be expected to have an effect on the pituitary also. Thus, the excess of circulating exogenous thyroid hormones should reduce the activity of both the thyroid gland and the pituitary because TSH secretion would be reduced to a minimum. Such treatment has indeed been found to bring about a significant decrease in the weight of the pituitaries of affected chickens (see Section VI.G.4.). Similarly, if the hyperthyroidism seen in DDT-dosed Bengalese finches is due to stimulation of the LATS system, then again pituitary activity should be reduced.

It is possible that many of the effects observed after induction of hyper- and hypothyroidism in animals by feeding thyroproteins, thyroidectomy and administration of goitrogens such as thiouracil and DDT, could be due to this secondary effect on the pituitary, e.g. the delay in ovulation in birds made hyperthyroid (see Sections VI.D.1. and VIII.B.4.) may be due to pituitary inactivity.

C. Production of Oestrogenic Effects

The oestrogenic effects of DDT, particularly by the *ortho–para* isomer, are thought to occur because this isomer mimics the molecule of the synthetic oestrogen diethylstilboestrol (see Sections VIII.A.16., VIII.B.21. and Fig. 8). Bitman and Cecil (1970) studied the oestrogenic activity and molecular configurations of several organochlorines and concluded that this activity is correlated with the presence of -H, -OH or -OCH$_3$ on the *para* positions of the basic diphenylalkane structure whilst halide or alkyl groups at these positions inactivate the compound. Thus, the two molecules do not have to be very similar before some mimicry occurs, although the differences probably explain why *op'*-DDT cannot produce all the effects of an oestrogen (see Section VIII.A.16.) and its activity is only one ten thousandth to one hundred thousandth that of oestradiol (Cecil *et al.*, 1971; Singhal *et al.*, 1970).

This explanation of oestrogenicity based on a simple similarity of the molecules in one or two points is not entirely satisfactory, however, when other, dissimilar, molecules are found to have oestrogenic properties also. Thus, Hertz *et al.* (1950) have shown that Amphenone B, a drug which is known to produce hyperplastic goitre of the thyroid in mammals (see Section XI.A.), causes similar oestrogenic effects on the genital tract of ovariectomized rats as those produced by *op'*-DDT. This very marked oestrogenic effect on the genital tract persisted and could still be produced after either hypophysectomy or adrenalectomy. It is possible that these effects produced by Amphenone B are again due to the similarity of its molecule to that of diethylstilboestrol (compare Figs 8 and 9), although if this is so, it means that the acceptor is even less specific, and will accept a molecule as an oestrogen mimic with -NH$_2$ groups at the *para* positions. Also, it means that both DDT and Amphenone molecules must be similar to both diethylstilboestrol and thyroxine as they are both goitrogens as well. On the other hand, perhaps DDT and Amphenone B have similar effects because both are goitrogens, i.e. the oestrogenic effect may be secondary and due to the induced hypothyroidism brought about by the similarity of their molecules to thyroxine (see Section XI.A.). However, the mechanism for such secondary oestrogenic effects is unknown. It cannot be the changes in pituitary activity noted in the last section. Although one would expect that augmented FSH could lead to increased production of oestrogen by the ovary, these oestrogenic effects occur even after ovariectomy, hypophysectomy and adrenalectomy.

D. Changes in Eggshell Thickness

Probably the most strongly supported hypothesis of a mechanism for the eggshell thinning seen in organochlorine insecticide-dosed birds is that of carbonic anhydrase inhibition within the shell gland (see Section VIII.B.20.). The reason for this strong support is that there is no good evidence so far of any marked reduction in blood calcium in laying birds dosed with organochlorines (Cooke, 1973). An effect within the shell gland itself could explain the presence of shell thinning without having any changes in blood calcium levels. However, it should be noted that DDT is capable of markedly reducing blood calcium levels in mammals (see Section VIII.A.15.) and there are difficulties in explaining shell thinning by inhibition of carbonic anhydrase alone. Thus, with sulphanilamide, which also causes thin-shelled eggs and inhibits carbonic anhydrase activity (Gutowska and Mitchell, 1945), there are thought to be other important factors concerned with the shell thinning (Tyler, 1954; Mueller, 1962). Also, carbonic anhydrase is known to be present in excess amounts in the shell gland (Heald *et al.*, 1968) and Dvorchik *et al.* (1971) have stated that the recorded reduction in activity with DDE and DDT (about 60 per cent by Peakall, 1970b; 18 per cent by Bitman *et al.*, 1970; see Section VIII.B.20.) is not usually enough for physiological inhibition. In addition, Pocker *et al.* (1971) have demonstrated that pesticides may not be true inhibitors of carbonic anhydrase.

It is possible that the thyroid changes recorded here may be involved in the production of thin eggshells by organochlorine insecticides and there is, in fact, much supporting evidence.

a. It is known that changes in thyroid activity have a marked effect on avian calcium metabolism. Thus, development of medullary bone (see Section VIII.B.20.) can be retarded by thyroidectomy (see Section VI.D.5.), so the reduction in medullary bone formation in DDT- and DDE-treated birds (see Section VIII.B.20.) could be due to the hypothyroidism produced by these materials. Also, the normal oestrogen-induced rise in plasma calcium can be prevented by both thyroxine and thiouracil in the hen and by thyroidectomy in the duck (Höhn, 1961). Reduction in thyroid activity has been suggested as the reason for the normal thinning of hens' eggshells occurring during the summer (see Section VI.D.4.), and experimental tests have shown that hypothyroidism does indeed cause the production of thin-shelled eggs in chickens whereas hyperthyroidism may cause the eggs to have thicker shells (see Section VI.D.4.).

b. The two species of birds which do not show thin-shelled eggs on dosing with DDT, the Bengalese finch and the chicken (see Section VIII.B.7.), are also the two species which show marked hyperthyroidism on treatment with this material (see Section IX.A.2. and A.3.) and which both show no change in liver weight (see Section VIII.B.17.).

c. The Bengalese finch produces thicker shells at low dose rates and thinner shells at high dose rates of DDT approaching lethal levels when clutch size and egg production are decreasing. This is what would be expected with mild hyperthyroidism turning to severe hyperthyroidism with increasing dose rate.

d. Experimental tests show that dieldrin produces little or no eggshell thinning (see Section VIII.B.7.). Also, eggshell thickness shows a much better negative correlation (i.e. a higher correlation coefficient) with the DDE residue in field specimens than it does with either dieldrin or PCB content (Anderson et al., 1969; Blus et al., 1971). Again, as with Bengalese finches and chickens fed DDT (see b. above), nearly all of the effects produced by dieldrin appear to be those of hyperthyroidism (see Section XI.A.) so if eggshell thinning is connected with hypothyroidism then thin eggshells would not be expected every time with this material.

e. There is much circumstantial evidence suggesting that the eggshell thinning observed in the field is due to DDT/DDE contamination (Ratcliffe, 1970). Also, this evidence appears to fit in with the known changes of thyroid activity with these materials. Ratcliffe compared the recent changes in eggshell thickness index for 14 species of birds with the mean organochlorine insecticide residue in their eggs. He found that high contamination in a species reduced this index and that the amount of thinning decreased with decreasing contamination. Species with low contamination levels showed increased indices, i.e. thicker shells. This could perhaps reflect the change from hypo-to hyperthyroidism with decreasing dose rate.

f. The drug sulphanilamide, which causes thin-shelled eggs in chickens (see above), is also a goitrogen: Larson et al. (1945) noted work showing that it inhibits the formation of thyroxine and diiodotyrosine. Thus, the production of thin-shelled eggs by this material and DDT/DDE may be brought about by the hypothyroidism that both induce as well as or instead of the carbonic anhydrase inhibition they cause.

Analysis of compounds and treatments known to cause changes in thyroid activity (Table V) shows that those treatments which inhibit carbonic anhydrase also thin eggshells (iv, viii) whereas when no inhibition occurs, thin eggshells are not produced (v, vii, ix). However, it is not just a matter of which exogenous molecules will bring about

Table V

The effect of thyroidectomy and a number of chemical agents on thyroid activity and eggshell thickness of various species of birds, with accompanying effects on the carbonic anhydrase system and the activity of the pituitary for purposes of correlation

Treatment	Species	Effect on thyroid activity	Effect on carbonic anhydrase	Effect on eggshell	Effect on pituitary
(i) Thyroidectomy	Chicken	Nil. Bird in state of hypothyroidism	?	Shell thinning observed (see VI.C.4.)	Weight and activity increased (see XI.B.)
(ii) Thiouracil in the diet	Chicken	Production of hyperplastic goitre. Reduced output of thyroid hormones results in hypothyroidism (see III.H.)	?	Shell thinning observed (see VI.C.4.)	Activity increased (see XI.B.)
(iii) Iodinated casein or thyroproteins added to diet	Chicken	Endogenous thyroid hormone secretion minimal due to excess exogenous thyroid hormones in circulation—result is hyperthyroidism (see III.F.)	?	Shell thickening observed (see VI.C.4.)	Weight and activity reduced (see XI.B.)
(iv) Sulphanilamide	Chicken	Production of hyperplastic goitre by inhibiting the formation of thyroxine intrathyroidally. Result is hypothyroidism (see XI.D.)	Inhibited (see XI.D.)	Shell thinning observed (see XI.B.)	Activity increased due to block in thyroxine formation (see XI.B.)
(v) Dieldrin	Various species	Production of hyperplastic goitre in pigeons (see IV.B.). Majority of effects on mammals, ring doves, pigeons, song thrushes are those of hyperthyroidism though some effects suggest that hypothyroidism can occur (see IX.A.1., IX.A.4., XI.A.)	No inhibition in chickens and ring doves (see VIII.B.20.)	No shell thinning in ring doves or chickens. Small amount of shell thinning in mallard (see VIII.B.7.)	Activity reduced as in (vi) below. (see XI.B.)

(vi) DDT or DDE	Bengalese finch	Production of hyperthyroidism only (see IX.A.2.)	?	Shell thickening at low dose rates with some shell thinning when dose rate approaches the the lethal level (see VIII.B.7. and XI.D.)	Pituitary activity reduced if, as appears, thyroid stimulation is not through the pituitary (see XI.B.)
(vii) DDT or DDE	Chicken	Mainly hyperthyroidism (see IX.A.3.)	No inhibition (see VIII.B.20.)	No shell thinning (see VIII.B.7.)	Activity reduced as in (vi) above (see XI.B.)
(viii) DDT or DDE	Various species	Production of hyperplastic goitre in pigeon. Result is the production of a phase of hyperthyroidism followed by hypothyroidism at most dose rates. Quail also show hypothyroidism (see IV.B. and V.B.) Many effects of hyper- and hypothyroidism (mainly the latter) are shown by various other species (see IX)	Inhibited in quail and ring doves (see VIII.B.20.)	Shell thinning in quail, ring doves, mallard, black ducks, American sparrowhawk (see VIII.B.7.)	Pituitary activity increased in attempt to correct hypothyroidism (see XI.B.) but may be reduced during the phase of hyperthyroidism (see (vi) above)
(ix) PCB	Various species	Production of large colloid goitre in lesser black-backed gull; thyroid involution with minimal secretion. Result is hypothyroidism. Various other species show effects of both hyper- and hypothyroidism, mainly the latter, as with DDT or DDE (viii) (see X)	No inhibition in chicken (see X.)	No shell thinning in ring doves, mallard, pheasant, chicken (see X)	Pituitary activity reduced if, as appears likely, thyroid involution is due to pituitary inhibition (see X and XI.A.)

inhibition of this enzyme system, as DDT/DDE will do this in one species (viii) but not in another (vii), which argues against a simple chemical effect. The physiological state of the animal is important too: carbonic anhydrase inhibition only occurs in cases where the animals are hypothyroid (iv, viii). Also, hypothyroidism, due to either thyroidectomy or thiouracil (i, ii), can cause eggshell thinning without any known effect on the carbonic anhydrase enzyme system, though, of course, this may occur. This suggests that the state of hypothyroidism is of importance in the pathogenesis of thin shells (i, ii, iv, viii). However, PCB treatment does not thin eggshells, although it does produce hypothyroidism (ix). The one factor which all treatments producing thin eggshells have in common, is that they increase pituitary activity (i, ii, iv, viii) whereas with decreased pituitary activity the eggshells are either unaffected or thickened (iii, v, vi, vii, ix). Increased pituitary activity usually follows hypothyroidism (see Section XI.B.) but it would not occur with PCB, as here hypothyroidism appears to be due to pituitary inhibition (see Sections X and XI.A.).

Although it may be thought that reduced pituitary activity, with the consequent reduction in oestrogen from the ovary, would be more likely to produce eggshell thinning than would increased pituitary activity, there are at least two ways in which the latter could act. First, there may be an imbalance in the relative amounts of the various hormones produced by the hyperactive pituitary. Thus, although the basophils were increased in the pituitaries of rats fed goitrogenic drugs, the acidophils were decreased (see Section XI.B.). This may mean an increase in the gonadotrophins but a decrease in the growth hormone (STH) and prolactin. As hormones never act in isolation but in complex coordination it is apparent that the imbalance may produce overt effects. In mammals, although STH has little effect on target organs when administered alone, it acts as a synergist to other hormones, such as oestrogen, and markedly enhances their effectiveness (Turner, 1966). If a similar relationship exists in birds then this could well affect eggshells. Secondly, the apparent connection between the inhibition of the carbonic anhydrase system and hypothyroidism coupled with increased pituitary activity (see above) suggests another mechanism. Hormones exert direct effects upon intracellular enzyme systems. These interactions may occur due to the hormones acting as co-enzymes or by their control of cell permeability thus making substrates available to semi-isolated enzyme systems, e.g. STH is thought to act by facilitating the entrance of amino acids into the cell contents (Turner, 1966). It has been demonstrated also, that hormones can act upon enzymes even in cell-free systems. These known modifications of enzyme systems by hormones suggest that a link between the hormone imbalance occasioned by increased pituitary activity and an effect on the carbonic anhydrase system is indeed possible. Thus, although the immediate mechanism for eggshell thinning may be an inhibition or a reduction in the rate of synthesis of carbonic anhydrase, this could be a secondary or tertiary effect stemming from the primary effect on the thyroid.

E. Actions Produced by Changes in Blood pH

It is possible that the hyperirritability of organochlorine-poisoned animals is linked to the hyperventilation that occurs initially with high doses of these materials. An increased rate of respiration (see Section VIII.A.3.) will decrease blood carbon dioxide to such an extent that alkalosis occurs. This can produce many of the signs of tetany, including spasms of the muscles and hyperexcitability of the peripheral nerves (Bell et al., 1952). Deichmann et al. (reported by Hayes, 1959) noted that in a DDT-dosed subject, both hyperexcitability and a rapid respiration rate started at the same time. Many of the symptoms of sub-lethal DDT poisoning in man (e.g. hyperirritability and muscular spasms, particularly that of carpopedal spasm in which the foot is firmly flexed), described in detail by Hayes (1959) are also features of tetany.

A reduction in the rate of respiration produces a different series of effects. When hypothyroidism slows the respiration rate (see Section III.F.), this elevates the blood CO_2 and brings about acidosis. This occurs with hypothyroidism in DDT-dosed animals as there are reported decreases in blood pH (see Section VIII.A.9.). Such acidosis could explain the suppression of salt gland secretion in DDE-dosed mallard (See Section VIII.B.24.): it is known that a low blood pH inhibits the activity of this gland (Sturkie, 1965). Another possible effect, suggested by Cooke (1973), might be on the thickness of egg-shells. Thus, experiments testing the effects of blood acidosis on the eggshell thickness of chickens have shown that both thinner (Helbacka et al., 1963; Hunt and Simkiss, 1967) and thicker (Frank and Burger, 1965) shells than normal may be produced.

XII. DISCUSSION AND CONCLUSIONS

The previous sections show that most of the sublethal effects of organo-chlorine insecticides may be due to the two main lesions on the thyroid producing hyper- and hypothyroidism. However, these materials are thought to kill by affecting the transmission of nervous impulses (see Hayes, 1959; Moriarty, 1969 and Casida and Maddrell, 1971 for discussions on possible lethal mechanisms). This finding that the main sublethal lesion of a group of toxins differs from the main lethal lesion is surprising. Usually one expects that the sublethal effects would be caused by a lesser degree of the lethal lesion. On the other hand, if a. the tremors seen in DDT-dosed animals follow hyperthyroidism (see Sections IX.A.1.d. and IX.A.2.a.), b. muscular spasms, tetany and hyperexcitability are caused by blood alkalosis (see Section XI.E.) and c. the complete usage of liver glycogen stores follows the increased BMR (see Section VIII.A.14.) then with interference with normal feeding due to a. and b. and reduced energy supplies due to c., the lesion on the thyroid may well contribute to death as well.

The literature recording the sublethal effects of the organochlorine insecticides shows that the results of different authors testing the same material vary considerably, even when using the same species. Also, the reactions of some species appear to be the opposite of others dosed with the same material. Thus, at first sight, the pattern of overt effects appears complex and sometimes contradictory. However, the reasons for some of these variations and contradictions are now clear. Chronic dosing may produce hyperthyroidism for some weeks before hypothyroidism develops and the opposite symptoms appear. With a severe acute dose of the same material given to the same species, on the other hand, the hyperthyroidism may be over very quickly. Certain species may never show a phase of hypothyroidism. Thus, what is recorded as the effect for a particular species/insecticide interaction will depend on the dose rate used, the length of time (or when) observations are made in relation to this dose rate and the rate and type of response of the species used. The effects of long-term dosing may depend on whether one is observing hypothyroidism with a functional pituitary or hypothyroidism without gonadotrophin production (see Section XI.B.). It should be remembered also, that at one point in time there may be a period of almost non-effect, at least with respect to the BMR.

As the sublethal effects of organochlorine insecticides seen in the laboratory appear to be due to lesions on the thyroid, it is important to determine if these effects on the thyroid are likely to occur at the 'background' contamination levels seen in wildlife in the field. Analytical results for the livers and brains of six pigeons from each of the dose rate groups fed DDT in the experiment described in Sections IV and V are given in Table I. One of the experimental pigeons fed 3 mg DDT/kg/day had a liver residue as low as 3·1 ppm DDT + 6·2 ppm DDE. This bird had a total thyroid weight (95 mg) larger than that of the largest control thyroid and also a very much reduced colloid content ($360 \ \mu^2$). The LD_{50} (for death within 56 days) for feral pigeons fed DDT is between 36 and 54 mg/kg/day (Jefferies and French, 1971; Jefferies et al., 1971) and a lethal residue of DDT + DDE in the liver of one bird was found to be $124 \cdot 5 + 258 \cdot 8$ ppm. Thus, this effect on the thyroid was very marked even at liver residues as low as one fortieth of the lethal residue and dose rates of about one fifteenth of the LD_{50}. This is, then, a true sublethal effect rather than an effect only occurring at high dose rates which are only just 'non-lethal'. Such liver residues are commonly found in avian specimens from the field (Moore, 1965; Jefferies and Prestt, 1966; Prestt, 1967; Walker et al., 1967). Thus, as many of the sublethal effects of the organochlorine insecticides noted in the laboratory have been observed in the field also (Lofts and Murton, 1966; Ratcliffe, 1967, 1970; Labisky and Lutz, 1967; Enderson and Berger, 1970; Peakall, 1970a; Prestt, 1970), it seems likely that thyroid lesions occur in the field and have overt effects.

Knowing the basic mechanism behind the sublethal effects produced by the organochlorine insecticides enables one to forecast further effects and particularly sensitive periods and groups. Turner (1966) noted that in mammals active throughout the year, the thyroids are necessarily more active during the cold winter months than during the summer. As Dempsey and Astwood (1943) showed that the thyroid response to a goitrogen was much more marked at low temperatures, these thyroid-induced aberrations are likely to show up more quickly and will have greater effect during the winter. Sublethal effects may then become lethal. In hibernating mammals, the thyroid tends to be inactive during the winter but needs to reach a peak of activity in the spring when the animals emerge from hibernation. The high levels of DDT in the organs of British bats, especially in the spring when the DDT-contaminated fat laid down for hibernation has been metabolized (Jefferies, 1972) suggest that this group may be in particular danger from environmental contamination. Another effect of organochlorines at present being studied at Monks Wood is the likely one on moulting. Changes in thyroid activity are known to affect both the onset of moulting and feather structure (see Section VI.G.1.). These are of major importance to birds, not only for flight but also for insulation. The latter is of particular importance to seabirds living in arctic waters.

Besides the more direct effect of organochlorines on the thyroid activity of adult mammals and birds and the reactions that this brings about within them, the present work shows that there are two other major effects, linked to the main lesion, which could be detrimental to contaminated populations. These are a. an effect on the pituitary and

b. an effect on the thyroid of the unhatched or unborn embryo. a. The lack of circulating thyroxine over a long period may exhaust the pituitary after continued stimulation to produce TSH (see Section XI.B.). This affects the production of gonadotrophins and exacerbates the effects that the lack of circulating thyroxine was already causing, i.e. the condition of an animal and the likelihood of it breeding at all would get progressively worse with time. Also, the work of Richert and Prahlad (1972) shows that once the thyroid and pituitary have been affected in this way their malfunction may persist long after removal of organochlorines from the diet (see Sections IV.B. and XI.B.). b. As the organochlorine insecticides can pass the placental barrier and accumulate in the mammalian embryo (Bäckström et al., 1965) and are passed by the female bird into its egg (Jefferies, 1971) these goitrogens can react with the embryonic thyroid just as in the adult animal (see Section VI.E.). The changing vitamin A status occurring among organochlorine-fed animals is passed on to the developing embryo also (see Section VII.). Thus, the young animal may be in a state of hypo-thyroidism before even the time of birth or hatching. In colonies of birds highly contaminated with organochlorine insecticides, such as those of the brown pelicans *Pelecanus occidentalis* of the Californian coast (Risebrough et al., 1970; Blus et al., 1972) the whole colony may be in a continuous state of hypothyroidism at all ages rather than this developing during the birds' lifetime.

Little is known about the effects of organochlorines on the thyroids of vertebrate groups other than mammals and birds. One group which may be affected is the Amphibia. Hughes and Astwood (1944) found that they could affect the thyroid and inhibit the metamorphosis of tadpoles by using the goitrogen thiouracil and one could expect a similar effect with the organochlorine insecticides. Recent work by Cooke (1972), exposing the frog *Rana temporaria* to DDT or dieldrin, has shown that abnormal development does indeed occur. Again, it is possible that the organochlorine insecticides may parallel the known effects of goitrogens on the invertebrate phyla. Thus, thiourea, in some unknown way, inhibits cleavage completely in sea urchin eggs (Bevelander, 1946).

The interest in the organochlorine insecticides as environmental contaminants may decrease with the drop in world usage and the decline in environmental residues (Coulson et al., 1972). However, when their effects are more fully understood they may have a future as physiological tools (O'Brien, 1969). Obviously much work remains to be done before we understand fully all the details of the thyroids' involvement in sublethal effects of organochlorine insecticides.

One general point though is worth making. The symptoms of sublethal poisoning may be many and diverse, and the mechanisms may be complicated and difficult to unravel, but at least in this instance, the results all appear to stem from a very few initial disturbances within the organism. This may well be so for the PCBs also.

REFERENCES

Adams, D. D. (1958). *J. clin. Endocr. Metab.* **18,** 699–712.

Adams, D. D. and Purves, H. D. (1956). *Proc. Univ. Otago Med. Sch.* **34,** 11–12.

Adams, R. D. and Rosman, N. P. (1971). *In* 'The Thyroid—a Fundamental and Clinical Text' (S. C. Werner and S. H. Ingbar, eds), pp. 771–780. 3rd edition. Harper, New York.

Albert, T. F. (1962). *Auk* **79,** 104–107.

Anderson, D. W., Hickey, J. J., Risebrough, R. W., Hughes, D. F. and Christensen, R. E. (1969). *Can. Fld Nat.* **83,** 91–112.

Andrews, F. N. and Schnetzler, E. E. (1945). *Endocrinology* **37,** 382–384.

Andrews, F. N. and Schnetzler, E. E. (1946). *Poult. Sci.* **25,** 124–129.

Asmundson, V. S. and Pinsky, P. (1935). *Poult. Sci.* **14,** 99–104.

Aydelotte, M. B. (1963). *Br. J. Nutr.* **17,** 205–210.

Azevedo, J. A., Hunt, E. G. and Woods, L. A. (1965). *Calif. Fish Game* **51,** 276–293.

Bäckström, J., Hansson, E. and Ullberg, S. (1965). *Toxic. appl. Pharmac.* **7,** 90–96.

Balasubramanian, A. (1972). *Diss. Abstr. Int., B.* **32,** 5230B.

Barger, E. H., Card, L. E. and Pomeroy, B. S. (1958). 'Disease and Parasites of Poultry'. 5th edition. Lea and Febiger, Philadelphia.

Bell, G. H., Davidson, J. N. and Scarborough, H. (1952). 'Textbook of Physiology and Biochemistry'. E. and S. Livingstone, Edinburgh.

Benoit, J. and Clavert, J. (1947). *C. r. Séanc. Soc. Biol.* **141,** 1256–1257.

Berg, L. R. and Bearse, G. E. (1951). *Poult. Sci.* **30,** 21–28.

Berliner, V. and Warbritton, V. (1937). *Rec. Proc. Am. Soc. Anim. Prod.* **1937,** 137–142.

Bernard, R. F. and Gaertner, R. A. (1964). *J. Mammal.* **45,** 272–276.

Bevelander, G. (1946). *Proc. Soc. exp. Biol. Med.* **61,** 268–270.

Beyer, R. E. (1952). *Endocrinology* **50,** 497–500.

Bitman, J. and Cecil, H. C. (1970). *J. agric. Fd Chem.* **18,** 1108–1112.

Bitman, J., Cecil, H. C., Harris, S. J. and Fries, G. F. (1968). *Science, N.Y.* **162,** 371–372.

Bitman, J., Cecil, H. C., Harris, S. J. and Fries, G. F. (1969). *Nature, Lond.* **224,** 44–46.

Bitman, J., Cecil, H. C. and Fries, G. F. (1970). *Science, N.Y.* **168,** 594–596.

Blackmore, D. K. (1963). *J. comp. Path. Ther.* **73,** 391–409.

Blakely, R. M. and Anderson, R. W. (1949). *Poult. Sci.* **28,** 185–188.

Blasi, F., Fragomele, F. and Covelli, I. (1969). *Endocrinology* **85,** 542–551.

Blivaiss, B. B. (1947). *J. exp. Zool.* **104,** 267–310.

Blivaiss, B. B. and Domm, L. V. (1942). *Anat. Rec.* **84,** 529.

Blus, L. J., Heath, R. G., Gish, C. D., Belisle, A. A. and Prouty, R. M. (1971). *Bio-Science* **21,** 1213–1215.

Blus, L. J., Gish, C. D., Belisle, A. A. and Prouty, R. M. (1972). *Nature, Lond.* **235,** 376–377.

Bogart, R. and Mayer, D. T. (1946). *Res. Bull. Mo. agric. Exp. Stn* **402.**

Booker, E. E. and Sturkie, P. D. (1949). *Poult. Sci.* **28,** 147–148.
Booker, E. E. and Sturkie, P. D. (1950). *Poult. Sci.* **29,** 240–243.
Brandstetter, W. E., Watterson, R. L. and Vineziano, P. (1962). *Anat. Rec.* **142,** 299.
Briggs, G. M. and Lillie, R. J. (1946). *Proc. exp. Biol. Med.* **61,** 430–432.
Brown, V. K., Richardson, A., Robinson, J. and Stevenson, D. E. (1965). *Food Cosmet. Toxicol.* **3,** 675–679.
Burlington, H. and Lindeman, V. F. (1950). *Proc. Soc. exp. Biol. Med.* **74,** 48–51.
Burlington, H. and Lindeman, V. F. (1952). *Fedn Proc. Fedn Am. Socs exp. Biol.* **11,** 20–21.
Burrow, G. N. (1965). *J. clin. Endocr. Metab.* **25,** 403–408.
Cameron, G. R. and Burgess, F. (1945). *Br. med. J.* **1,** 865–871.
Casida, J. E. and Maddrell, S. H. P. (1971). *Pestic. Biochem. Physiol.* **1,** 71–83.
Cecil, H. C., Bitman, J. and Harris, S. J. (1971). *J. agric. Fd Chem.* **19,** 61–65.
Cecil, H. C., Fries, G.F., Bitman, J., Harris, S.J., Lillie, R.J. and Denton, C. A. (1972). *Poult. Sci.* **51,** 130–138.
Cecil, H. C., Harris, S. J., Bitman, J. and Fries, G. F. (1973). *Bull. environ. Contam. Toxicol.* **9,** 179–185.
Chaudhuri, S. and Sadhu, D. P. (1961). *Nature, Lond.* **192,** 560–561.
Cheftel, C. and Bouchilloux, S. (1968). *Biochim. biophys. Acta* **170,** 15–28.
Coates, M. E. (1971). In 'Physiology and Biochemistry of the Domestic Fowl' (D. J. Bell and B. M. Freeman, eds), Vol. 1, pp. 373–396. Academic Press, London and New York.
Cohlan, S. Q. (1954). *Pediatrics, N.Y.* **13,** 556–567.
Collins, K. J. and Weiner, J. S. (1968). *Physiol. Rev.* **48,** 785–839.
Conney, A. H., Welch, R. M., Kuntzman, R. and Burns, J. J. (1967). *Clin. Pharmac. Ther.* **8,** 2–10.
Cooke, A. S. (1970). *Bull. environ. Contam. Toxicol.* **5,** 152–157.
Cooke, A. S. (1972). *Environ. Pollut.* **3,** 51–68.
Cooke, A. S. (1973). *Environ. Pollut.* **4,** 85–152.
Coulson, J. C., Deans, I. R., Potts, G. R., Robinson, J. and Crabtree, A. N. (1972). *Nature, Lond.* **236,** 454–456.
Crew, F. A. (1925). *Proc. R. Soc. Edinb.* **45,** 252–260.
Dahlgren, R. B. and Linder, R. L. (1971). *J. Wildl. Mgmt* **35,** 315–319.
Dahlgren, R. B., Linder, R. L. and Ortman, K. K. (1970). *J. Wildl. Mgmt* **34,** 957–959.
Danowski, T. S., Sarver, M. E., Moses, C. and Bonessi, J. V. (1964). *Am. J. Med.* **37,** 235–250.
Davidson, K. L. and Sell, J. L. (1972). In 'Trace Substances in Environmental Health' (D. D. Hemphill, ed.), pp. 257–265. (Proceedings of University of Missouri 5th Annual Conference on Trace Substances in Environmental Health, 1971).
Deichmann, W. B. and Keplinger, M. L. (1966). *Toxic. appl. Pharmac.* **8,** 337–338.
Dempsey, E. W. and Astwood, E. B. (1943). *Endocrinology* **32,** 509–518.
DeWitt, J. B. (1955). *J. agric. Fd Chem.* **3,** 672–676.
DeWitt, J. B. (1956). *J. agric. Fd Chem.* **4,** 863–866.
Doxey, D. L. (1971). 'Veterinary Clinical Pathology'. Baillière, Tindall and Cassell, London.
Draize, J. H., Nelson, A. A. and Calvery, H. O. (1944). *J. Pharmac. exp. Ther.* **82,** 159–166.
Duby, R. T., Travis, H. F. and Terrill, C. E. (1971). *Toxic. appl. Pharmac.* **18,** 348–355.
Dustman, E. H., Stickel, L. F., Blus, L. J., Reichel, W. L. and Wiemeyer, S. N. (1971). *Trans. N. Am. Wildl. nat. Resour. Conf.* **36,** 118–133.

Dvorchik, B. H., Istin, M. and Maren, T. H. (1971). *Science, N.Y.* **172,** 728–729.
Enderson, J. H. and Berger, D. D. (1970). *BioScience,* **20,** 355–356.
Falconer, I. R. (1971). *In* 'Physiology and Biochemistry of the Domestic Fowl' (D. J. Bell and B. M. Freeman, eds) ,Vol. 1, pp. 459–472. Academic Press, London and New York.
Farer, L. S., Robbins, J., Blumberg, B. S. and Rall, J. E. (1962). *Endocrinology* **70,** 686–696.
Ferm, V. H. (1967). *Life Sci.* **6,** 493–497.
Fitzhugh, O. G. (1948). *Ind. Engng Chem.* **40,** 704–705.
Flick, D. F., O'Dell, R. G. and Childs, V. A. (1965). *Poult. Sci.* **44,** 1460–1465.
Fowler, J. F., Newsom, L. D., Graves, J. B., Bonner, F. L. and Schilling, P. E. (1971). *Bull. environ. Contam. Toxicol.* **6,** 495–501.
Frank, F. R. and Burger, R. E. (1965). *Poult. Sci.* **44,** 1604–1606.
Frape, D. L., Speer, V. C., Hays, V. W. and Catron, D. V. (1959). *J. Nutr.* **68,** 333–342.
Fregly, M. J., Waters, I. W. and Straw, J. A. (1968). *Can. J. Physiol. Pharmacol.* **46,** 59–66.
French, M. C. and Jefferies, D. J. (1969). *Science, N.Y.* **165,** 914–916.
Frieden, E. and Winzler, R. J. (1948). *J. biol. Chem.* **176,** 155–163.
Friend, M. and Trainer, D. O. (1970). *Science, N.Y.* **170,** 1314–1316.
Friend, M., Haegele, M. A. and Wilson, R. (1973). *Bull. environ. Contam. Toxicol.* **9,** 49–53.
Frienkel, H. and Lewis, D. (1957). *J. Physiol., Lond.* **135,** 288–300.
Fukuto, T. R. and Metcalf, R. L. (1969). *Ann. N.Y. Acad. Sci.* **160,** 97–111.
Gabuten, A. R. and Shaffner, C. S. (1954). *Poult. Sci.* **33,** 47–70.
Genelly, R. E. and Rudd, R. L. (1956). *Auk* **73,** 529–539.
Gillett, J. W., Chan, T. M. and Terriere, L. C. (1966). *J. agric. Fd Chem.* **14,** 540–545.
Gillie, R. B. (1971). *Scient. Am.* **224,** (6), 93–101.
Golberg, L. (1966). *Proc. Eur. Soc. Study Drug Toxicity* **7,** 171–184.
Goldsmith, E. D., Gordon, A. S. and Charipper, H. A. (1945). *Am. J. Obstet. Gynec.* **49,** 197–206.
Good, E. E. and Ware, G. W. (1969). *Toxic. appl. Pharmac.* **14,** 201–203.
Gutowska, M. A. and Mitchell, C. A. (1945). *Poult. Sci.* **24,** 159–167.
Haag, H. B., Finnegan, J. K., Larson, P. S., Dreyfuss, M. L., Main, R. J. and Riese, W. (1948). *Ind. Med. Surg.* **17,** 477–484.
Harris, G. W. and Woods, J. W. (1958). *J. Physiol., Lond.* **143,** 246–274.
Hayes, W. J. (1959). *In* 'DDT: the Insecticide Dichlorodiphenyltrichloroethane and its Significance' (P. Müller, ed.), Vol. 2, pp. 11–247. Birkhäuser Verlag, Basel.
Hays, F. A. (1948). *Poult. Sci.* **27,** 84–86.
Heald, P. J., Pohlman, D. and Martin, E. G. (1968). *Poult. Sci.* **47,** 858–862.
Heath, R. G., Spann, J. W. and Kreitzer, J. F. (1969). *Nature, Lond.* **224,** 47–48.
Heath, R. G., Spann, J. W., Hill, E. F. and Kreitzer, J. F. (1972). *Spec. scient. Rep. U.S. Fish Wildl.* Serv. No. 152.
Helbacka, N. V., Casterline, J. L. and Smith, C. J. (1963). *Poult. Sci.* **42,** 1082–1084.
Hendrich, C. E. and Turner, C. W. (1965). *Proc. Soc. exp. Biol. Med.* **117,** 218–222.
Heninger, R. W. and Newcomer, W. S. (1964). *Proc. Soc. exp. Biol. Med.* **116,** 624–628.
Hertz, R., Allen, M. J. and Tullner, W. W. (1950). *Proc. Soc. exp. Biol. Med.* **75,** 627–630.
Hogness, J. R., Lee, N. D. and Williams, R. H. (1953). *Endocrinology* **52,** 378–389.
Höhn, E. O. (1961). *In* 'Biology and Comparative Physiology of Birds' (A. J. Marshall, ed.), Vol. 2, pp. 87–114. Academic Press, New York and London.
Hughes, A. M. and Astwood, E. B. (1944). *Endocrinology* **34,** 138–139.

Hunt, J. R. and Simkiss, K. (1967). *Comp. Biochem. Physiol.* **21,** 223–230.

Huston, T. M. and Wheeler, R. S. (1961). *Poult. Sci.* **40,** 440–442.

Irwin, M. R., Reineke, E. P. and Turner, C. W. (1943). *Poult. Sci.* **22,** 374–380.

Jefferies, D. J. (1967). *Ibis* **109,** 266–272.

Jefferies, D. J. (1969a). *Nature, Lond.* **222,** 578–579.

Jefferies, D. J. (1969b). *J. Zool.* **157,** 429–436.

Jefferies, D. J. (1971). *Meded. Fakult. Landbouwwetenschappen Gent* **36,** 34–42.

Jefferies, D. J. (1972). *J. Zool.* **166,** 245–263.

Jefferies, D. J. (1973). *J. Reprod. Fert., Suppl.* **19,** 337–352.

Jefferies, D. J. and Davis, B. N. K. (1968). *J. Wildl. Mgmt* **32,** 441–456.

Jefferies, D. J. and French, M. C. (1969). *Science, N.Y.* **166,** 1278–1280.

Jefferies, D. J. and French, M. C. (1971). *Environ. Pollut.* **1,** 235–242.

Jefferies, D. J. and French, M. C. (1972). *J. Wildl. Mgmt* **36,** 24–30.

Jefferies, D. J. and Parslow, J. L. F. (1972). *Bull. environ. Contam. Toxicol.* **8,** 306–310.

Jefferies, D. J. and Prestt, I. (1966). *Br. Birds* **59,** 49–64.

Jefferies, D. J. and Walker, C. H. (1966). *Nature, Lond.* **212,** 533–534.

Jefferies, D. J., French, M. C. and Osborne, B. E. (1971). *Br. Poult. Sci.* **12,** 387–399.

Jensen, S., Johnels, A. G., Olsson, M. and Otterlind, G. (1969). *Nature, Lond.* **224,** 247–250.

Johnson, C. L. and LaRoche, G. (1968). *Aerospace Med.* **39,** 365–375.

Johnson, R. M. and Baumann, C. A. (1947). *J. biol. Chem.* **171,** 513–521.

Jones, G. E. S., Delfs, E. and Foote, E. C. (1946). *Endocrinology* **38,** 337–344.

Judah, J. D. (1949). *Br. J. Pharmacol.* **4,** 120–131.

Keil, J. E., Sandifer, S. H., Finklea, J. H. and Priester, L. E. (1972). *Bull. environ. Contam. Toxicol.* **8,** 317–320.

Keith, J. O., Woods, L. A. and Hunt, E. G. (1970). *Trans. N. Am. Wildl. nat. Resour. Conf.* **35,** 56–64.

Kempster, H. L. and Turner, C. W. (1945). *Poult. Sci.* **24,** 94–96.

Kenny, A. D., Dacke, C. G., Wagstaff, D. J., Musacchia, X. J. and Volkert, W. A. (1972). *In* 'Trace Substances in Environmental Health' (D. D. Hemphill, ed.), pp. 247–255. (Proceedings of University of Missouri 5th Annual Conference on Trace Substances in Environmental Health, 1971).

Koeman, J. H., Oudejans, R. C. H. M. and Huisman, E. A. (1967). *Nature, Lond.* **215,** 1094–1096.

Koeman, J. H., ten Noever de Brauw, M. C. and De Vos, R. H. (1969). *Nature, Lond.* **221,** 1126–1128.

Koger, M., Hurst, V. and Turner, C. W. (1942). *Endocrinology* **31,** 237–244.

Koster, R. (1947). *Fedn Proc. Fedn Am. Socs exp. Biol.* **6,** 346.

Labisky, R. F. and Lutz, R. W. (1967). *J. Wildl. Mgmt* **31,** 13–24.

Larson, R. A., Keating, F. R., Peacock, W. and Rawson, R. W. (1945). *Endocrinology* **36,** 160–169.

Laug, E. P. and Fitzhugh, O. G. (1946). *J. Pharmac. exp. Ther.* **87,** 18–23.

Läuger, P., Pulver, R. and Montigel, C. (1945a). *Experientia* **1,** 120–121.

Läuger, P., Pulver, R. and Montigel, C. (1945b). *Helv. physiol. pharmac. Acta* **3,** 405–415.

Leathem, J. H. (1945). *Endocrinology* **36,** 98–103.

Leathem, J. H. (1946). *Proc. Soc. exp. Biol. Med.* **61,** 203–205.

Lee, M., Harris, K. and Trowbridge, H. (1964). *J. Nutr.* **84,** 136–144.

Lehner, P. N. and Egbert, A. (1969). *Nature, Lond.* **224,** 1218–1219.

Leutskaja, Z. K. (1963). *Dokl. Akad. Nauk SSSR* **153,** 243–245.

Leutskaja, Z. K. (1964). *Dokl. Akad. Nauk SSSR* **159,** 464–465.

Levin, W., Welch, R. M. and Conney, A. H. (1968). *Fedn Proc. Fedn Am. Socs exp. Biol.* **27**, 649.

Lillie, R. D. and Smith, M. I. (1944). *Publ. Hlth Rep., Wash.* **59**, 979–984.

Lillie, R. J., Denton, C. A., Cecil, H. C., Bitman, J. and Fries, G. F. (1972). *Poult. Sci.* **51**, 122–129.

Locke, L. N., Chura, N. J. and Stewart, P. A. (1966). *Condor* **68**, 497–502.

Lofts, B. and Murton, R. K. (1966). *Br. Birds* **59**, 261–280.

Longcore, J. R., Samson, F. B., Kreitzer, J. F. and Spann, J. W. (1971a). *Bull. environ. Contam. Toxicol.* **6**, 345–350.

Longcore, J. R., Samson, F. B. and Whittendale, T. W. (1971b). *Bull. environ. Contam. Toxicol.* **6**, 485–490.

Lundberg, C. and Kihlström, J. E. (1973). *Bull. environ. Contam. Toxicol.* **9**, 267–270.

March, B. E., Coates, V. and Biely, J. (1966). *Can. J. Physiol. Pharmacol.* **44**, 295–300.

March, B. E., Coates, V. and Goudie, C. (1972). *Poult. Sci.* **51**, 891–896.

Maren, T. H. (1967). *Physiol. Rev.* **47**, 595–781.

Marshall, J. S. and Tompkins, L. S. (1968). *J. clin. Endocr. Metab.* **28**, 386–392.

McCartney, M. G. and Shaffner, C. S. (1949a). *Endocrinology* **45**, 396–402.

McCartney, M. G. and Shaffner, C. S. (1949b). *Poult. Sci.* **28**, 223–228.

McCune, E. L., Savage, J. E. and O'Dell, B. L. (1962). *Poult. Sci.* **41**, 295–299.

McEwen, L. C. and Brown, R. L. (1966). *J. Wildl. Mgmt* **30**, 604–611.

McKenzie, J. M. (1965). *J. clin. Endocr. Metab.* **25**, 424–431.

McNamara, B. P., Bing, R. J. and Hopkins, F. (1946). *Fedn Proc. Fedn Am. Socs exp. Biol.* **5**, 67–68.

Mellen, W. J. and Hardy, L. B. (1957). *Endocrinology* **60**, 547–551.

Metcalf, R. L. (1955). 'Organic Insecticides—Their Chemistry and Mode of Action'. Interscience, New York.

Meyer, A. E. and Ranson, G. V. (1945). *Endocrinology* **36**, 259–265.

Moore, N. W. (1965). *Bird Study* **12**, 222–252.

Moore, T. (1957). 'Vitamin A', Elsevier, Amsterdam.

Moore, T. (1967a). *In* 'The Vitamins' (W. H. Sebrell and R. S. Harris, eds), Vol. 1, pp. 245–266. 2nd edition. Academic Press, New York and London.

Moore, T. (1967b). *In* 'The Vitamins' (W. H. Sebrell and R. S. Harris, eds), Vol. 1, pp. 280–294. 2nd edition. Academic Press, New York and London.

Moriarty, F. (1969). *Biol. Rev.* **44**, 321–357.

Mueller, W. J. (1962). *Poult. Sci.* **41**, 1792–1796.

Naevested, R. (1947). *Tidsskr. norske Laegeforen.* **67**, 261–263.

Neal, P. A., von Oettingen, W. F., Smith, W. W., Malmo, R. B., Dunn, R. C., Moran, H. E., Sweeney, T. R., Armstrong, D. W. and White, W. C. (1944). *Publ. Hlth Rep., Wash. Suppl.* No. 177, 1–32.

Negherbon, W. O. (1959). 'Handbook of Toxicology', Vol. III, 'Insecticides.' W. B. Saunders, Philadelphia.

Neill, D. D., Muller, H. D. and Shutze, J. V. (1971). *Bull. environ. Contam. Toxicol.* **6**, 546–551.

Nelson, A. A., Draize, J. H., Woodard, G., Fitzhugh, O. G., Smith, R. B. and Calvery, H. O. (1944). *Publ. Hlth Rep., Wash.* **59**, 1009–1020.

Nelson, J. R., Wookey, L. E., Nockels, C. F. and Shutze, J. V. (1972). *Poult. Sci.* **51**, 747–751.

Newton, I. (1972). 'Finches'. Collins, London.

Nockels, C. F. and Phillips, R. W. (1971). *Poult. Sci.* **50**, 174–181.

O'Brien, R. D. (1967). 'Insecticides: action and metabolism'. Academic Press, New York and London.

O'Brien, R. D. (1969). In 'Essays in Toxicology' (S. D. Blood, ed.), Vol. 1, pp. 1–59. Academic Press, London and New York.

O'Brien, R. D. and Matsumura, F. (1964). Science, N.Y. 146, 657–658.

Oestreicher, M. I., Shuman, D. H. and Wurster, C. F. (1971). Nature, Lond. 229, 571.

Ogilvie, R. F. (1962). 'Histopathology', 6th edition. E. and S. Livingstone, Edinburgh.

Oppenheimer, J. H. and Tavernetti, R. R. (1962). J. clin. Invest. 41, 2213–2220.

Örberg, J., Johansson, N., Kihlström, J. E. and Lundberg, C. (1972). Ambio 1, 148–149.

Ortega, P. (1966). Lab. Invest. 15, 657–679.

Ottoboni, A. (1969). Toxic. appl. Pharmac. 14, 74–81.

Panda, B. and Combs, G. F. (1963). Proc. Soc. exp. Biol. Med. 113, 530–534.

Parker, J. E. (1943). Proc. Soc. exp. Biol. Med. 52, 234–236.

Patton, A. R., Wilgus, H. S. and Harshfield, G. S. (1939). Science, N.Y. 89, 162.

Peakall, D. B. (1967). Nature, Lond. 216, 505–506.

Peakall, D. B. (1969). Nature, Lond. 224, 1219–1220.

Peakall, D. B. (1970a). Scient. Am. 222 (4), 73–78.

Peakall, D. B. (1970b). Science, N.Y. 168, 592–594.

Peakall, D. B. (1971). Bull. environ. Contam. Toxicol. 6, 100–101.

Peterle, A. F. and Peterle, T. J. (1971). Bull. environ. Contam. Toxicol. 6, 401–405.

Petrásek, R. and Placer, Z. (1965). Čslká Hyg. 10, 183–188.

Philips, F. S. and Gilman, A. (1946). J. Pharmac. exp. Ther. 86, 213–221.

Phillips, W. E. J. (1963). Can. J. Biochem. Physiol. 41, 1793–1802.

Phillips, W. E. J. (1965). Can. J. Physiol. Pharmacol. 43, 649–656.

Phillips, W. E. J. and Hidiroglou, M. (1965). J. agric. Fd Chem. 13, 254–256.

Pocker, Y., Beug, W. M. and Ainardi, V. R. (1971). Science, N.Y. 174, 1336–1339.

Porter, R. D. and Wiemeyer, S. N. (1969). Science, N.Y. 165, 199–200.

Prestt, I. (1967). Proc. Br. Insectic. Fungic. Conf. 4th 1, 26–35.

Prestt, I. (1970). Pap. Proc. Tech. Meet. int. Un. Conserv. Nat. nat. Resour. 11th, New Delhi, 1969. 1, 95–102. Morges, I.U.C.N.

Prestt, I., Jefferies, D. J. and Moore, N. W. (1970). Environ. Pollut. 1, 3–26.

Ratcliffe, D. A. (1958). Br. Birds 51, 23–26.

Ratcliffe, D. A. (1960). Br. Birds 53, 128–130.

Ratcliffe, D. A. (1967). Nature, Lond. 215, 208–210.

Ratcliffe, D. A. (1970). J. appl. Ecol. 7, 67–115.

Ray, A. K. and Premachandra, B. N. (1964). Endocrinology 74, 800–802.

Reineke, E. P. (1946). In 'The Problem of Fertility' (E. T. Engle, ed.), pp. 233–239. Princeton University Press, Princeton.

Reineke, E. P. and Turner, C. W. (1945). Poult. Sci. 24, 499–503.

Reineke, E. P., Mixner, J. P. and Turner, C. W. (1945). Endocrinology 36, 66–67.

Revzin, A. M. (1966). Toxic. appl. Pharmac. 9, 75–83.

Richert, E. P. and Prahlad, K. V. (1972). Poult. Sci. 51, 196–200.

Riker, W. F., Huebner, V. R., Raska, S. B. and Cattell, M. (1946). J. Pharmac. exp. Ther. 88, 327–332.

Risebrough, R. W., Menzel, D. B., Martin, D. J. and Olcott, H. S. (1967). Nature, Lond. 216, 589–591.

Risebrough, R. W., Rieche, P., Peakall, D. B., Herman, S. G. and Kirven, M. N. (1968). Nature, Lond. 220, 1098–1102.

Risebrough, R. W., Davis, J. and Anderson, D. W. (1970). *In* 'The Biological Impact of Pesticides in the Environment' (J. W. Gillett, ed.), pp. 40–53. Environmental Health Sciences Center, Oregon.

Robbins, J. and Rall, J. E. (1967). *In* 'Hormones in Blood' (C. H. Gray and A. L. Bacharach, eds), Vol. 1, pp. 383–490. 2nd edition. Academic Press, New York and London.

Rogler, J. C., Parker, H. E., Andrews, F. N. and Carrick, C. W. (1959). *Poult. Sci.* **38**, 1027–1032.

Rudd, R. L. (1964). 'Pesticides and the Living Landscape'. University of Wisconsin Press, Madison.

Sadhu, D. P. and Brody, S. (1947). *Am. J. Physiol.* **149**, 400–404.

Sarett, H. P. and Jandorf, B. J. (1946). *Fedn Proc. Fedn Am. Socs exp. Biol.* **5**, 151–152.

Sarett, H. P. and Jandorf, B. J. (1947). *J. Pharmac. exp. Ther.* **91**, 340–344.

Scott, T. G., Willis, Y. L. and Ellis, J. A. (1959). *J. Wildl. Mgmt* **23**, 409–427.

Shaffner, C. S. and Andrews, F. N. (1948). *Poult. Sci.* **27**, 91–102.

Shellenberger, T. E. and Newell, G. W. (1965). *Lab. Anim. Cent. coll. Pap.* **15**, 119–130.

Singhal, R. L., Valadares, J. R. E. and Schwark, W. S. (1970). *Biochem. Pharmac.* **19** 2145–2155.

Smith, M. I. and Stohlman, E. F. (1944). *Publ. Hlth Rep., Wash.* **59**, 984–993.

Snedecor, J. G. (1968). *Gen. comp. Endocrinol.* **10**, 277–291.

Snedecor, J. G. (1971). *Poult. Sci.* **50**, 237–243.

Sprague, J. B. (1971). *Wat. Res.* **5**, 245–266.

Srivastava, B. K., Saxena, K. C. and Sharma, J. C. (1960). *Nature, Lond.* **186**, 172–173.

Stanbury, J. B. (1967). *In* 'Endocrine Genetics' (S. G. Spickett, ed.), pp. 107–136. University Press, Cambridge.

Stephen, B. J., Garlich, J. D. and Guthrie, F. E. (1970). *Bull. environ. Contam. Toxicol.* **5**, 569–576.

Stickel, L. F. (1968). *Rep. Dir. Fish Wildl.* Serv. No. 119.

Straw, J. A., Waters, I. W. and Fregly, M. J. (1965). *Proc. Soc. exp. Biol. Med.* **118**, 391–394.

Sturkie, P. D. (1954). 'Avian Physiology'. 1st edition. Comstock, New York.

Sturkie, P. D. (1965). 'Avian Physiology'. 2nd edition. Baillière, Tindall and Cassell, London.

Tarján, R. and Kemény, T. (1969). *Food Cosmet. Toxicol.* **7**, 215–222.

Tarsitano, F. (1948). *Folia med., Napoli* **31**, 297–306.

Tata, J. R. and Shellabarger, C. J. (1959). *Biochem. J.* **72**, 608–613.

Taylor, J. C. and Blackmore, D. K. (1961). *Vet. Rec.* **73**, 232–233.

Taylor, L. W. and Burmester, B. R. (1940). *Poult. Sci.* **19**, 326–331.

Taylor, T. G., Morris, K. M. L. and Kirkley, J. (1968). *Br. J. Nutr.* **22**, 713–721.

Thompson, J. A. and Goldberg, I. H. (1968). *Endocrinology* **82**, 805–817.

Thompson, J. N., Howell, J. M., Pitt, G. A. J. and Houghton, C. I. (1965). *Nature, Lond.* **205**, 1006–1007.

Thornton, P. A. and Moreng, R. E. (1959). *Poult. Sci.* **38**, 594–599.

Tucker, R. K. and Haegele, M. A. (1970). *Bull. environ. Contam. Toxicol.* **5**, 191–194.

Turner, C. D. (1966). 'General Endocrinology'. 4th edition. W. B. Saunders Company, Philadelphia and London.

Turner, C. W., Irwin, M. R. and Reineke, E. P. (1945a). *Poult. Sci.* **24**, 171–180.

Turner, C. W., Kempster, H. L., Hall, N. M. and Reineke, E. P. (1945b). *Poult. Sci.* **24**, 522–533.

Tyler, C. (1954). *J. agric. Sci., Camb.* **45**, 156–163.

Tyler, C. and Geake, F. H. (1960). *J. Sci. Fd Agric.* **11**, 535–547.

Ulfstrand, S., Södergren, A. and Raböl, J. (1971). *Nature, Lond.* **231**, 467–468.

Velbinger, H. H. (1947a). *Pharmazie* **2**, 268–274.

Velbinger, H. H. (1947b). *Dte GesundhWes.* **2**, 355–358.

Walker, C. H., Hamilton, G. A. and Harrison, R. B. (1967). *J. Sci. Fd Agric.* **18**, 123–129.

Ware, G. W. and Good, E. E. (1967). *Toxic. appl. Pharmac.* **10**, 54–61.

Wassermann, D., Wassermann, M., Djavaherian, M., Gorin, I., Barish, M. and Tavor, R. (1971). *Bull. environ. Contam. Toxicol.* **6**, 85–88.

Wassermann, M., Wassermann, D., Kedar, E., Djavaherian, M. and Cucos, S. (1972). *Bull. environ. Contam. Toxicol.* **8**, 177–185.

Welch, R. M., Levin, W. and Conney, A. H. (1967). *J. Pharmac. exp. Ther.* **115**, 167–173.

Welch, R. M., Levin, W. and Conney, A. H. (1969). *Toxic. appl. Pharmac.* **14**, 358–367.

Wheeler, N. C. and Andrews, F. N. (1943). *Poult. Sci.* **22**, 361–367.

Wheeler, R. S. and Hoffman, E. (1948). *Endocrinology* **42**, 326–328.

Wheeler, R. S., Hoffman, E. and Graham, C. L. (1948). *Poult. Sci.* **27**, 103–111.

Wiemeyer, S. N. and Porter, R. D. (1970). *Nature, Lond.* **227**, 737–738.

Wilson, W. O. (1949). *Poult. Sci.* **28**, 581–592.

Wilwerth, A. M., Martinez-Campos, C. and Reineke, E. P. (1954). *Poult. Sci.* **33**, 729–735.

Wolbach, S. B. and Hegsted, D. M. (1952). *Archs Path.* **54**, 13–29.

Woodwell, G. M., Craig, P. P. and Johnson, H. A. (1971). *Science, N.Y.* **174**, 1101–1107.

Wrenn, T. R., Wood, J. R., Fries, G. F. and Bitman, J. (1970). *Bull. environ. Contam. Toxicol.* **5**, 61–66.

Wrenn, T. R., Weyant, J. R., Fries, G. F. and Bitman, J. (1971). *J. Anim. Sci.* **33**, 1288–1292.

Wright, A. S., Potter, D., Wooder, M. F., Donninger, C. and Greenland, R. D. (1972). *Food Cosmet. Toxicol.* **10**, 311–332.

5. Effects of Organochlorine Insecticides on Animal Populations

J. P. DEMPSTER

Institute of Terrestrial Ecology,
Monks Wood Experimental Station,
Abbots Ripton, Huntingdon, England

I. INTRODUCTION

Virtually all pesticides and other organic pollutants are non-specific poisons. That is to say they are poisonous to a wide range of different organisms. There are, however, very considerable differences between different species of animal in their sensitivity to any one chemical. Even closely related species may differ enormously in this respect (see

Chapter 3). This variation in toxicity to different species means that a chemical may virtually eliminate one species from an area, but have little or no effect upon another.

The persistence of a toxic pollutant may also vary considerably between different parts of a habitat (see Chapter 1), so that different species differ in their likelihood of coming into contact with a poison. For example, DDT may virtually disappear from the foliage of a crop in six to eight weeks, but it may persist for many years in soil in temperate regions, so that a soil-living animal may be at a far greater risk than a plant-living one. This adds considerably to variations in the effect of pollutants on different species, since the chemical may have a far more permanent effect in one part of a habitat than in another.

The direct toxic effects of a chemical on individual organisms may be comparatively easy to determine. Its effects on populations of that organism in the field are far more difficult to ascertain. The numbers of any one animal are determined by a complex of factors, including the actions of other species, such as enemies, competitors, and food species, and the effect of a toxic chemical on these other species can lead to a range of indirect effects which are difficult to unravel in the field. This interdependence of the populations of different species can make the overall effect of a pollutant on any one species extremely complex and difficult to predict. Populations of some species may crash, while others show remarkable increases in the presence of a toxic chemical. The precise effect depends upon the sensitivity to the chemical of the species in question and upon the sensitivity of other species which are influencing its numbers. It is primarily these indirect effects of pollutants on animal populations that I shall be discussing in this chapter.

Many of the examples which I shall take concern species of arthropod, particularly insects. This is because far more is known of the factors determining their numbers than for other animals. Vertebrates tend to occur at low densities and are more difficult to study, so that although much is known about their natural survival rates, very little is known about precise causes of death.

The only intensive studies on the effects of persistent organic pollutants on animal populations have been those with the organochlorine insecticides. Virtually nothing is known about other pollutants, such as the extremely widespread polychlorinated biphenyls (PCBs). On the other hand, PCBs have many properties in common with the organochlorine insecticides (e.g. persistence, fat solubility, similar biological activity), which makes it possible to generalize about the impact that they can have on animal populations.

II. REDUCTIONS IN POPULATIONS

A. Direct Toxic Effects

The killing of a large number of individual animals by a toxic chemical does not necessarily result in an adverse effect on the population. High death rates may be extremely local, and if the polluted area is not large, recolonization may rapidly make good any losses. Even when immigration does not occur, the population may recover quickly, since both natural mortality and reproduction can be dependent upon population density, and a reduced density may automatically result in a more rapid rate of population increase. On the other hand, populations of particularly sensitive species can be completely eliminated from large areas by the direct toxic effect of a chemical. There are many examples in the literature of the apparent elimination of species from areas following applications of organochlorine insecticides. For example, Croker and Wilson (1965) recorded a complete kill of the fish, *Menidia beryllina* and *Fundulus similis*, in a sample ditch, following an application of 0·22 kg/ha DDT to a tidal marsh in Florida. Similarly, Hoffman *et al.* (1949) showed that many invertebrates were apparently eliminated by applications of DDT (1·1–4·5 kg/ha) to forests in the U.S.A. It is often difficult to be certain when a population of any particular species has been eliminated, since very low numbers may be present without obtaining any by sampling. On the other hand, some studies have failed to find a previously abundant species for years after application of a persistent organochlorine insecticide: for example, the millipede, *Glomeris marginata*, was eliminated from grassland plots for six years by a single application of dieldrin (5·4 kg/ha) (Davis *et al.*, 1969).

B. Secondary Poisoning

Besides coming into direct contact with a pollutant, an animal may also pick up the poison as a result of eating another poisoned animal. This secondary poisoning can be the most important source of a pollutant for some predators and scavengers. An example of this is seen with the use of aldrin, dieldrin and heptachlor as cereal seed-dressings. These chemicals are all highly toxic to birds and many seed-feeding birds were killed in Britain during the springs of 1956–1960 as a result of feeding on dressed seed. Bird casualties were locally so large that the use of these materials in spring was discontinued by agreement between Government and Industry. During the period when they were still in use many foxes were found dead on agricultural land. These had died as a result of eating dead, poisoned birds (Blackmore, 1963). This increased mortality had no permanent effect on the fox population in Britain, but during the same time several species of birds of prey crashed in numbers. The sparrowhawk (*Accipiter nisus*), peregrine falcon (*Falco peregrinus*), barn owl (*Tyto alba*) were particularly affected (Ratcliffe, 1963; Prestt, 1965. From being one of the commonest and most widely distributed diurnal birds of prey, a survey in 1964 showed that there was not a single county in England where the sparrowhawk could be considered common. Declines of this species were most marked in eastern and midland regions, where it is now either scarce or extinct as a breeding species. These population declines appear to have resulted from the acute poisoning of large numbers of adult birds by feeding on poisoned prey (birds and small mammals), which had themselves fed on dressed seed. Only a few heavily contaminated prey are needed to kill these predatory birds, since in some cases they are more sensitive to the chemical than are their prey (Jefferies and Prestt, 1966). Added to this, a poisoned prey tends to be erratic in its movements just prior to death and so may well attract special attention from predators. In this way a predator may tend to select heavily contaminated prey.

Most living animals contain far higher concentrations of the organochlorine insecticides than occur in their physical environments (see Chapter 1). The main reason for this is that these substances are fat-soluble and so can concentrate in animal lipids, especially in adipose tissue. Some species are particularly good at concentrating these chemicals and so can present a considerable hazard to predators feeding on them. A good example of this is seen in the now famous case of the western grebe (*Aechmophorus occidentalis*) at Clear Lake, in California.

Clear Lake is a shallow lake, about 100 miles north of San Francisco, and is an important tourist and fishing centre. A small gnat (*Chaoborus astictopus*) breeds in the mud at the bottom of the lake and its adults reach such huge numbers that it can be of considerable nuisance. In order to control the gnat, the lake was sprayed with DDD (TDE) in 1949, 1954 and 1957. Before the first application of DDD more than a thousand pairs of western grebe regularly bred on the lake. Observations during the breeding seasons of 1958–61 showed that a few pairs were present, but that no young were fledged (Hunt and Bischoff, 1960; Rudd and Herman, 1972). Throughout the period of spraying, however, grebes continued to visit the lake in large numbers during the winters. In December, 1954, many deaths were reported amongst these overwintering birds and in March of the following year many more died. In both cases, no signs of disease could be found. In 1957, following the third application of DDD, more grebes were reported dead, and since again no diesase could be identified, the visceral fat from two grebes was analysed. These samples contained 1,600 ppm of DDD. Subsequently, samples of other organisms from Clear Lake were analysed and some species of fish were found to contain very high residues of DDD, in some cases even higher than those obtained from the grebes. It is clear that the grebes were poisoned by feeding on highly contaminated fish. There has been some argument as to how the fish obtained these high residues, but it is probable that they absorbed and accumulated most of their DDD directly from the water (Moriarty, 1972; and see Chapter 2). As in the case of the seed-dressing incidents, some of the prey species (the fish) proved to be more resistant to the pesticide than were the predators (the grebes).

The best documented examples of secondary poisoning are of vertebrate predators and scavengers. Invertebrate animals may, however, also be killed in this way: for example, van Halteren (1971) demonstrated secondary poisoning of mantid nymphs fed on *Drosophila* which had been reared on a larval diet containing ten ppm dieldrin. Kiritani and Kawahara (1973) showed that spiders (*Lycosa pseudoannulata*) were killed by feeding on leafhoppers (*Nephotettix cincticeps*) which had picked up BHC systemically from rice plants. It is probably more common, however, for invertebrate predators and scavengers to pick up toxic chemicals by direct contact, rather than via their food.

C. Elimination of Prey Organisms

Any reduction in the numbers of an animal is likely to affect the abundance of its natural enemies, particularly when these enemies are feeding only on the one species of animal. Thus the catastrophic crash in a pest's population after spraying may eliminate a specific parasite or predator, even if the latter is not itself sensitive to the pesticide.

Polyphagous predators or parasites may survive the elimination of one prey species by switching their attention to another. An example of this is seen in the change of diet of brook trout (*Salvelinus fontinalis*) and rainbow trout (*Salmo gairdnerii*) following the spraying of forests with DDT (1·1 kg/ha) in Idaho, U.S.A. (Adams *et al.*, 1949). With the elimination of many of their normal food organisms, these fish fed heavily upon crayfish after spraying. A change in diet may not be possible for a more stenophagous species, in which case the predator may emigrate in search of food, or may die of starvation. Whatever the outcome, a violent change in the numbers of an abundant food organism will inevitably have repercussions on those animals feeding on it.

In the field, it is difficult to distinguish this type of effect from that resulting from direct toxicity of a chemical to a predator. For example, a reduction in the numbers of a predator may be noted after a pesticide application, but this does not necessarily indicate that the predator has been killed directly by the pesticide. The reduction may simply be the result of elimination of the predator's prey.

III. INCREASES OF POPULATIONS

A. Pest Populations

The control of pest populations brought about by pesticides is often disappointing, since pests often recur surprisingly quickly after spraying. Many cases have now been reported of pests recurring in far higher numbers after spraying than occurred before. This phenomenon is known as pest resurgence and it invariably owes its origin to the elimination of the pest's natural enemies or competitors (Ripper, 1956). In the absence of these, the pest population can build up to a higher level than occurred before spraying.

A good example of how pest resurgence can be brought about can be seen from the control of the small white butterfly (*Pieris rapae*) with DDT (Dempster, 1968a). This butterfly is a pest of *Brassica* crops (cabbage, sprouts, swedes, turnips, kale, mustard) throughout Europe, Asia, North America and Australia. In Britain it has two, sometimes three, generations a year. The female butterfly lays its eggs on the new, fully expanded leaves of the food plant but as the caterpillar grows, it moves into the heart of the plant. There are five larval stages and the heart is normally occupied from the third instar onwards. The fully grown caterpillar leaves the plant to pupate on a fence, tree, or building. There is little mortality during the egg stage, but mortality is high amongst the newly hatched caterpillars. This is due mainly to arthropod predators, such as ground beetles (Carabidae) and harvest spiders (Phalangida), which feed on the very small caterpillars (Dempster, 1967). As the caterpillars grow, they become too big to be taken by these predators, but mortality is again high amongst the fully grown caterpillars, due to insect parasites and to bird predators. Over 90 per cent of the young stages of the pest normally die between the egg and pupation. By far the most important cause of death is predation by arthropods, for these normally take 50–60 per cent of the caterpillars each year, while they are still too small to do much damage to the crop. All of these arthropods are polyphagous, that is they feed on a wide variety of prey besides *Pieris*. Some, such as hoverfly larvae (Syrphidae), spiders and plant bugs, live on the crop plants and weeds. Others, such as the ground beetles and phalangids, are nocturnal and live in the soil and litter under the plants during the day and climb the plants at night to feed. The most important of these is the ground beetle, *Harpalus rufipes*.

DDT is a very effective insecticide against the caterpillars of *Pieris*. If it is applied correctly it will kill virtually all of the caterpillars present on the crop at the time of spraying. Control may however be rather short lived and within a few weeks after spraying the pest can recur in large numbers. The reason for this is that the crop plants are growing rapidly during the summer and new leaves, on which the pest lives, are free from the insecticide. In all three years of this study, the build up of the pest's population was more rapid on the sprayed crop than on an unsprayed control crop. This was due to a far lower mortality of caterpillars on the sprayed crop owing to the elimination of many of the arthropod predators.

Much of the DDT put onto a crop as a foliage application finishes up in the surface layers of the soil. Some lands on the soil during spraying, some gets washed off the leaves by rain, while dead leaves falling off the plants bring more down onto the soil. Once in the soil, DDT is extremely persistent: its half life is between one and five years depending on the type of soil (Edwards, 1966). Because of its persistence in soil, DDT affects the ground-living predators of *Pieris* long after its effect on the pest is lost. For this reason residues of DDT left in the soil from applications in previous years can greatly reduce the mortality inflicted by these ground-living predators of *Pieris*.

In this example, resurgence results from the fact that the pest lives in that part of the habitat where the effect of the chemical is soon lost (the growing plant), while its principal enemies live where the effect of the chemical persists longest (the soil).

B. Non-target Species

Increases of animal populations after the use of pesticides are not confined to pests. Similar population increases have been reported for many different types of organism.

A chemical aimed at killing one pest may cause the increase of another pest. For example, DDT applied to citrus orchards in California to control mosquitoes led to an outbreak of cottony cushion scale (De Bach, 1947). This is a particularly interesting example because cottony cushion scale (*Icerya purchasi*) is one of the classical examples of biological control. This pest was accidentally introduced into California at the end of the last century, when it became a major pest of citrus orchards: so much so that the whole future of citrus growing in that State was threatened. *Icerya* was completely brought under control by the introduction of a ladybird predator (*Rhodolia cardinalis*) from its native Australia. The subsequent outbreak of *Icerya* following DDT applications was due to *Rhodolia* being eliminated. *Rhodolia* is far more susceptible to the chemical than *Icerya*.

Besides this effect on known pests, chemical control may lead to new pests developing. One of the best documented examples of this is the fruit-tree red spider mite, *Panonychus ulmi*. This mite, in common with a number of other Tetranychidae, has risen in importance over the past 50 years, to become an important pest of apples and other fruit.

Before about 1925, *Panonychus ulmi* was virtually unknown in British orchards. From that date, however, there has been a gradual build up in its importance in commercial orchards. Even today, however, its numbers are low in orchards not treated with chemicals. This increased importance of *Panonychus* has been paralleled in other parts of the world since the use of certain pesticides. Pickett for example, showed as early as 1929 in Nova Scotia, that orchards treated with copper fungicides were clear of red spider, while those treated with sulphur sprays had heavy infestations. He also noted that sulphur sprays led to an increase in damage by codling moth (*Ernarmonia pomonella*). Now in Nova Scotia, lead arsenate was used extensively for codling moth control up to about 1949. The moth developed resistance to it, however, and many growers gradually turned to DDT. This led to huge outbreaks of red spider, far greater than had been known before (Pickett and Patterson, 1953). In southern England, there are over 40 species of predaceous insects and mites occurring in apple orchards which will feed on red spider. Few survive the battery of sprays, particularly DDT, applied to commercial orchards, while neglected orchards contain many predators (Collyer, 1953a,b; Morris, 1968). Red spider, on the other hand, is very resistant to chemical sprays. The detailed effect of any one chemical may be extremely complicated. DDT, for example, kills predators of the mite, while low concentrations of it may also affect the mite's reproductive rate, tendency to disperse and the nutritive status of the food plant (see p. 242).

One of the most consistently found effects of DDT applications is the increase of soil Collembola (Hoffman *et al.*, 1949; Sheals, 1956; Menhinick, 1962; Edwards, 1965; Edwards *et al.*, 1967; Dempster, 1968b). Sheals (1956) was the first person to study this in any detail and he suggested that this was primarily due to the reduction in the numbers of predatory mites (Mesostigmata) which feed on Collembola. All workers have found that DDT reduces the numbers of these mites and so it seems likely that the increase of Collembola is, at least in part, the result of this (see Table I). On the other hand, Dempster (1968b)

Table I

The numbers of Collembola and Mesostigmata in 25 soil samples

	Unsprayed	Sprayed with DDT	Significance of difference
Collembola (total)	4538	14041	P < 0·001
Poduroidea	1953	4396	0·01 < P < 0·02
Hypogastura denticulata	1773	3899	0·02 < P < 0·05
Entomobryoidea	2235	8818	P < 0·001
Symphypleona	350	827	0·02 < P < 0·05
Mesostigmata	379	30	P < 0·001

Data from Dempster (1968b).

recorded an increase of *Hypogastura denticulata* in the first year of using DDT before any reduction of the Mesostigmata could be detected. Collembola are fed on by a large number of predatory species, so that it is possible that some other enemy was involved in the case of *Hypogastura*. More research is required to elucidate this.

All of the examples discussed in this section are caused by the same phenomenon as that causing pest resurgence. In all cases, the species which increases in abundance after spraying is either relatively tolerant of the chemical, or fails to come in contact with the chemical (as with *Pieris rapae*, p. 236). In all cases, the natural enemies of the species are more susceptible to the chemical and with the removal of these enemies the species can build up to far higher numbers than occurred before spraying.

Not all predatory species are so susceptible to pesticides, and when this is the case, it is possible for a predator to increase in abundance in response to an increase of its prey. Examples of this are difficult to find, because one can expect a response of this sort only when the predator is having little or no effect on the prey's population. If the predator is efficient it will probably prevent the increase of its prey in the first place. Two examples are described by Dempster (1968b): both concern ground-beetle predators of Collembola, *i.e. Trechus quadri-striatus* and *Nebria brevicollis*. These beetles occur at rather low densities on arable land and so probably have an insignificant effect on the numbers of Collembola. Adults of both species are relatively resistant to DDT and their numbers increased after applications of this chemical, probably in response to increases in the abundance of their prey. The larvae of *Nebria* are large and active and they probably also feed on Collembola. Their number also increased on the sprayed plot. Added to this, their rate of growth was significantly greater on the sprayed plot (Table II) as a result of the abundance of prey. In contrast,

Table II

Mean length of body (mm) of *Nebria* larvae on unsprayed and sprayed plots

	Unsprayed	Sprayed with DDT	Significance of difference
December	4·31	6·52	$P < 0.001$
January	6·68	7·52	$0.01 < P < 0.02$
February	8·36	7·99	N.S.

Data from Dempster (1968b).

Trechus larvae did not increase in number and it is probable that the large populations of *Trechus* adults immigrated from surrounding unsprayed land to feed on the high densities of Collembola on the sprayed plot.

C. Replacement of One Species by Another

The removal of one species from a habitat may enable another species to expand to take its place. In such situations the expanding species is less sensitive to the toxic chemical, and had previously been kept at low numbers, or excluded from the habitat, by competition with the species which the chemical eliminates.

An example of this was seen during the programme to eradicate the mosquito, *Anopheles labranchiae*, from Sardinia (Trapido and Aitken, 1953; Aitken and Trapido, 1961). At the beginning of the programme, in 1947, *A. labranchiae* was the dominant and most widespread species of *Anopheles* inhabiting fresh water streams in south-east Sardinia. This is a malaria-carrying mosquito and attempts to eradicate it were made by spraying the adult resting sites in houses and farm buildings with DDT, and later with chlordane, and by spraying the larval habitats with DDT. The last spraying was carried out in 1949, after which no *A. labranchiae* larvae were found during routine sampling for two years. After the control operations, *A. hispaniola* became the most common species of mosquito inhabiting the *A. labranchiae* habitats. This species does not transmit malaria, and previously it occurred in such low numbers that it was not found during a survey of the mosquito fauna of the area in 1946.

A. hispaniola differs from *A. labranchiae* in two respects, which make it less affected by the control measures. First, its adults rarely rest in houses or farm buildings and so are far less affected by the spraying programme against adult mosquitoes. Secondly, larvae of *A. hispaniola* stay underwater far longer than *A. labranchiae* larvae. Mosquito larvae need to come to the surface occasionally to breathe. The DDT tends to stay on the water's surface as an oil film, and in flowing water the larvae of *A. hispaniola* may avoid much of the spray. These two factors give it a considerable advantage over *A. labranchiae* in sprayed areas.

Very similar replacements of one species by another after chemical control have been reported for other mosquitoes. Gillies and Smith (1960) report the replacement of *A. funestris* by *A. rivulorum* after the virtual elimination of the former species by spraying of dieldrin against adults in East Africa. Service (1965) reported a similar replacement of *Culex nebulosus* by *C. pipiens fatigans* in towns in Nigeria after the use of DDT larvicides. In this case the mosquito nuisance was increased by spraying, since *C. nebulosus* rarely feeds on man, whereas *C. p. fatigans* does.

IV. SUBLETHAL EFFECTS

Sublethal doses of toxic chemicals may affect both the survival and reproduction of animals (see Chapter 4). These effects may occur whenever insufficient of a toxic chemical is picked up to cause death.

The persistent organochlorine insecticides frequently show a delayed toxicity in that the lethal effect is not seen until some time after contact with the chemical. These chemicals are fat-soluble and so can accumulate in the body fat of an animal. Lethal doses may then be released into the blood stream when fat reserves are used, at such times as starvation, moulting, reproduction, or migration. This delayed toxicity is, strictly speaking, a lethal not a sublethal effect, although the toxic chemical may accumulate as a result of repeated sublethal exposures to the chemical.

A toxic chemical may also affect the likelihood of death from some other cause. For example, sublethal doses of the organochlorine insecticides often cause hyperactivity and erratic movement, and this may attract a predator to a poisoned prey. Selective predation by newts (*Triturus cristatus*) on frog tadpoles (*Rana temporaria*) treated with DDT has been demonstrated in the laboratory by Cooke (1971). Stress caused by a toxic chemical may also increase the chance of death from disease. Dempster (1968a) found that a higher percentage of *Pieris rapae* caterpillars died from a granulosis virus disease on plots sprayed with DDT than on control plots.

Sublethal effects of a chemical on a predator may result in improved survival of its prey. Examples of this have scarcely been looked for, but Dempster (1968c) showed that concentrations of DDT in soil, which were far less than those required to kill adult *Harpalus rufipes*, significantly reduced their rate of feeding. This suggests that residues of DDT in soil may reduce the efficiency of some predators, without actually killing them.

Sublethal doses of the organochlorine insecticides may also affect reproductive potential in a number of ways. First, differential survival can have repercussions on reproduction. For example, larger individuals of insect tend to be more fecund, and if these tend to survive an application of a chemical, the survivors will, on average, tend to be more fecund. This differential survival is the cause of many of the examples of increases in fecundity which have been reported for arthropods following the use of organochlorines (Moriarty, 1969). There have been cases, however, where selection cannot account for the increases in fecundity observed in the laboratory, for example, in *Sitophilus granarius* (Kuenen, 1958) and *Panonychus ulmi* (Hueck *et al.*, 1952). In the case of *Sitophilus* there appears to be a direct stimulatory effect of DDT on egg production, although one cannot be certain of this. Kuenen counted only adult offspring resulting from reproduction by *Sitophilus* when kept in wheat containing different concentrations of DDT. It is possible that higher numbers of eggs were laid by the controls, but that the survival of these was poorer (Moriarty, 1969). In *Panonychus* the effect appears to be complicated because of indirect effects of DDT on the nutritive status of the mite's food plants. Added to this, different workers have obtained conflicting results from their studies of the effect of DDT on this mite's reproduction (Pielou, 1960; Seifert, 1961; Attiah and Bondreaux, 1964; Saini and Cutkomp, 1966). It seems likely that the main effect of DDT on the mite's reproduction is through the plant, but more thorough study is required to resolve this.

More commonly the effect of a sublethal dose of a toxic chemical is to reduce, not increase, fecundity. For example, Moriarty (1968) found that the fecundity of adults of *Aglais urticae* and the fertility of their eggs was reduced by sublethal doses of dieldrin received in the larval stage. Survivors from a dose around the LD_{50} were completely sterile. In birds reproductive potential may be reduced by organochlorine insecticides through delayed egglaying, reduced fertility, reduced hatchability, and thinner eggshells (see Chapter 4).

It is extremely difficult to predict the impact which sublethal effects of toxic chemicals can have on animal populations. In the field, sublethal effects are frequently accompanied by an array of lethal effects which makes their identification difficult. No study has yet been made in which the various direct and indirect, lethal and sublethal, effects of a toxic chemical on an animal population can be quantified. One can, therefore, draw only tentative conclusions on the effect that sublethal doses of toxic chemicals can have on populations.

Sublethal effects on survival simply result in an increased mortality from the chemical. Effects on reproductive potential, however, may be far more important in determining the size of subsequent populations. As we have seen, sublethal doses of some chemicals may cause either increases or decreases in reproduction, depending upon the species, the chemical and its concentration (see Chapter 4). Usually, reproductive potential is reduced by organochlorine pesticides, but this may have little or no effect upon population size. An example of this is seen in the golden eagle (*Aquila chrysaëtos*) in Britain.

In western Scotland there was a marked reduction in the breeding success of the golden eagle between 1963–6 (Lockie *et al.*, 1969). This coincided with a decrease in its average eggshell thickness and an increase in egg breakage by the parent birds (Ratcliffe, 1970). In the Western Highlands the eagle feeds predominantly on sheep carrion from which it picks up high residues of dieldrin, which is used as a sheep dip. In eastern Scotland, where it feeds mainly on wild prey, rather than carrion, breeding success and eggshell thickness remained normal. With the ban on the use of dieldrin as a sheep dip in 1966, there was a marked improvement in the eagle's breeding success in western Scotland, which was paralleled by a significant increase in eggshell thickness. Throughout the period the population of eagles in western Scotland did not decline, in spite of the reduced breeding success. The golden eagle is a long-lived bird, so that one might expect a reduced rate of reproduction to make only a slow impact on population size. Added to this, the effect of dieldrin occurred in only part of the species range. Immigration of young birds produced in eastern Scotland, or elsewhere, may have been making good any effects of reduced reproduction in western Scotland.

In some other birds of prey, such as the peregrine falcon and sparrow-hawk, there have been population declines together with reduced breeding success (Ratcliffe, 1970). In these, however, the populations crashed due to the acute poisoning of large numbers of adult birds during the seed-dressing incidents in the late 1950s (see p. 234). Just what impact the reduced reproduction is now having on populations of these species is uncertain. Both species are showing a very slow recovery with the reduction in use of the organochlorine insecticides (Ratcliffe, 1972; Newton, 1972), but without a better understanding of the population dynamics of these species, one cannot be certain that this recovery would be any quicker in the absence of sublethal effects on reproduction. This does seem likely, however.

The impact of increases in reproduction brought about by sublethal doses of the organochlorine insecticides, such as in the fruit tree red spider mite, is no better documented than those involving decreases. In the case of red spider mites, there is little doubt that the increase of populations following the use of DDT is due mainly to the elimination of the mite's natural enemies. Huffaker and Spitzer (1950) concluded, however, that in California, the rapid increase of the mite on pears after DDT applications could not be accounted for entirely by lack of predators. They believe that changes in reproduction of the mite brought about by the effects of DDT on the nutritive status of the plant, contributed considerably to the pest's increase. Once again, this can be proved only by a thorough study of the population dynamics of the mite.

V. GENETIC CHANGES

The last effect which requires mention is the change in the genetic constitution of animal populations after a high death rate from a toxic chemical. We have seen one example of this in the tendency for sur-viving insects to be larger and therefore more fecund than average after an insecticide application (p. 242). By far the best documented example of selection through differential survival is the development of insecticidal resistance in pests. The development of resistance is due to the fact that within any large population of an animal, a small number of individuals exist which are naturally more resistant to the chemical and so survive dosages which kill the rest. All subsequent young are progeny of these survivors and many of them will inherit resistance from their parents. With continued exposure to the chemical, due to its persistence or due to repeated applications, the proportion of the population showing resistance may increase to such an extent that some other means of control has to be found. Resistance is frequently due to an ability to detoxify the chemical, but it can be due to some other factor, such as reduced penetration of an insect's cuticle, or to a behaviour pattern which reduces the individual's contact with the chemical, or to a combination of these factors (see Chapter 3). In such cases, an increased proportion of individuals with these characteristics may affect the percentage survival from some other mortality, such as predation. Selection for more resistant individuals can occur only in the presence of the chemical. In an environment free from the chemical, selection pressures will differ. On the other hand, if subsequent populations stem from survivors of the chemical application—that is, there is little immigration of new individuals—genetic variability within the population may be greatly reduced by the chemical. This could alter the 'fitness' of the species in a chemical-free environment.

VI. CONCLUSIONS

Because of the complex interdependence of different species inhabiting any habitat, it is extremely difficult to predict the detailed effects of introducing a persistent toxic substance into a habitat. The precise effect depends partly upon the relative sensitivity of the different interacting species to the chemical. Although most toxic chemicals are not specific in their action, different species do differ considerably in their sensitivity to any one chemical.

Added to this, the precise effect of a chemical will depend upon the amount and way in which it is applied and its persistence in different parts of the habitat under the particular environmental conditions which prevail. The size of the area covered by the chemical will also influence the outcome, since this will affect the chance of recolonization of the area by those species which have been reduced in number or eliminated. The larger the area affected, the smaller will be the chance of recolonization.

There are, however, some generalizations which can be made. First, toxic chemicals have frequently been found to cause the reduction, or elimination, of predatory species. These often appear to be more sensitive to toxic chemicals than other species, and since they tend to have relatively low rates of reproduction, their ability to recover after a heavy mortality is often poor.

Secondly, this reduction, or elimination, of predators frequently leads to the increase of populations of herbivores. Many examples of this were seen in Section III of this chapter. This phenomenon is so common that there has been a tendency to attribute all increases of animal populations after chemical applications to the elimination of natural enemies, without any evidence to show that these enemies are capable of controlling the animal's numbers in the absence of the chemical. Interactions between species are not as simple as this and increases can result from the elimination of competitors (e.g. mosquitoes, p. 240), changes in the abundance of food species (e.g. *Nebria*, p. 240), or other, more subtle, sublethal effects (e.g. *Panonychus*, p. 242). Many of these effects have scarcely been looked for in the field.

Thirdly, many of the effects which have been described are the inevitable outcome of any form of pest control. One cannot drastically reduce the numbers of one abundant species, such as a pest, by any means, without this having repercussions on other species. The numbers of many other organisms will be directly, or indirectly, dependent upon the abundance of the pest. The more closely dependent the species are, the bigger the effect will be. On top of this, there is the direct toxic effect of a chemical on other species and the effect of differential persistence in different parts of the habitat.

Lastly, the persistence of the organochlorine pesticides poses special problems. Persistence increases the likelihood of drastic changes in the fauna since it may affect one species more than another, it may prevent recolonization, and it may cause secondary poisoning and sublethal effects.

The overall effects of any one chemical on an animal's population may be extremely complicated. We are still a long way from understanding the intricacies of this for any one chemical and species. In particular, we know far too little about the sublethal effects of persistent chemicals. Laboratory studies on individual animals suggest that sublethal effects on reproduction could have important effects on populations in the field. Field evidence on this is completely lacking.

As we have seen, the demonstration of a harmful effect of a toxic substance on individual animals does not necessarily imply that it is having a harmful effect on populations of that animal. Large increases in mortality, or reductions in natality, can occur with no permanent effect on a population. One can only determine the effect of a chemical on the trend in abundance, from one generation to the next, by intensive study of populations in the field.

REFERENCES

Adams, L., Hanavan, M. G., Hosley, N. W. and Johnston, D. W. (1949). *J. Wildl. Mgmt* 13, 245–254.

Aitken, T. H. G. and Trapido, H. (1961). I.U.C.N., 8th Tech. Meeting, Warsaw, 1960, 106–114.

Attiah, H. H. and Bondreaux, H. B. (1964). *J. econ. Ent.* 57, 53–57.

Blackmore, D. K. (1963). *J. comp. Path. Ther.* 73, 391–409.

Collyer, E. (1953a). *J. hort. Sci.* 28, 85–97.

Collyer, E. (1953b). *J. hort. Sci.* 28, 246–259.

Cooke, A. S. (1971). *Nature, Lond.* 229, 275–276.

Croker, R. A. and Wilson, A. J. (1965). *Trans. Am. Fish Soc.* 94, 152–159.

Davis, B. N. K., Moore, N. W., Walker, C. H. and Way, J. M. (1969). *In* 'The Soil Ecosystem' (J. G. Sheals, ed.). Pub. No. 8, pp. 217–228. Systematics Association, London.

De Bach, P. (1947). *Calif. Citrograph* 32, 406–407.

Dempster, J. P. (1967). *J. appl. Ecol.* 4, 485–500.

Dempster, J. P. (1968a). *J. appl. Ecol.* 5, 451–462.

Dempster, J. P. (1968b). *J. appl. Ecol.* 5, 463–475.

Dempster, J. P. (1968c). *Entomologia exp. appl.* 11, 51–54.

Edwards, C. A. (1965). *In* 'Ecology and the Industrial Society', Fifth Symposium of the British Ecological Society, (G. T. Goodman, R. W. Edwards and J. M. Lambert, eds), pp. 239–261.

Edwards, C. A. (1966). *Residue Rev.* 13, 83–132.

Edwards, C. A., Dennis, E. B. and Empson, D. W. (1967). *Ann. appl. Biol.* 60, 11–22.

Gillies, M. T. and Smith, A. (1960). *Bull. ent. Res.* 51, 243–252.

van Halteren, P. (1971). *J. econ. Ent.* 64, 1055–1056.

Hoffman, C. H., Townes, H. K., Swift, H. H. and Sailer, R. I. (1949). *Ecol. Monogr.* 19, 1–46.

Hueck, H. J., Kuenen, D. J., den Boer, P. J. and Jaeger-Draafsel, E. (1952). *Physiol. comp. Oecol.* 2, 371–377.

Huffaker, C. B. and Spitzer, C. H. (1950). *J. econ. Ent.* 43, 819–831.

Hunt, E. G. and Bischoff, A. I. (1960). *Calif. Fish Game* 46, 91–106.

Jefferies, D. J. and Prestt, I. (1966). *Br. Birds* 59, 49–64.

Kiritani, K. and Kawahara, S. (1973). *Botyu-Kagaku* 37, 69–75.

Kuenen, D. J. (1958). *Entomologia exp. appl.* 1, 147–152.

Lockie, J. D., Ratcliffe, D. A. and Balharry, R. (1969). *J. appl. Ecol.* 6, 381–389.

Menhinick, E. F. (1962). *Ecology* 43, 556–561.

Moriarty, F. (1968). *Ann. appl. Biol.* 62, 371–393.

Moriarty, F. (1969). *Biol. Rev.* 44, 321–357.

Moriarty, F. (1972). *Sci. total Environ.* 1, 267–288.

Morris, M. G. (1968). *J. appl. Ecol.* 5, 409–429.

Newton, I. (1972). *Scott. Birds* 7, 5–23.

Pickett, A. D. and Patterson, N. A. (1953). *Can. Ent.* 85, 472–478.

Pielou, D. P. (1960). *Can. J. Zool.* 38, 1147–1151.

Prestt, I. (1965). *Bird Study* 12, 196–221.

Ratcliffe, D. A. (1963). *Bird Study* 10, 56–90.

Ratcliffe, D. A. (1970). *J. appl. Ecol.* 7, 65–115.

Ratcliffe, D. A. (1972). *Bird Study* 19, 117–156.

24 pp.

Ripper, W. E. (1956). *A. Rev. Ent.* **1,** 403–438.

Rudd, R. L. and Herman, S. G. (1972). *In* 'Environmental Toxicity of Pesticides' (F. Matsumura and G. Mallory Boush, eds), pp. 471–485. Academic Press, New York and London.

Saini, R. S. and Cutkomp, L. K. (1966). *J. econ. Ent.* **59,** 249–253.

Seifert, G. (1961). *Z. angew. Zool.* **48,** 441–452.

Service, M. W. [1965 (1966)]. *Bull. ent. Res.* **56,** 407–415.

Sheals, J. G. (1956). *Bull. ent. Res.* **47,** 803–822.

Trapido, H. and Aitken, T. H. G. (1953). *Am. J. trop. Med. Hyg.* **2,** 658–676.

6. Persistent Pesticides: An Economic and Legal Analysis

P. A. VICTOR and W. M. MANSELL

Ministry of the Environment,
Toronto, Ontario,
Canada
and
Eliot College,
The University of Kent,
Canterbury, Kent, England

I. PERSISTENT PESTICIDES: AN ECONOMIC ANALYSIS

A. Introduction

The increasing use of persistent pesticides in agriculture and public health programmes has been met with responses ranging from unqualified praise to blind condemnation. The lack of reliable information and the intractability of some methodological problems relating, in particular, to the evaluation and comparability of the costs and benefits associated with persistent pesticides, enormously complicate the answer to any question concerning the advisability of their use. This lack of information about intended and unintended effects of various kinds of pesticides is well known and indeed, it is one of the purposes of this book to help remedy this situation. But, even if all the biological effects of persistent pesticides were known and there was full information about their effects on agricultural productivity and public health, by what common denominator could all these costs and benefits be related to enable a rational assessment of the use of persistent pesticides? There are some people, including many economists of high repute, who would have little hesitation in answering this question. Money would be offered up as the required measuring rod and the extensive literature on cost-benefit analysis, ably surveyed by Dasgupta and Pearce (1972), would be brought into the debate.

The principle which underlies the evaluative technique of cost-benefit analysis is that things are worth what people are willing and able to pay for them. Once this is accepted, then any activity, including the application of pesticides, can, in principle, be assessed for its contribution to 'social well-being' by comparing the sum of money that those who desire the activity are willing to pay for it with the sum of money that those who would bear the costs of the activity require as compensation. In fact, most cost-benefit analyses value costs by assessing the sum of money that people would be prepared to pay in order to avoid them and only in special circumstances would this sum be as great as the sum necessary for compensation. Whether or not the compensation is actually paid is crucial since only if it is can the argument be made that all people affected by the activity in question benefit from it. If compensation is not paid, and it is doubtful if there has ever been a case involving cost-benefit analysis where all the potential losers have been compensated, then the supposed 'gain to society' that is revealed by the analysis dissolves into a conflict of interests between the gainers and losers which no cost-benefit analysis can resolve.

When the specific application of cost-benefit analysis to the use of persistent pesticides is considered additional problems are introduced. It may well be impossible for the cost-benefit analyst to identify those people who suffer or will suffer from the possible harmful effects of the pesticide in question. This is particularly difficult when future generations are involved. Moreover, the use of willingness to pay as a measure of value, which can so easily bias any cost-benefit analysis in favour of those with high incomes, makes little sense where the people concerned are without adequate information.

Cost-benefit analysis, therefore, does not provide a useful analytical tool for evaluating the use of persistent pesticides. The purpose of this chapter, however, is not to evaluate but to explain. Taking the mixed economies of Western Europe, North America, Australasia and Japan as the focus of attention, the economic and political framework within which the decisions of farmers to use persistent pesticides are made will be outlined. This will be followed by a fairly detailed micro-economic analysis of pest control in agriculture. The last part of the chapter will be concerned with the existing voluntary system of control over the use of persistent pesticides in Britain and the actual and potential role of legislated controls.

B. The Economic and Political Context of Agriculture in Mixed Economies

The essence of a mixed economy is that the means of production—capital and land—are owned in substantial amounts both by the private sector, which includes companies and individuals, and by the public sector, which encompasses the different levels of government, nationalized industries and public corporations. In Britain, 1970, approximately 60 per cent of the means of production were owned privately and 40 per cent were owned publicly, though as Preston (1965) has shown, the actual relationship is very difficult to measure precisely. Within the private sector of the economy, the ownership of the means of production is concentrated in very few hands, though again, accurate figures are hard to obtain. It is incontestable, however, that the vast majority of people who live in a mixed economy depend for their livelihood on the sale of their capacity for work. Only a very few rely on profits from private ownership for their income. In the U.K., in 1970, more than 70 per cent of all income came from employment, less than 8 per cent came from self-employment, 11 per cent came from rent, dividends and interests, and 10 per cent came from national insurance benefits and other current grants from public authorities (Anon., 1971). Though differing in detail, this pattern is representative of the situation in all the mixed economies of the developed world.

The relationship between the public and private sectors of a mixed economy is highly complex and can only be sketched here. Primarily, the economic links between the public and private sectors consist of the tax and expenditure decisions of the government, the government's control over the availability of credit and the rates of interest prevailing in the economy, and the direct regulation of private economic activity. It would be a mistake to think, however, that the private sector is a passive partner in this relationship. The competing interests of capital and labour both seek to secure the kind of government intervention in the private sector which suits them best, and various means, including lobbying and contributions to the funds of political parties, are used for this purpose. The important point is that the economic and political context of agriculture in mixed economies prescribes the framework within which the agricultural sector operates. In particular, agricultural resources are almost all privately owned and the farmers' concern is with profits. The same is true of those companies which manufacture persistent pesticides. But these productive activities are subject to government legislation of one form or another. As a method of approach, therefore, it is useful to analyse the purely economic aspects of the farmer's decisions concerning pest control and to see how those decisions can be modified by different forms of government regulation and control.

C. A Micro-economic Analysis of the Farmer's Decision to Use a Persistent Pesticide

The method of micro-economics is essentially deductive. By examining the logical implications of a set of simplifying assumptions concerning a decision maker's objective and the constraints within which he must operate, economists seek to say something concrete about the very much more complicated world in which we live. It is an ongoing debate among economists and philosophers whether or not it is sufficient for the conclusions of the deductive analysis to be testable against experience in order to validate the analysis. Some people argue that validation also requires that the initial set of assumptions be shown to satisfy some additional criteria of realism. Doubtless, nothing is lost wherever this is possible, and when policy recommendations are regarded as an important outcome of an analysis then the view that the assumptions underlying the analysis require support over and above mere arguments of plausibility is particularly compelling.

In the following analysis, which deals with the decisions of a farmer to use persistent pesticides, little or no evidence is offered in support of the various assumptions on which the argument rests. The number of variables under consideration is kept particularly small so that graphical techniques may be employed. Furthermore, the relations between the variables are assumed to be very simple and although many of them may be plausible they are not intended to be accurate representations of the quantitative relations involved.

Apart from the fact that the necessary data for building a detailed micro-economic model of agriculture are not available, the main justification for this approach is that it highlights some key relationships which are important to understanding the farmer's decision to use persistent pesticides. Moreover, the analysis provides a guide to the kind of data that a more empirically based study of the decision to use persistent pesticides would require.

In all that follows it is assumed that the farmer seeks to maximize his profits from farming. The conditions and constraints under which he must act are defined by the following assumptions:

a. two forms of pest control are available to the farmer: PC_1 and PC_2, which can be used separately or in combination;
b. only one type of food is produced, which can be sold in any quantity at a price which cannot be altered by an action of the individual farmer;
c. land L (combined with labour and capital in fixed proportions and available at constant prices) and pest control are the variable inputs, the quantities of which are to be selected by the farmer.

This designation of land as a variable input is substantiated for the United States by the work of Langham et al. (1972) who have investigated, for various regions in the United States, the extent to which land and insecticides may be substituted for one another without affecting agricultural output. For the country as a whole, they estimate that if the area of cropland in use were increased by 1 per cent then the use of insecticides could be reduced by as much as 6·5 per cent with no change in the production of food.

In Fig. 1 the two methods of pest control, PC_1 and PC_2, are measured on the axes in appropriate units per acre. Any point on the graph represents a particular combination of these methods of pest control. The curved lines I_1, I_2 and I_3 indicate pest control programmes of equal effectiveness, with effectiveness measured in terms of the percentage of pests eliminated per acre for a given period of time. Thus, any combination of PC_1 and PC_2 along I_1 results in the same percentage reduction in the target population of pests. I_2 and I_3 represent progressively more effective programmes of pest control. These 'isocontrol' lines, which probably reflect a greater degree of continuity than would obtain in practice, are drawn convex to the origin on the assumption that combinations of PC_1 and PC_2 are more effective than complete dependence on either of the available methods of pest control.

In order to maximize his profits the farmer has to minimize his costs. The costs to the farmer of pest control are shown in Fig. 1 by the isocost lines $E_1 F_1$, $E_2 F_2$, $E_3 F_3$. Each of these lines represents a fixed level of expenditure on pest control, with their slopes determined by the relative prices of PC_1 and PC_2. The greatest degree of pest control that can be obtained by each of the progressively larger sums of money represented by these isocost curves is shown at N, M, and T. Note that even though $E_2 F_2$ represents a greater level of expenditure than $E_1 F_1$, if this larger

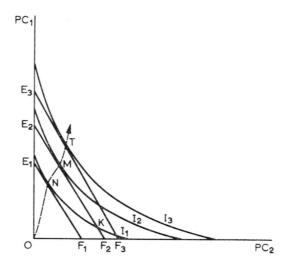

Fig. 1. The farmer's choice of pest control methods.

budget is spent in the manner indicated by point K, the same level of pest control I_1 that the smaller budget makes possible at N, is achieved via this 'inefficient' use of the larger budget. The locus of all the 'efficient' patterns of spending budgets of varying size is given by $ONMT$. This line shows the last cost method of achieving any pre-scribed level of pest control, and so the farmer who seeks maximum profit will attempt to locate himself somewhere along $ONMT$ according to the level of pest control that he requires.

The next stage of the analysis is concerned with the farmer's choice of different inputs. In this case his choice is between varying degrees of pest control and the quantity of land he farms. The same technique can be used here as for analysing the farmer's choice of pest control

methods. The lines B_1, B_2, B_3 in Fig. 2 show the technical possibilities
open to the farmer of combining land and pest control to produce food.
The combinations of these two agricultural inputs indicated along any
particular line, or isoquant, produce exactly the same quantity of food.
The further an isoquant is from the origin, the greater is the quantity
of food it represents. Thus B_3 shows combinations of pest control and
land which produce more food than those combinations shown by B_2.
These isoquants are convex to the origin to reflect the assumption that
from a position in which a substantial amount of one input is used in

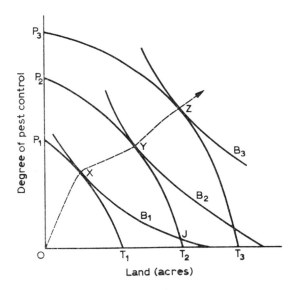

Fig. 2. The farmer's choice of pest control and land.

conjunction with a small amount of the other (e.g. at point J on B_1)
output is held constant by decreasing the greatly used input (at J it is
land) by a larger percentage than the necessary complementary percentage increase in the other input.

The curves $P_1\ T_1$, $P_2\ T_2$, $P_3\ T_3$ correspond to the budget lines of
Fig. 1. They are curved and not straight even though the price per
unit of land may be assumed constant for any farmer. This reflects the
assumption that the price per unit of pest control rises with the amount
of pest control purchased by the farmer. They represent fixed levels
of expenditure on land and pest control. The farmer can purchase a
degree of pest control, OP_2 or quantity of land OT_2 or any combination of the two that is shown by $P_2\ T_2$. If he spends this money on these

agricultural inputs so that he purchases the quantities indicated by
point J then his food output will be that of the B_1 isoquant. He can
do better however, with this level of expenditure, by moving along
$P_2 T_2$ to point Y so that his food output rises to that of the B_2 isoquant.
Once again the tangents formed between the budget lines and the
isoquants show the cheapest way of producing any particular quantity
of food, or, what is the same thing, the most food from a particular level
of expenditure on inputs. The locus of all these 'efficient' patterns of
expenditure is given by $OXYZ$, and so the profit maximizing farmer,
who will be concerned to minimize his costs whatever his most profitable
output of food happens to be, will operate at some point along this
curve.

If it is assumed that the cost of the inputs and their technical productivity are such that a proportional increase in food output requires a
more than proportional increase in costs, then such a relationship
between costs and output is shown in Fig. 3 by OTC.

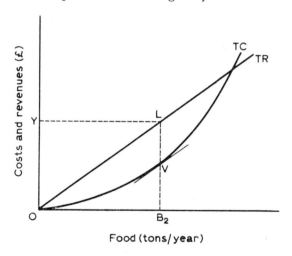

Fig. 3. The output of food which maximizes the farmer's profit.

The assumption made at the start of the analysis that the farmer can
sell as much food as he likes at the same market price implies that the
farmer's total revenue from sales rises in the same proportion as does
the output of food he sells. This relationship between total revenue
and output is shown as OTR in Fig. 3. Since the farmer's objective is
to maximize his profits, and given that he knows the costs he must
incur in order to produce food (OTC in Fig. 3) and the revenue he
gains from selling food (OTR in Fig. 3), he will select that output

which maximizes the difference between his revenue and his costs. In Fig. 3, the profit maximizing output is OB_2 tons/year of food, which provides a profit of $£LV$. This is at the point where the total revenue and total cost curves are parallel.

Working back from this particular output of food in Fig. 3 through the other Figures it can be seen that it corresponds to some combination of land and pest control shown by some point on $OXYZ$ in Fig. 2, say point Y, which in turn corresponds to some particular cost of pest control shown as point M on E_2F_2 in Fig. 1. Thus the farmer's goal of maximum profit has been related to his decision about the type and extent of pest control to use.

To summarize, on the basis of some assumptions concerning technical agricultural relationships and the market for agricultural outputs and inputs, a decision-making framework for a farmer has been constructed which links various key choices that he must make if he is to maximize his profits. In particular, his choice between two different methods of pest control has been highlighted within a more broadly based decision-making framework.

Subsequently (in Section D), the implications of some different assumptions from those that have been made so far will be examined. In the next few pages, however, the decision-making framework that has been established will be used to consider the farmer's decision about pest control within the context of the following five issues:

a. the relationship between the decisions of individual farmers and the 'social contribution' of agriculture;
b. the implications of unintended side-effects from pest control;
c. the implications of regulations concerning pest control;
d. the implications of land use planning;
e. the implications of government subsidies to agriculture and protection from foreign imports of food.

These are by no means the only issues which this decision-making framework can help elucidate, although there are other important issues for which this decision-making framework is inappropriate. For example, a similar approach to the decisions of a manufacturer of persistent pesticides would also indicate the set of conditions which must obtain if the manufacturer is to maximize his profits. Without substantial modification, however, the analysis is not suitable in cases where uncertainty predominates. It may be necessary, for example, to introduce probability functions in order to describe the relationships among the variables in the model. The use of 'objective' probabilities can allow for relationships which are known to be probabilistic, and the use of 'subjective' probabilities can be a convenient way of coping with a decision maker's ignorance about specific relationships with which he is concerned.

These micro-issues aside, there are the broader macro-economic problems of employment, prices, and foreign trade that may well be associated with the control of the use of pesticides, and these require a different kind of approach altogether than that presented here.

The following five issues are sufficient to show the use and limitations of this kind of economics for analysing some of the problems surrounding the control of pesticides.

1. The Relationship between the Decisions of Individual Farmers and the 'Social Contribution' of Agriculture

This issue has, in less specific terms, occupied a large number of economists for at least 200 years. Whilst we cannot hope to provide anything like a complete treatment of this issue here, and to do so would not be very relevant to our concern with the control of pesticides, a brief account of the main arguments does help give a standard by which to judge the significance of points that will arise when we turn to the next four questions.

Providing farmers take account of all the costs associated with the production of food and that these costs are registered in the total cost curve (OTC) of Fig. 3, then these costs can be aggregated over all farmers to arrive at a curve which shows the aggregate total costs for the production of food. In economics, the cost of an item is taken to mean the value of what must be foregone in order to obtain the item concerned. This 'opportunity cost' may be measured in terms of money but it need not be. Similarly, an aggregate total revenue curve for the agricultural sector can also be constructed and the cost and revenue curves of Fig. 3 can be reinterpreted so as to apply to the entire agricultural sector. Although the assumptions that the prices of food and land are constant, irrespective of the quantities traded, are less satisfactory when applied to all agriculture rather than to a single farmer, it is reasonable in the case of a country with a relatively small agricultural sector and unhindered access to the world food market. In Fig. 4 these assumptions underlie the aggregate cost and revenue curves TC_A and TR_A. Fig. 4 also shows a total revenue curve, TR_B, for agriculture when the quantity of food sold does have a negative effect on price.

It can now be asked whether from a social point of view the total output of food is too large or too small in each of the cases represented in Fig. 4. The assumed competitive agricultural sector of the economy will produce food up to the point where the cost of a marginal increment in the output of food just equals the price at which the food can be sold. This is indicated by point B_A for the aggregate revenue curve TR_A, and point B_B for the curve TR_B.

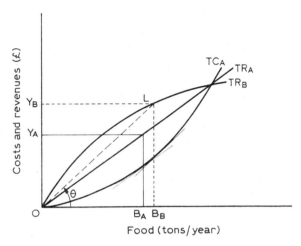

Fig. 4. The output of food from a competitive agricultural sector.

The output B_B occurs where the tangent to the total cost curve TC_A is parallel to the line through L and the origin. The angle θ indicates the average revenue, or price, of food.

Provided that the distribution of incomes is socially equitable and consumers have full information about all commodities then it may be said that the social worth of the marginal unit of food just equals the social worth of what must be forgone in order to produce it. Consequently, given the many assumptions that have been made so far, and some others which have not been mentioned (see de V. Graaff, 1957), a competitive agriculture sector will utilize resources in such a way that they satisfy the assumed autonomous demands of consumers. It is in this limited sense that economists assess the 'social contribution' of any economic activity.

2. The Implications of Unintended Side Effects from Pest Control

One of the key behavioural assumptions in the analysis of a farmer's choice of agricultural inputs, including his method of pest control, is that he is concerned solely with the costs that he incurs himself and the benefits he receives. He is assumed to completely neglect any costs or benefits that might accrue to others as a result of his agricultural activities. These include any deleterious effects that pesticides may have on:

a. the farmer or his employees, of which they are not aware;
b. the consumers of the food, of which they are not aware;
c. any third party, born or unborn, of which they are not aware, or of which they are aware but have no economic or legal remedy.

This third set of effects is particularly broad and includes such things as the effects of pesticides on wildlife, to which people may object without having a legal or economic remedy. Also included is the resistance to insecticides which may result from one or several farmers' actions and hence increase the difficulty of pest control for other farmers. It is the existence of these three categories of effects of pesticides which gives rise to what is sometimes referred to as the 'pesticide problem'. Fortunately, they can all be dealt with in a similar manner within the decision-making framework that has been established, although each of the three cases may call for different kinds of policies. Perhaps more important, the existence of these unintended side effects creates problems which can only be resolved within a broader context of agricultural and economic policy. This aspect of the 'pesticide problem' is too often ignored by economists and policy makers. It can, however, be accommodated in the decision-making framework, as will be seen when we turn to the subsequent issues. For the moment, it will be assumed that all else is well with agriculture except for the existence of the three categories of unintended side effects which were cited above.

The right hand quadrant of Fig. 5 is a repeat of Fig. 1 which was used to analyse the farmer's choice of pest control methods for varying degrees of pest control. The left hand quadrant of Fig. 5 relates the quantity of PC_1, which can be regarded as some variety of persistent pesticide, to the side effects caused by the use of this pesticide. Depending on the kind of side effects it may be easy, difficult or impossible to attribute a monetary value to them. This important issue, which was discussed in the introduction, has received a great deal of attention elsewhere, but since it is not crucial to the present argument the difficulties and impossibilities will be neglected here. There are two significant features of this assumed side effects function: any positive use of the pesticide causes some side effects, and there is a threshold level after which the damage increases very rapidly with increases in the use of the pesticide. For simplicity of exposition, the other method of pest control, PC_2, is assumed to have no unintended side effects.

The essential idea illustrated by Fig. 5 is that the farmer selects his method of pest control according to his perception of the gains and losses that he expects to experience. In doing this he neglects any costs (and benefits) that others incur as a result of his decision. It has become conventional to refer to these two categories of costs as private costs and social costs respectively.

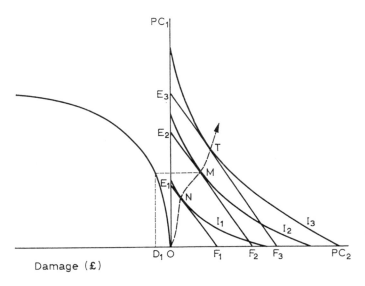

Fig. 5. The unintended side effects of a farmer's choice of pest control methods.

In Fig. 5 it is seen that the farmer who operates at the profit maximizing point M causes damage OD_1. Since it is possible to relate each point on that curve to a point on the cost minimization path ONMT in Figs 1 and 5, it is possible to determine the damage from pesticides associated with each level of the farmer's agricultural output. Thus, in Fig. 6, the total cost (OTC) and total revenue (OTR) curves of Fig. 3 are reproduced together with a curve $(O\overline{TC})$ which relates the private and social costs of a farmer's output to the quantity of food he produces.

Although there may well be other social costs of agriculture besides those associated with persistent pesticides it is only the latter which are of interest here. Consequently, the difference between the two curves TC and $\overline{TC}$ is due entirely to the unintended side effects of using persistent pesticides, as shown in Fig. 5.

Earlier, before the social costs of using persistent pesticides were introduced into the analysis, it was suggested that the farmer's aim for
maximum profit is not without social significance. This is because he
will tend to produce that output at which the incremental cost of an
increase in production is just equal to the incremental benefit of the
food produced, and this will apply to all farmers so that their total
output may be considered socially desirable. Now that an element of
social cost has entered the analysis this conclusion is untenable, since

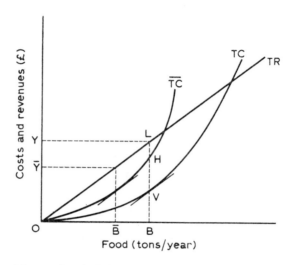

Fig. 6. The social costs of agriculture.

in failing to take account of these costs in their production decisions,
the farmers will produce an output of food at least part of which will
require costs in excess of the benefits provided by the food. In Fig. 6
at the output of food OB selected by the farmer who maximizes his
profit, the rate at which all costs, private and social, are increasing
exceeds the rate of increase of benefits, as measured by sales revenue:
the slope of $O\overline{TC}$ at H exceeds the slope of OTR at L. This means that a
smaller output of food is called for and, by the now familiar argument
concerning incremental benefits and costs, the socially optimal output
of food is $O\overline{B}$.

This argument applies equally to the individual farmer or the agricultural sector as a whole. If each farmer is over-producing food because
he is ignoring the costs that are associated with his use of persistent
pesticides, then the output of the agricultural sector is also too large
and, to the extent that output affects price, the price of food too low.

3. The Implications of Regulations Concerning Pest Control

In principle this issue can be dealt with very simply since the effect of virtually any kind of regulation governing the use of pesticides will increase the costs to the farmer of producing food. The farmer who maximizes profits can be expected to respond to such an increase in his private costs by using less of the regulated pesticides and absolutely or relatively more of the other agricultural inputs, which, in the simplified case under examination, means less of pest control method one (PC_1) and more of pest control method two (PC_2), and more land. The added response of a shift to crops requiring less pest control should not be forgotten, though it cannot be allowed for in the present decision-making framework in which only one agricultural output is recognized. Overall the farmer will tend to reduce his output of food and insofar as his response is typical of all farmers subjected to the pest control regulations, the total output of food will decline. If the food is being sold at world prices and imports are unrestricted then there will be no increase in the price of food although imports from the international market are likely to rise. This assumes, of course, that the regulations on pest control are national rather than international. In any other case the reduction in the output of food, consequent on the imposition of pest control regulations, will tend to raise the price of food to the consumers.

Having outlined the general direction of the changes which are induced by the imposition of regulations concerning pest control, it is possible, with the use of the decision-making framework, to analyse more precisely the effects of different kinds of regulations. Three types of regulation will be considered:

a. complete prohibition of a pesticide;
b. partial prohibition of a pesticide whereby an upper limit is placed on its use;
c. compulsory expenditure by the farmer on safety measures such as protective clothing for himself and his employees.

In addition to these regulations a policy of taxing pesticides, so as to deliberately raise their price to the farmer and thereby discourage their use, will also be analysed.

Figure 7, which is very similar to Fig. 5, shows the effects of the three types of pesticide regulation on a farmer's decision to use the two methods of pest control, PC_1 and PC_2. It has been seen that when there are no regulations concerning pest control a farmer will obtain the desired degree of pest control by selecting the appropriate mix of the two available pest control methods at some point along the line of minimum costs, $ONMT$. In the previous analysis this point was M, leading to the unintended damage, OD_1. One way of analysing the effects of the various forms of pesticide regulation is to consider what happens to the line $ONMT$ as a result of the regulations.

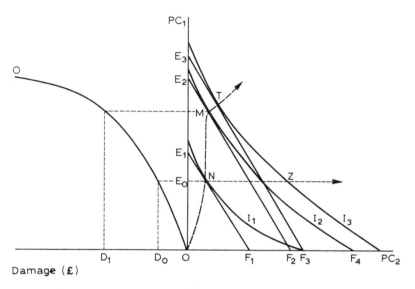

Fig. 7. The effect of complete and partial prohibition on the farmer's choice of pest control methods.

a. Complete prohibition. If PC_1 is prohibited then the farmer is obliged to use PC_2 to achieve whatever degree of pest control he desires. In this case his line of minimum cost becomes coincidental with the horizontal axis.

By means of pesticide regulation, the unintended side effects of the regulated pesticide are eliminated and the farmer's costs of controlling pests are increased. This is shown in Fig. 8 by a decrease in the degree of pest control that can be obtained from the expenditure of given sums of money. Before the prohibition of the pesticide PC_1, the farmer could obtain from a specific level of expenditure a degree of pest control OP_1^1, or an amount of land OT_1, or any combination of the two along $P_1^1T_1$. After the prohibition of the pesticide the same amount of money will only purchase a degree of pest control, OP_1^2 or any combination of land and pest control $P_1^2T_1$. By the same argument, the budget line $P_2^1T_2$ shrinks to $P_2^2T_2$. As a result of this increase in the price of pest control the farmer is unable to produce as much as before from any given level of expenditure on agricultural inputs. Prior to the prohibition of the pesticide he could produce an output of food B_1 with the budget constraint given by $P_1{}^1 T_1$ by operating at point X in Fig. 8. After the pesticide prohibition his food output for the same level of expenditure on inputs must drop to B_0 at point U on the budget line $P_1{}^2 T_1$. Similarly for the larger level of expenditure represented by the budget line $P_2{}^1 T_2$ before the prohibition, and $P_2{}^2 T_1$ after it, the farmer's output of food drops from B_3 at point Y to B_2 at

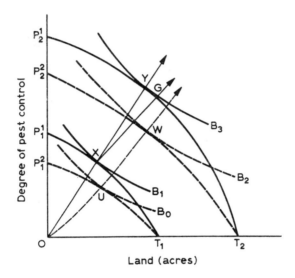

Fig. 8. The effect of legislation on the farmer's choice of pest control and land.

point W. Moreover, the original line of minimum cost OXY is replaced by the new line OUW, characterized, in comparison with OXY, by a greater use of land and a smaller use of pest control for each and every level of food output. It should be noted, however, that this does not necessarily mean that the farmer's use of land will increase in absolute terms as a result of the prohibition of pesticides. This will depend on the extent to which the output of food declines when the costs of food production increase. It is quite possible that the output of food will decrease so much that the substitution of land for pest control induced by the change in their relative prices will be outweighed by the absolute decrease in the use of both inputs due to the increased costs of food production.

b. Partial prohibition. Referring to Fig. 7, if a farmer is allowed to use up to an amount OE_0 of the first method of pest control, PC_1, then his cost minimization path for pest control becomes ONZ. If he is to achieve a degree of pest control greater than that indicated by the isocontrol curve I_1, then he must rely solely on increasing his use of the second method of pest control, PC_2. It is clear from Fig. 7 that this will increase the farmer's cost of pest control, beyond I_1, though to a lesser extent than in the case of complete prohibition. For example, he can obtain a degree of pest control I_2 by spending a sum of money large enough to buy OF_3 of PC_2, though he spends some of this money to buy OE_0 of PC_1. In the case of complete prohibition of PC_1 he would have to spend a sum of money large enough to buy OF_4 of PC_2, for a degree of control I_2, but if there was no prohibition of either kind all he would have to spend would be a sum of money large enough to buy OF_2 of PC_2 to attain point M on I_2.

The effect of partial prohibition on the farmer's choice between pest control and land, illustrated in Fig. 8, is to raise the price of pest control relative to the price of land and change the farmer's cost minimization path to OXG. This path is coincidental with the unrestricted path OXY up to point X, beyond which the pesticide prohibition comes into effect, and the cost minimization path begins to approach that which applies in the case of complete prohibition, OUW. Except in the case where partial prohibition is irrelevant to a farmer, in that he does not want to use all of the pesticide that he is allowed to, the effects of partial prohibition on his costs and output are qualitatively similar to the effects of complete prohibition. There would, however, be some damage from the use of the partially prohibited pesticide, given as the amount OD_0 in Fig. 7.

c. Compulsory expenditure on safety measures. Regulations which compel a farmer to undertake expenditure to protect himself and his employees from the pesticides they use fall into two economic categories. The extra expenditure by the farmer may be a 'lump sum', e.g. for a new kind of spraying equipment, or 'per unit', e.g. for protective clothing which must be provided for farm workers (assuming there is a direct relation between the number of farm workers and the amount of pesticide used). The essential difference between lump sum and per unit costs, in the context of the decision-making framework, is that once a farmer has decided to incur the required lump sum expenditure there will be no incentive for him to change his methods of pest control. As will be seen, momentarily, he will tend to use less of both methods of pest control, even though the lump sum expenditure is required for only one of them. In contrast to this situation, if safety regulations affect the unit cost to the farmer of one method of pest control and not the other, then he will tend to substitute the safe method of control for the method from which protection is required. Even in this case, however, it is quite possible for both methods of pest control to be used less than before.

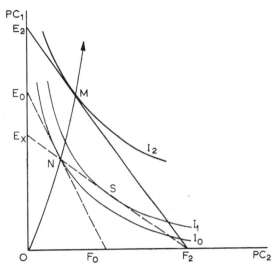

Fig. 9. The effect of compulsory expenditures on the farmer's choice of pesticides.

In Fig. 9 it is assumed that, before the imposition of compulsory expenditure of either kind, the farmer is operating at point M. The obligation to pay a fixed sum for safety purposes should he use any quantity of PC_1 is shown by a shift in his budget line from E_2F_2 to $E_0F_0F_2$. This is explained as follows: for the sum of money represented by the initial budget line E_2F_2, the farmer can buy an amount OF_2 of PC_2, and no amount of PC_1 at all. Because of the regulations, if he wishes to use some positive quantity of PC_1 then he must incur some fixed costs, which, by assumption, are just sufficient to buy an amount F_0F_2 of PC_2. Once he has paid these costs he is then able to substitute PC_1 for PC_2 at the same rate as before because the unit costs of both methods of pest control are unaffected by the safety regulations. Therefore E_0F_0 is parallel to E_2F_2.

The price of pest control rises as a result of the regulations, and only the degree of control indicated by the isocontrol curve I_0 can now be purchased with the same quantity of money as could previously buy the amount of pest control indicated by I_2. The farmer's response to this increase in costs will be qualitatively similar to his response to complete and partial prohibition of a pesticide. With the increase in the cost of pest control he will tend to use more land and less pest control, as shown in Fig. 8. Whether or not the substitution of land for pest control leads to an absolute increase in the farmer's use of land will depend on the extent to which the increase in his total costs of producing food leads to a reduction in his profit maximizing output of food.

The decline in the farmer's use of pest control, irrespective of whether or not he increases his use of land, will be achieved by a contraction along the unchanged line of minimum costs, ONM in Fig. 9, so that the farmer will end up using less of both methods of pest control. An important exception to this result would be complete specialization in the second method of pest control which would be justified in cases where the relevant isocontrol curve intersected the horizontal axis in a manner which justified complete dependence on PC_2. For example, if I_0 intersected the horizontal axis between F_0 and F_2 then the greatest degree of pest control from the budget indicated by $E_0F_0F_2$ would be obtained not at point N but at point F_2.

When investigating the effects of an increase in the unit cost of the regulated pesticide it is useful to make a comparison with the effects of the lump sum expenditure. In Fig. 9 the increase in the unit cost of using PC_1 is shown by rotating the budget line E_2F_2 around F_2. The sum of money which previously could purchase OE_2 of PC_1, or OF_2 of PC_2, or any combination of PC_1 and PC_2 shown by E_2F_2 can now only purchase OE_x of PC_1, OF_2 of PC_2 or a combination of PC_1 and PC_2 shown by E_xF_2. This reflects the fact that only PC_1 and not PC_2 has become more expensive. The farmer could, as in the case of the lump sum expenditure, move to point N and obtain a measure of pest control given by I_0. He can however, do better than this from the same budget and move to a point S where he obtains a higher measure of control than at point N. There is, therefore, a greater incentive for the farmer to substitute the harmless method of pest control for the harmful one when their relative prices are altered than when he is only subject to a lump sum cost, except when the lump sum cost causes complete specialization in PC_2.

Apart from this important difference between the effects of the two types of compulsory charges, the other effects on land use and food output are much the same with both types of increased costs. It is quite possible, of course, that in any real situation, required expenditures for safety measures would involve lump sum costs and unit costs, in which case the effects would be a mixture of the two extremes analysed in this section.

It is convenient to note at this point that the policy measure favoured by a substantial number of economists such as Kneese and Bower (1968) in other contexts, of imposing a 'tax on pollution' so as to deliberately raise the price of a product with which social costs are associated, corresponds analytically to the case of increased unit costs resulting from enforced safety precautions. The principle behind this tax proposal is not to raise revenue in order to compensate those who suffer damage, but to bring the price of the product, pesticide or any other, into line with all the costs that are involved in its production and use. The farmer's economic response to an increase in the price of the pesticide, PC_1, due to the imposition of a tax parallels exactly his response to an increase in unit costs for safety measures. It is quite possible, however, that the farmer would prefer a policy of regulated safety procedures rather than a tax on pesticides, largely because the rationale behind the two policies is likely to differ: the former is usually intended to directly benefit himself and his employees, and the latter to bring some benefit, probably immeasurable and even undetectable, to an unknown public.

4. The Implications of Land Use Planning

It has been seen that the farmer who seeks to maximize his profit will attempt to combine his agricultural inputs of pest control and land so as to produce food at the lowest possible cost to himself (see Fig. 2 and the accompanying analysis). The farmer's decisions concerning pest control are likely, therefore, to be significantly influenced by the price and availability of agricultural land. If land is cheap he will tend to use less pest control, and hence less persistent pesticide, than if land is expensive. The government may have a land use policy which has little or nothing to do with any concern it may have for persistent pesticides. This will inevitably affect the price and availability of farm land. Depending on the nature of the land use policy, agricultural land will become more or less available, and less or more expensive. As a consequence of this, the farmer will adjust his mix of pest control and land and hence his use of persistent pesticides.

5. The Implications of Government Subsidies to Agriculture and Protection from Foreign Imports of Food

Virtually every industrialized country in the world subsidizes and protects its agriculture. Although the reasons for such policies vary from country to country and from time to time, they usually include a desire for a degree of self-sufficiency for strategic purposes, concern for the balance of payments, and the maintenance of farm incomes. They also reflect, to some extent, the long standing power of the landed classes.

Such a wide variety of goals has given rise to an ever wider variety of agricultural support policies, each of which has implications for the use of persistent pesticides, irrespective of whether this was intended by those who formulated the policies. The use of persistent pesticides will be affected by the extent to which agricultural output is stimulated and the other agricultural inputs such as land, manpower, and capital equipment are favoured as compared with pesticides.

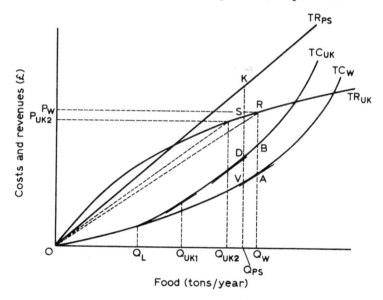

Fig. 10. The effect of agricultural subsidies and import restrictions on the output of food.

This section will be concerned with the effects of three agricultural support policies on pesticide use:

a. subsidies paid to farmers so that they can compete with lower cost imports;
b. import restrictions to keep out cheaper foreign imports;
c. import restrictions to keep out cheaper foreign imports combined with government guaranteed prices for agricultural output.

Figure 10, which is similar to Fig. 4, describes, say, the British agricultural market under different conditions. The curve OTC_W describes the total cost of supplying Britain with food from British and foreign farmers. The curve OTC_{UK}, which is coincident with OTC_W over a range and then lies above it, describes the total cost of supplying Britain with food solely from British farms: the cost curves are coincident up to the output of food OQ_L, all of which is produced most cheaply in Britain. The demand for food in Britain is represented by the total revenue curve OTR_{UK}. When the government guarantees the price of food in Britain the total revenue curve facing British farmers is OTR_{PS}.

It can now be seen that if British agriculture was completely unprotected from foreign competition then the quantity of food purchased on the British market would be OQ_W, and it would sell at a price per unit of $£OP_W/OQ_W$. This price is just equal to the cost of producing the marginal unit of food, as given by the slope of TC_W at A. Moreover, in view of the competition between British and foreign farmers, the cost of producing a marginal unit of food for importation (including transport costs) must equal the cost of producing a marginal unit on a British farm. If this were not the case then competitive market processes would alter the mixture of home produce and imports in the total output of food, until the marginal cost of food from the two sources of supply were equal. Consequently, the contribution of British agriculture to the total supply, OQ_W, of food in Britain, is found by locating the point on the curve TC_{UK} at which the slope of this curve is equal to the slope of the curve OTC_W at A. Thus, the British output of food in the absence of protection is OQ_{UK1}.

Having established the output of the British agricultural sector in the case of free trade in food it is possible to deduce the output of food from each British farm. Every farmer, all of whom are faced with the same market price for food, $£OP_W/OQ_W$, will expand his output of food up to the point where a further expansion would involve him in greater costs than revenue. Since the increase in revenue from the sale of an extra unit of food is the same for all farmers, i.e. $£OP_W/OQ_W$, all will operate their farms so that the cost of a marginal change in output is equal to this and, therefore, the same for all farms.

Turning now to the implications of agricultural subsidies, Fig. 10 shows the extent of the subsidy which must be paid to British farmers if they are to be induced to supply any prescribed quantity of food. The extra cost of supplying a quantity of food OQ_W from domestic sources alone, rather than importing some of it $(Q_{UK1}Q_W)$, is given by the vertical distance between the two total cost curves at that point, i.e. AB. It follows therefore that a subsidy of this magnitude, designed to lower the costs that are associated for each farmer with an increase in output, would lead to the expansion of agricultural output in Britain, with a corresponding increase in the use of persistent pesticides.

A smaller or larger subsidy would have qualitatively the same results as the subsidy AB, although the magnitude of the effect would be different. This kind of agricultural support prevailed in Britain prior to entry into the European Community. A qualitative difference in the effects of a subsidy would obtain, however, when, as often happens, the agricultural subsidies (or tax exemptions, which amount to the same thing) are given for the purchase of specific types of agricultural input rather than as a general reduction in the costs borne by the farmers. The effect of such specific subsidies (such as those currently given in Britain for the purchase of fertilizer) is to encourage the replacement of unsubsidized inputs by the subsidized inputs. In terms of the decision-making framework, a pest control subsidy which lowered the farmer's cost of purchasing the harmless pest control method PC_2 would reduce the slope of the isocost curves in Fig. 1 and lower the expansion path. The effects are equivalent to those analysed in Fig. 9. This means that any specified level of pest control would be achieved by a greater use of PC_2 and a smaller use of PC_1 than in the absence of the subsidy.

The second form of agricultural support to be considered is the imposition of import restrictions to keep out cheaper foreign food. Figure 10 shows that complete prohibition of imported food level would raise the output of food in Britain from the OQ_{UK1}, which prevails when agriculture is not supported, to a level OQ_{UK2}. At this point the price of food in Britain would be £OP_{UK2}/OQ_{UK2}, which is just equal to the cost of producing the marginal unit of food on British farms, indicated by the slope of the cost curve OTC_{UK} for this output of food. By comparison with the previous case of general agricultural subsidies, the output of food produced in Britain when imports are prohibited would be less and therefore the use of persistent pesticides would be less.

It is quite possible that a prohibition of food imports would be regarded by the government as leading to an output of food that is too small. Something of a compromise between this situation and that of the general subsidy discussed earlier can be achieved by prohibiting imports and, at the same time, by guaranteeing the price of farm produce that is paid to farmers. This approximates to the agricultural support policies of the Euopean Economic Community and is the third of the agricultural policies to be considered here though, for convenience, the analysis will remain in an entirely British context.

The total revenue curve OTR_{PS} in Fig. 10 reflects a guaranteed price for agricultural output irrespective of the quantity sold. The guaranteed price is indicated by the slope of this curve. Under these conditions, with all food imports prohibited, British farmers will expand their output of food up to OQ_{PS} where the price they receive for food just equals the cost of producing a marginal increment in the output of food, indicated by the slope of the cost curve TC_{UK}. The vertical distance between the two total revenue curves at this point, SK, shows the cost to the government of supporting prices and this must be added to the vertical distance between the two cost curves at this point, VD, to ascertain the total cost of protecting agriculture. With this policy the degree to which British use of persistent pesticides will be affected will depend on the size of the guaranteed prices and on the extent of import prohibition, which has only been assumed to be complete for expositional purposes. If account is also taken of the probable decline in the use of persistent pesticides abroad in response to greater protection for British agriculture, then it becomes more difficult to be confident about the effect of the policies on their total use. The general conclusion remains, however, that the protection of agriculture will have implications for the use of persistent pesticides, even though this may not be the intention of the policy maker, and these may conflict with other policies designed to control the use of persistent pesticides.

D. The Decision-making Framework: Concluding Comments

The analysis which has been presented in the preceding pages is a highly simplified representation of the way in which farmers decide on their use of pesticides, and of the ways in which their decisions may be influenced by pesticide control regulations and agricultural support policies. Nevertheless, many of the insights gained from this simplified examination apply to the more complicated situation which prevails in mixed economies throughout the world.

A more complete analysis would recognize the many forms of pest control, the many forms of agricultural inputs and the many varieties of farm products. This would not, however, detract from the fundamental conclusion that the profit maximizing farmer will attempt to combine the cheapest form of pest control with other agricultural inputs so as to produce various types of food as cheaply as possible. He will tend to neglect, unless compelled otherwise by legislation, all those costs, including those associated with the use of persistent pesticides, which fall on others as a result of his activities. Furthermore, government policies which may or may not be designed to control the farmer's use of persistent pesticides will have their effect on the farmer's use of persistent pesticides by influencing the profitability of the alternative modes of farming open to him.

Having said this, it remains that the precise results obtained in the above analysis of the simple case depend crucially on a number of assumptions which have not yet been made explicit. First of all there is the assumed competitive nature of the agricultural sector which implies that no farmer or group of farmers is able to influence the price for which they sell their food or the price they pay for their agricultural inputs. All farmers are price takers, although the farming community is not precluded from influencing the government's policies towards agriculture. This institutional assumption of competitive agriculture is reasonable when applied to some mixed economies: in 1971 there were 329,073 farms in the United Kingdom and in the European Economic Community, before enlargement, there were 4,977,800 farms in 1970 (Anon., 1972).

The assumption that farmers try to maximize their profits might be thought somewhat extreme in that it allows little room for the romantic view of farming that some people, particularly non-farmers, still hold. Despite this, however, it does not seem an unreasonable assumption to make in the context of the 1970s. Moreover, it should be noted that many of the results obtained in the analysis depend on the assumption that farmers seek to minimize their private costs, which is only a necessary condition for maximum profit. Whatever a farmer's goal, if he wants to achieve it at the least cost to himself he will tend to ignore the costs of his activities, such as those from the use of persistent pesticides, which he does not bear himself.

It was assumed during most of the analysis that the farmer had full information about the production process in which he is involved, and would know how much food to produce with what inputs given the prevailing price structure and his profit maximizing objective. This is possibly the least accurate assumption reviewed so far since farmers are usually accustomed to a particular method of farming and are not in a position to compare other methods which differ substantially from the one they know. Thus, whilst farmers may well be aware of the effects of minor changes in their use of the various agricultural inputs, having learnt this from past experience, they will know far less about significantly different forms of farming. This lack of knowledge will restrict the range of the farmer's response to pesticide controls even though substantial changes in the type or extent of farming may be in his own economic interest. This argument suggests that government should make available to farmers detailed accounts of alternative modes of farming and, in particular, information concerning the very wide variety and effects of pest control methods.

An example, based on the decision-making framework, will illustrate these points. Suppose that the relationship between the degree of pest control and the cost of pest control for a farmer is represented by the curve OC, in Fig. 11. The relationship assumed throughout the earlier analysis is shown by the broken line.

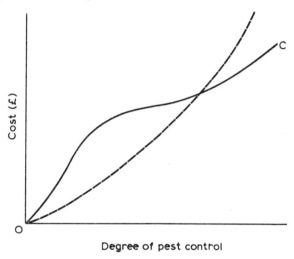

Fig. 11. Alternative assumptions about the cost of pest control.

The 'hump' in the OC curve reflects a threshold in the costs of pest control after which the extra cost of additional pest control declines and subsequently increases again. This might be because the cheapest means of obtaining a prescribed degree of pest control calls for a change in technique rather than more of the same. Eventually, the extra cost of additional pest control rises again due, perhaps, to the decreasing effectiveness of the available means of pest control to achieve higher and higher degrees of pest control.

When the information from Fig. 11 concerning the cost of pest control is combined with an assumed fixed price of land, the farmer's use of pest control and land may be analysed using Fig. 12, which is a variation on Fig. 2.

In Fig. 12 the food isoquants of Fig. 2 are combined with isocost curves that are consistent with the farmer's cost of pest control, as shown in Fig. 11, and a fixed price of land. There are two equally cheap methods of producing the two quantities of food, B_1 and B_2. Consequently, there are two expansion paths OX_1Y_1 and OX_2Y_2 along which the farmer who seeks maximum profits might operate. These paths differ substantially in the relative use of pest control and land, and hence in the use of persistent pesticides.

An interesting implication of this analysis is that very different mixes of agricultural inputs might be equally costly to farmers but have, for the rest of society, very different side effects. Moreover, a farmer may be unaware of the alternative option(s) open to him. For example, a

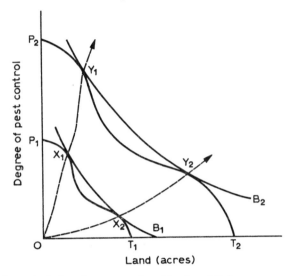

Fig. 12. The farmer's choice of pest control and land revisited.

farmer who is operating along the expansion path OX_1Y_1, which is pest control intensive, might only have information about the cost and productivity of input mixes in the region of this expansion path. He would, therefore, tend to respond to relatively small changes in the regulations and controls governing the use of pesticides by very small changes in his method of production, when, in the interests of profit maximization and the rest of the community, a major change in method might be called for.

This possibility is particularly relevant when the efficacy of certain forms of pesticide control which raise the unit cost of pest control is considered. A policy of imposing a tax on inputs such as persistent pesticides, which involve undesirable side effects, can only be properly effective if those concerned, in this case farmers, are fully aware of the range of options open to them. In Fig. 12 this would mean the farmer would have to know about both expansion paths, and he may not, insofar as they involve very different farming techniques.

In a conclusion such as this it is possible to go on indefinitely adding comments on and qualifications to the analysis. Furthermore, the analysis itself is by no means directly relevant to all of the economic issues surrounding the use of persistent pesticides, and to that extent the discussion cannot be considered comprehensive. In other respects, however, the analysis has a wider relevance than is, perhaps, apparent. It can be used, for example, to examine the decisions of the chemical companies who manufacture the pesticides. Unless they are subjected to legislated control, or participate in voluntary agreements, they too will tend to neglect any undesirable side effects of the products they develop, manufacture and sell. Similarly, they and all other manufacturers who are concerned to maximize their profits, or, at least, to minimize their costs, will tend to ignore any pollution caused by them in the process of production. Whether or not legislation and voluntary agreements can serve as effective controls in these circumstances will be the main topic of discussion in the second part of this paper. Once again, almost all of the examples chosen to illustrate the argument will deal with persistent pesticides but, equally, many of the points raised in that context apply just as much to the control of other pollutants, particularly those which are long lived and widely dispersed.

II. THE REGULATION OF PESTICIDES

A. Introduction

Any system of compulsory controls over pesticides must of course be founded in the law. Controls do in fact exist, and these will be examined in due course, but there are fewer than might have been expected, and not all the existing controls are backed by sanctions. Such legal controls as there are seem rather haphazard in effect and if examined as a united body of law many gaps become apparent. This probably arises from the disjointed appraisal which law making bodies—the Courts and the Legislature—have given to pesticides. Only rarely are the problems which accompany the manufacture and use of pesticides dealt with by the law as pesticide problems. More often the law attempts to place the problems which do arise into categories which were created before the development of pesticides, or at least before the discovery of the potential dangers which accompany their use, and consequently are not wholly appropriate. This is particularly true of common law controls. Had the legal significance of pesticide manufacture and use been examined as such, the controls might well be quite different. Such an examination would have involved the isolation of potential problems requiring regulation and also the isolation of the problems of creating effective and sensible legal controls. This is not to suggest that pesticides give rise to a set of totally unique problems. They do not. They have a good deal in common with other products of a technological age such as pharmaceutical drugs or even nuclear power but in at least some aspects the possible problems are unique, because these non-specific poisons are released deliberately into the environment.

At this point it may be useful to outline the general difficulties which pesticides pose for the law. Throughout the remainder of the paper it should be remembered that the remarks made apply to Britain, though experience in other countries will be drawn upon where necessary or useful. It is a feeling common among lawyers that the law may prescribe, proscribe, or regulate anything, so long as those requiring the controls can explain exactly what they want and the criteria which they wish applied in order to achieve the end. But the criteria for control of pesticides are by no means decided, even by those who have access to the most information about pesticide use and effects. Until such decisions are taken, whether by politicians, scientists, economists, or the public, the difficulties in promulgating workable legislation are immense. This is not to say that because unanimous opinion is lacking on some matters the legal institution is totally impotent, but the role of the non-scientist in the debate on controls is not an easy one. Again, though this too should not be overemphasized, dealing with sophisticated scientific data in the courts or tribunals presents problems, largely because if sanctions are to be applied, a Court will require proof beyond reasonable doubt of a transgression of any controlling legislation. And as will be shown later the type of proof a Court might require, that harm resulted from a particular pesticide, might be difficult to provide.

Perhaps an even more difficult problem lies in asking pesticide manufacturers to pay for all the costs which might result from pesticide use. English law has traditionally protected both the person and property of the person. If one has a claim at law for harm which has been done, the law will reimburse but generally it cannot reimburse a person for things in which he had no property interest. Thus if pesticide spraying results in the disappearance of certain species of wildlife or plant life in a particular area an individual would not be able to show that he had suffered damage such that he should receive compensation. And monetary compensation would be hardly appropriate anyway. Thus the sort of losses which might result could well be social costs of which it is difficult for Courts to take cognizance. In such cases though it may be thought more appropriate to provide penal sanctions—of the type as have, for instance, recently been provided for the discharge of oil by ships.[1] Again however the problem of proof of the cause of the damage will arise.

Controls over the use of pesticides present problems of effective supervision. Apart from random checks, which are likely to be quite ineffectual, it is hard to see how the law can directly control the application of pesticides legally obtained. The law can proscribe the over-application or misapplication of pesticides but enforcement is quite a separate matter and if it were to be effective would require extraordinarily expensive enforcement machinery.

The isolation of the potential problems requiring control is rather easier. The stages involved in the creation and use of a pesticide are research and development, manufacture and sale, and use. All controls will be directed to one or more of these stages. As to research there would seem to be little that the law would achieve by directing controls of a special nature to pesticide research. The controls applicable to other scientific research (e.g. duty of the employer to take care, the liability of an employer for the acts of his servants etc.) seem equally appropriate to pesticide research.

At the manufacturing and sale stage however the problems are of a quite different nature from the problems attached to the manufacture and sale of other products. There are, of course, controls applicable to all, but pesticides have special qualities arising out of their use. The possibility of control after sale poses enormous difficulty and this affects both the desirability and the type of regulations required before sale is permitted. Control of the use through control of the manufacture is however unlikely to be totally effective. Simple control of the manufacture and sale would require approval procedures to ensure the acceptability of both effects and side effects of the product and regulation of the sale by ensuring that complete and explicit information was provided about any necessary precautions in use together with full instructions for the pesticides application. It might also be necessary to state the persons to whom, and the conditions under which, the pesticide might be sold. These problems are dealt with by the voluntary Pesticides Safety Precautions Scheme (Ministry of Agriculture, Fisheries and Food, 1971), the Pharmacy and Poisons Act, 1933, and

---

[1] See the Oil in Navigable Waters Act, 1971 and the Prevention of Oil Pollution Act, 1971.

the Farm and Garden Chemicals Act, 1967, which will be discussed in due course.

The use stage, as has been said, produces the most problems for control primarily because of the difficulties of enforcement. Ideally one would want to regulate the quantity of a pesticide used, the occasions on which it is used, and the precautions taken when applied. The law has primarily been concerned only with the last of these— through the Agriculture (Poisonous Substances) Act, 1952—and even under that Act enforcement has not been easy.

Before examining such rules as do exist in pesticide control, mention must be made of the voluntary Pesticides Safety Precautions Scheme. Largely because of the problems of control outlined above, the necessity of cooperation between government and the manufacturer of pesticides has been regarded as extremely important. Also the prevention of harm and the importance of 'safeguarding human beings (whether they be users, consumers of treated produce, or other members of the public), livestock, domestic animals and wildlife, against risks from pesticides'[2] was of mutual benefit to companies and government. For these reasons the major control over pesticides is to be found in a voluntary scheme agreed between the government and industry. That it is voluntary and without apparent sanction should not though, hide the fact that the scheme will remain voluntary only as long as it is regarded as a sufficient safeguard. This has always been stated by government. Because of this the scheme is outlined and examined even though it cannot at present be regarded as a strictly legal control.

B. Common Law and the Regulation of Pesticides

There are, in essence, two methods by which the law may directly regulate the use of pesticides, by statute and regulations pursuant to statute, and by the common law. It is to the latter that we first turn.

The common law is of course a system of judge-made law which has evolved over a long period of time, and its propositions are contained in the reports of decided cases. It is a system of resolving disputes which depends on the doctrine of *stare decisis*. This provides that individual judge-made decisions on points of law have relevance not only to the particular dispute before the court but also to future disputes with facts which give rise to the same point of law. The rules which dictate this relevance create the system. Basically they provide that

---

² 'Pesticides Safety Precautions Scheme', para. 2.

where material facts are the same in a later case as in an earlier one then the later case will be decided in the same way as the earlier one. They also provide that, with a few limited exceptions, every court binds lower courts (and often the court itself) to follow the rulings of superior courts. Hence if the Court of Appeal should decide a case and 30 years later a case with the same material facts should come to the High Court then the High Court will follow the ruling of the Court of Appeal even if it disagrees with that previous decision.[3] Of course it would probably be possible to appeal the case to the Court of Appeal and then to the House of Lords but because of the cost involved it may not be practicable. Thus a case which is no longer appropriate to changed conditions may remain good law, and so long as it represents the law, people will order their affairs in accordance with it.

It might be thought that since the problems raised by persistent pesticides have only recently been created or observed the common law would be able to commence afresh in creating rules to deal with cases of damage or injury arising from their use. This is not so, for the principles of the law of tort will be applied to any new situation which arises. Almost all common law actions which might arise from harm caused by pesticides will be actions concerning the torts of negligence, or nuisance, and examination of the principles of these torts may be useful.

The area of law which comes under the heading of tort is concerned with securing indemnity against certain forms of harm by neighbours to one's person, reputation or estate. Generally, it is concerned with the allocation or redistribution of losses. The remedies for torts are civil, not penal (though a tort may also be a crime in which case a penalty may be exacted for the crime), and the usual aim of the remedy is to put the party who has suffered the tort as nearly as possible into the position he would have been in had the tort not occurred.

Obviously not all damage is actionable but rather only that damage which has been caused in circumstances which amount to a tort and which comes within the relevant rules of liability of the common law. Examples of torts which may be familiar are trespass, negligence, false imprisonment, defamation, and conversion.

A person injured by a pesticide who brings an action in negligence

---

[3] Instances where a court has expressed regret at being bound by a decision which it considers ill related to modern conditions—i.e. where the changed conditions are not regarded as a material fact—are not difficult to discover. See e.g. *Radcliffe* v. *Ribble Motors* [1939] A.C. 215.

will have to show that the person against whom he claims damages has in some way failed to discharge a duty of care owed to the claimant and that damage to him has resulted. If this sounds deceptively simple it may be aided by the words of Lord Aitken in the famous case of *Donoghue* v. *Stevenson*[4] when in discussing what was meant by an owed duty of care he said

> 'You must take reasonable care to avoid acts or omissions which you can reasonably foresee would be likely to injure your neighbour. Who, then, in law is my neighbour? The answer seems to be—persons who are so closely and directly affected by my act that I ought reasonably to have them in contemplation as being so affected when I am directing my mind to the acts or omissions which are called in question.'

And also by the words of Alderson B. in *Blyth* v. *Birmingham Waterworks Co.*[5]

> 'Negligence is the omission to do something which a reasonable man, guided upon those considerations which ordinarily regulate the conduct of human affairs, would do, or doing something which a prudent and reasonable man would not do.'

The problem of what amounts to damage for which compensation is payable will be mentioned shortly. The final qualification is that the only damage in such circumstances which will be compensated is that which is legally not too remote from the cause. The criterion for this is one of foreseeability i.e. would a reasonable man have foreseen the consequences, granted the negligent act?

It should be apparent that the negligence principles pose some problems for those injured through pesticides even though the burden of proof they will have to discharge in proving the cause of their injury will only be the balance of probabilities.

The first problem is that the damage which may be caused by persistent pesticides may be of a kind with which the law is ill-equipped to deal for it may not manifest itself for a number of years or even, conceivably, for more than a generation. And even if after that time the cause of the harm can be identified it would be difficult to show a breach of duty of care if, at the time of production, the manufacturer had complied with all requirements of the Pesticides Safety Precautions Scheme, of which more will be shortly said.

---

[4] [1932] A.C. 562, 580.
[5] [1856] 11 Ex. 781, 784.

A second and related problem is that small quantities of a pesticide may be quite harmless but the cumulative effect over many years might be injurious. If there are many manufacturers of the pesticide, it would be almost impossible to prove any one of them negligent if the ill-effects rose from overapplication by numerous users. And it would be impossible to show any one manufacturer to be the cause of any particular injury.

Further, the losses which have been, and could be, caused by pesticides may not of themselves be the sort of which the law takes account. Before one can bring an action in negligence one must be able to show injury which affects the claimant in a way in which it does not affect everyone else. The damage for which compensation is payable is usually damage either to one's person or to one's property, i.e. one must suffer quantifiable harm. But the harm which pesticides may cause can be unrelated to either. No-one has property in much of the wildlife of Britain. No individual will have a cause of action if negligent spraying leads to, for instance, the deaths of large numbers of skylarks or hares. Of course if the birds killed were a protected species the sprayer could possibly be prosecuted but clear proof would be required of the link between the spray and the deaths—in the case of prosecution the evidence has to provide proof beyond reasonable doubt—and this would be difficult as would the proof of culpability. If the injury sustained by the wildlife is less direct, affecting nesting habits, thickness of eggshells and such like, then tortious remedies are totally inapplicable. The cost is a social one rather than a private one and tort seldom recognizes the former.

Furthermore though damage might be attributed to pesticides it will often be impossible to attribute the damage to a particular application of a pesticide or even to a particular manufacturer. This is especially true of the indirect damage which might be caused because of the distance which persistent pesticides can travel.

It is clear then that the tort of negligence is of limited use if damage arises from pesticides. Its usefulness lies in those rare cases where one can show clearly foreseeable damage arising from defects in the research, production, or application of the pesticide.

The tort of nuisance is the other major cause of action at common law if injury results from pesticides. Private nuisance is 'unlawful interference with a person's use or enjoyment of land, or some right over, or in connection with it.'[6] If the nuisance merely affects the enjoyment of property (as opposed to damaging or interfering with rights over

---

[6] *Read* v. *J. Lyons and Co., Ltd.*, [1945] K.B. 216, 236 per Scott L. J.

the property) then it will not be actionable unless it is unreasonable. To determine whether or not it is unreasonable one must have regard to the character of the neighbourhood. The tort of private nuisance is essentially aimed at balancing the right of an occupier to use his land as he will with that of his neighbour to the quiet enjoyment of his land. But in deciding this, as has been said, regard will be had to the nature of the neighbourhood. 'What would be a nuisance in Belgrave Square would not necessarily be so in Bermondsey'.[7]

The possibility of using the tort of private nuisance against a user of pesticides is not great because a nuisance which is actionable must be either continuous or recurrent and it must be affecting land in which the claimant has some property interest. Generally, if such conditions are met, an action will lie in negligence anyway but there may be three reasons for bringing an action in nuisance rather than negligence. Firstly, and obviously, the claimant need not show a duty of care though generally that will exist anyway. Secondly, and more importantly, as well as the remedy of damages the plaintiff may obtain an injunction from the Court prohibiting future activity of the kind giving rise to the claim. This is related to the third reason which is that the damage complained of may, in a nuisance action, be an interference with the enjoyment of the land and changes in vegetation or wildlife may amount to such an interference.

Public nuisance as opposed to private nuisance is a crime and it is anything 'which materially affects the reasonable comfort and convenience of life of a class of Her Majesty's subjects who come within the sphere or neighbourhood of its operation' (Jolowicz, 1971). It is only a civil wrong (i.e. a case where an individual may ask for compensation) if a person can show that he suffered some special loss over and above that suffered by the public at large. Generally with pesticides the nuisance would create such special damage. The only real importance of public nuisance is that a local authority might institute a prosecution.

It is also conceivable that a person injured or harmed by pesticides could have an action in the tort of trespass to land i.e. interference with the possession of land. The qualification however, that for trespass to occur the injury must be direct and immediate, means that almost invariably other torts will be more appropriate. Trespass could be used in such cases as where empty or partially empty canisters are dumped on ground though again the only person in a position to claim would be the possessor of the land.

---

[7] *Sturges* v. *Bridgman* [1879] 11 Ch.D. 852, 865 per Thesiger L. J.

That there are problems in these common law controls is obvious. Primarily, tort law is concerned with resolving disputes which have occurred and only indirectly with the ordering of behaviour in the future. This means that the rules laid down in the solving of cases may not always be the best way of directing future conduct. Though it might not be just to ask a party to pay damages in a situation where he has taken all reasonable precautions it is certainly unjust that parties injured, for instance by pesticides duly approved under the voluntary control scheme, should have no remedy. The law has taken cognizance of this situation on other occasions in two ways: firstly by a common law method clearly applicable to some pesticide situations and secondly by use of statute with reference to other problems not unrelated to pesticides.

The common law method of dealing with such complications arises from the rule laid down in the case of *Rylands* v. *Fletcher*.[8] In that case a mill-owner wished to create a water reservoir on his land to provide water for his mill. He employed apparently competent contractors who, while preparing the land, discovered old mine shafts. Unbeknown to anyone these connected to a mine worked under a neighbour's land. The contractors did not seal the mines. As a consequence when the reservoir began to fill, the neighbour's mines were flooded. He sued the mill-owner but the mill-owner was found out not to have been negligent. Nevertheless he was held liable for the damage caused and the rule laid down by Blackburn J. and approved by the House of Lords is contained in these words:

> 'We think that the true rule of law is that the person who for his own purposes brings on his lands and collects and keeps there anything likely to do mischief if it escapes, must keep it at his peril, and if he does not do so, is *prima facie* answerable for all the damage which is the natural consequence of its escape.'[9]

The original rule has been applied to such things as fire, oil, noxious fumes, and gas, and pesticides would seem to fit with the general category. Thus it is probable that if a person suffers damage because of pesticides emanating from a neighbouring property it will not be necessary to show negligence. In most cases it would be equally easy to claim under nuisance but an important distinction is that the rule under *Rylands* v. *Fletcher* protects not only the interests of occupiers of land but also those of non-occupiers.

---

[8] [1868] L.R. 3 H.L. 330.
[9] [1866] L.R. 1 Ex. 265, 279–280.

Under the rule a defendant can be liable even though he has taken all reasonable care and is without fault. The problem for the defendant is that no similar common law rule exists to enable such a user to bring an action in turn against a non-negligent manufacturer. If the manufacturer has taken all reasonable care, undertaken the accepted tests of the product, acted in accordance with the voluntary control scheme, and fulfilled the requirements of act and regulation, then he will escape liability. It may be that in view of the potential harm of pesticides the courts would demand a very high standard of care indeed before agreeing that harm arose in spite of the absence of negligence but it is not impossible that such circumstances could arise. Statute has reacted to this possibility in such areas as the law concerned with nuclear installations by imposing strict liability. This concept is not unrelated to the *Rylands* v. *Fletcher* rule.

The statute relating to nuclear installations provides a good example of how the duty of care by pesticide manufacturers could be increased. Section 7(1) of the Nuclear Installations Act, 1965 provides:

'It shall be the duty of the licensee to secure that
a. no such occurrence involving nuclear matter as is mentioned in sub-section (2) of this section causes injury to any person or damage to any property of any person other than the licensee, being injury or damage arising out of or resulting from the radioactive properties, or a combination of those and any toxic, explosive or other hazardous properties, of that nuclear matter, and
b. no ionizing radiations emitted during the period of the licensee's responsibility
   i. from anything caused or suffered by the licensee to be on the site which is not nuclear matter, or
  ii. from any waste discharged (in whatever form) on or from the site cause injury to any person or damage to any property of any person other than the licensee'.

The effect of the Act is that if damage within the provisions of the Act is shown to have occurred there need be no finding of negligence. Damages will be payable on proof of cause of injury. Thus a much higher standard of care than is usual in the common law is clearly imposed. Legislation of this type would seem at least a minor improvement in the law relating to pesticides. Of course radioactive materials tend to be used by more highly trained people than are pesticides, and the legislation would have to take this fact into account in listing the types of damage for which liability would automatically accrue to the pesticide manufacturer. But generally the risk of non-negligent harm may be better borne by the producer rather than the user or the sufferer both because the manufacturer is more able to insure against such losses and because their financial ability to recompense loss is greater. It would also seem reasonable that these costs should be a charge upon the profits from pesticide manufacture.

Even so, the importance of this type of legislation to the control of pesticides should not be over-rated since it still leaves unsolved the problem of proving the cause of injury to the satisfaction of a court, and the problem arising from social costs.

C. Statutory Law and the Regulation of Pesticides

As they are at present then, the common law controls over the manufacture and use of pesticides are not great, but what of statute and regulation? Existing controls are not extensive. If they have not so far been shown to be grossly defective this is as likely to be because harmful conduct is not always proscribed, and even when proscribed is not always identifiable, as it is to be because of the success of the regulations. It should be added however that for reasons to be explained the legal control of the manufacture and use of pesticides is fraught with a great number of problems and to some extent the voluntary controls have been regarded as successful because of the problems raised by alternative methods of control.

There are two Acts which primarily control pesticide manufacture and use. The first of these is The Agriculture (Poisonous Substances) Act, 1952 the enforcement of which, and of the Regulations made under it, is in the hands of a Safety Inspectorate of the Ministry of Agriculture, Fisheries and Food. The concern of the Act is to protect workers who may use toxic chemicals either on farms or in enclosed areas. Essentially the protection the Act gives is by providing for the provision, use, and maintenance of protective clothing and equipment, and the keeping and inspection of records. Regulations made pursuant to the Act name some 40 active ingredients of pesticides grouped into four classes of different toxicities and provide that in 19 described operations workers must wear specified protective clothing in the manner which is deemed appropriate for the particular operation. Problems in this legislation are manifest though, it has been argued, unavoidable. Not everyone who uses the pesticide will be an employee yet the Act extends only to them. A man in one field using pesticides without protective clothing may be creating an offence under the Act, the man in the next, engaged in an identical enterprise on his own behalf, may not. Of course the intention of the Act was to give protection to workers but there are obvious difficulties in enforcing the legislation and from 1963 to 1972 there were only 31 prosecutions under the Act. Anyway the object of the Act is exceedingly limited for it provides protection, if complied with, only for those actually engaged in the pesticide operation whereas it may be that the resulting dangers are to a much wider number of people. But the Act itself is broad enough to enable regulations to be made (unfortunately only for the protection of employees) imposing restrictions or conditions as to the purposes for which, the circumstances in which, and the methods or means by which, a pesticide may be used. On balance though the Act is narrow in scope and of limited though not negligible use.

The second Act of direct importance is the Farm and Garden Chemicals Act, 1967. This is an important Act but also limited in scope since it is concerned only with the labelling of pesticides. It is an Act providing for regulations to be made governing the form and content of labels on farm and garden chemicals. Pursuant to the Act regulations now provide that all pesticide products designed to prevent plant damage must name clearly and conspicuously on the label the active ingredient.

Other legislative control is to be found in the Pharmacy and Poisons Act, 1933 and the Poison Rules made under the Act which deal with the sale, purchase, and labelling of poisons, and provides for their storage and transportation and also names obligatory additives. The intention of the Act was to limit the number of persons who might sell and obtain poisons to those qualified to handle them and who had a real need for them. Pesticides which were included in Part II of the Poisons List and subject to Schedule 5, part B, of the Poisons Rules may only be sold to professional farmers or growers who need no further qualification. But the amounts used cannot be regulated by this Act and the greatest users are able to buy as they wish i.e. certain people have been deemed to have a real need for the pesticides. So the Act has little effect on the use of these pesticides except to limit the number of people who can obtain them.

Less directly concerned with pesticides but of relevance are the Rivers (Prevention of Pollution) Act, 1951, section 2(1) (a) of which creates an offence if a person 'causes or knowingly permits to enter a stream any poisonous, noxious, or polluting matter'; and the Dangerous Litter Act, 1971, which provides penalties if litter of a dangerous nature is deposited.

Statute and regulation do not therefore substantially directly affect the use of pesticides. This is seemingly regarded as a satisfactory position by the legislature which has confidence in the voluntary Pesticides Safety Precautions Scheme which we shall now examine. It had been anticipated that this scheme would be replaced by legislation but on 11th April 1972 Mr Prior, then Minister of Agriculture, stated in Parliament that

'The Advisory Committee on Pesticides and Other Toxic Chemicals which was invited to consider the (recommendations in the second report of the Royal Commission on Environmental Pollution on pesticides) tells me that the Pesticides Safety Precautions Scheme is now working so effectively to ensure safe use of pesticides in agriculture, food storage and related areas that legislation is not at present required. In the light of this, the Royal Commission has advised me that it would not wish to press for the immediate introduction of legislation although it maintains, as a matter of principle, that it should not be ruled out as the ultimate sanction to control those substances which, when misused, can harm—and in its view have harmed—the environment. I therefore do not propose to introduce legislation at this stage'.[10]

What then is the scheme and why is it thought desirable that it should be voluntary rather than mandatory? The scheme provides that distributors (including manufacturers and importers) will notify the relevant Ministries of new pesticides and new uses for existing pesticides and that such pesticides will not be put on the market before clearance. To enable a clearance to be given the manufacturers undertake to provide all necessary information to the Department of Education and Science so that they may ascertain the precautions necessary in the use of the pesticide which the manufacturer must then include in the label. There is also an undertaking that the product will be withdrawn from the market if the Ministries so recommend.

When given the information they require the Ministries, usually advised by the Advisory Committee on Pesticides and Other Toxic Chemicals, may refuse clearance for any product they consider unduly hazardous. Alternatively they may grant clearance with or without qualification. Such qualification may amount to trials clearance which clears the product only for use for a limited period on crops for trial purposes only with no sales of the pesticide being permitted or to limited clearance, which means that small quantities may be sold for limited periods, to certain commercial users. In that case the manufacturer is under an obligation to present confidentially any further adverse data which have been obtained at the end of the period. The

---

[10] H.C. Deb., Vol. 834, col. 172.

other possibility is a limited commercial clearance which provides for sales on the open market for a limited period during which tests will be made on the effects and side effects of the product.

It should be added that since the scheme's inception it is reported that there have been only two discovered evasions by U.K. distributors (McLoughlin, 1972).

Various arguments have been put forward in support of this voluntary scheme. It is claimed that it is working smoothly and with reasonable speed and that a more formal scheme could lead to delays in approval to the detriment of the manufacturing companies not least in their competitiveness on the international market. It is also said that being voluntary the scheme encourages frank disclosure which would not be so with legislation backed by penalties. But the very existence of such a scheme is a clear admission of the necessity of control in the manufacture and use of pesticides. And if this is admitted what is the advantage of applying the controls only to those willing to conform? Of course, the very threat of a compulsory scheme may be sanction enough to ensure compliance, but there is no evidence of this, and even if so there would then seem to be little advantage in maintaining the scheme as voluntary. The element of compulsion is only felt if a manufacturer is not willing to cooperate. Indeed a mandatory scheme has already been adopted by the other common market countries.

The scheme is limited in many ways anyway. Although it may control the manufacture it does not control the use. Once a purchaser has acquired a persistent pesticide there is no way of ensuring that he uses it for the purpose for which it is recommended nor yet in the quantities appropriate to the problem. Further the scheme relies upon a spirit of cooperation from private enterprises which many would regard with considerable cynicism. Though there is no evidence available of any withholding of information or of any malpractice by the producers of pesticides in this country under this scheme, in the United States the behaviour of the producers of persistent pesticides outlined in 'Since Silent Spring' (Graham, 1970) should give pause for thought. And the established activities of big business in the manufacture of pharmaceutical drugs might add to this feeling of unease (Kefauver, 1966; Sjostrom and Nilsson, 1972). This might in turn be aggravated by the knowledge that in making decisions about whether to grant clearances the Ministry advisers are primarily concerned to ensure that an adequate programme of tests was followed by those who developed the product rather than in making independent tests themselves.

Another defect concerns the secrecy of data submitted to the Ministry. All data supplied to the scientific sub-committee is regarded as secret and can only be made known to a person with the agreement of the notifier or after he has signed an undertaking of secrecy. This is understandable in that commercial secrets require protection and also because the scheme is voluntary, but there should be other ways of ensuring protection not least by patent or, as has been suggested (Price, 1973), by temporary patent protection which could be granted while testing continued.

The effect of the secrecy is that parties who may be interested in the direct or indirect toxicity of a product will not be able to make tests, without the consent of either the producer or the Ministry, until the pesticide is marketed. Further, the evidence given to the Ministry may not be challenged or even debated by outsiders since it remains confidential. This may be contrasted with the fact that if there is evidence from any source that the use of an active ingredient or pesticide product is responsible for, or appears to be responsible for, a hazard or degree of risk which is novel or was not studied prior to notification, the producer will be informed of the intention to review the product and supplied with all the evidence and given the opportunity to comment. And if after the original application the Ministries' recommendations are influenced to the detriment of the producer by data obtained, other than from the producer himself, then the producer will be informed and given an opportunity to discuss the matter in confidence with the Ministry.

Of course the Ministry is understandably intent on retaining the cooperation of an industry it is unable to coerce in the event of non-cooperation but it cannot be doubted that it is in the public interest that as much informed discussion as possible should take place before a pesticide receives approval.

D. International Aspects of Pesticide Regulation

A factor which must be taken into account in providing new controls is the international consequences created both by pesticide control and by pesticide use. Pesticides have already been the study of international groups and it is to be anticipated that this work will continue and increase. A 1971 report (OECD, 1971) which made a study of the problem of persistent chemicals drew attention to the effects that national legislation might have on other countries—for instance a food exporting country might have forced upon it the use of certain chemicals if countries importing food required it to be free of certain pests and diseases. Implications such as these should encourage internationally accepted controls—though having regard to differing circumstances.

Already the controls which exist in many countries have distinct similarities. Among the countries in the Organization for Economic Cooperation and Development (OECD) none actually regulates the amounts of pesticides produced even though there may be legislation to protect those who manufacture, sell, and use the product. Almost all countries require the registration of pesticides though only in Britain is this registration on a voluntary basis. Some countries classify the pesticides according to toxicity and have different regulations for different classes. For the most toxic, some allow only persons with special training to sell or use the product, and in some special permission must be obtained before purchase.

The control method of several countries is by reference to residue tolerance levels in food stuffs. For example in the United States, control has been largely through the sanctions of Federal Food Drug and Cosmetic Acts under which

> 'an agricultural product is considered adulterated if it contains any pesticide chemical unless a registration limiting the quantity is in effect and the use or intended use of such substances conforms to the terms prescribed by the regulation'.[11]

Problems have been caused however, by the fact that certain pesticides were given a tolerance rating of zero, i.e. no trace of the pesticide was permitted in the commodity. As testing became more and more sophisticated residues have been discovered and this makes the crop of the user of the pesticide subject to seizure even if the residue is negligible. As a result of the Mrak Report (U.S. Dept. of Health, 1969) which urged the strengthening of controls over the registration of chemical pesticides and also urged the restriction of certain persistent pesticides in the United States

> 'to specific essential uses which create no known hazard to human health or the quality of the environment and which are unanimously approved by the Secretaries of the Departments of Health Education and Welfare, Agriculture, and Interior', (U.S. Dept. of Health, 1969, Recommendation IV).

U.S. controls are unlikely to be relaxed and will almost certainly be increased.

In the United Kingdom only arsenic, lead, fluorine and ethoxyquin

---

[11] 'Persistent Pesticides' [1970] 6 Colum. J. L. & Soc. Prob. 122, 132–133.

have statutory tolerance limits though the Food and Drugs Act, 1955 is indirectly important. This prohibits (by Section 2) the sale of food which is not of the nature substance or quality demanded by the purchaser and also prohibits (Section 8) the sale of food unfit for human consumption. The voluntary safety scheme too provides recommendations where possible stating the maximum residues to be expected in a crop or animal tissue.

E. Pesticides and the Law : Some Concluding Comments

Having looked at the controls over pesticides which exist some general appraisal is required. It has been suggested that defects in the controls lie to a large extent in the piecemeal way with which the law deals with pesticides. A unified code of pesticide law would have clear advantages. This need not displace the common law but could take care of those situations where the common law seems inadequate. Such legislation would have to be geared more to social costs than to private costs and this might mean providing heavy penalties for the misuse of pesticides, providing not only a deterrent against such misuse, but also a fund for the repair of the environment. The regulation of use, as has been explained, does present problems for the law because of the need for supervision of the application. To some extent this could be countered by heavy sanctions for misuse clearly explained on pesticide labels, but it is still unlikely to be very effective. There would also seem good reason for providing strict liability in the case of offences against controls of pesticides. This would mean that if misapplication contrary to the legislation could be proved then the person responsible would be liable to conviction regardless of his excuse for that misapplication. The effect of this would be to demand a higher standard of care when using pesticides than would otherwise be the case. It would also seem desirable to make an employer criminally liable for the acts of his employees in misapplying pesticides though this would necessarily have to be restricted to situations where the employer could have prevented the employee from so acting.

Because of this difficulty in controlling the use of pesticides other methods of control should be considered such as the rationing of the quantities which might be purchased by users or by pricing the pesticides with a special tax to ensure that they are not over used. Neither type of control poses substantial problems for the law but either would be dependent for success upon being the implementation of a considered and coherent policy. And again the supervision would not be easy.

Having shown that the harm which results from pesticide use is often either difficult to prove, or a widely experienced social cost, such general controls seem preferable to those based upon providing recompense for individual losses provable at common law. This does not mean that the common law actions should not remain, for they provide a useful means of obtaining compensation when there is financial loss or injury to the person. And this would be equally true even if the common law were extended, as already suggested, by legislation of the type enacted for nuclear installations.

Thus at the use stage, in addition to the common law and the few existing statutes, it is suggested that there is a good case for providing substantial penalties for use of pesticides other than in accordance with the approved instructions; for providing strict liability for the manufacturers of pesticides; and also for consideration, by those with the necessary skills to isolate criteria, for the provision of legislation which would restrict the quantity of pesticides obtainable.

As for the controls governing the manufacture and sale it has been argued that these should be made mandatory rather than voluntary. Ideally financial provision would be made (by the manufacturer if not the state) for the independent testing of pesticides but at any rate the argument that delays might occur and cooperation might decline if the controls were mandatory seems false. Though cooperation is obviously desirable the burden of proving to the Ministry that a pesticide is safe within the requirements of the scheme lies with the would-be manufacturer and it must be in his interests to provide satisfactory information as quickly as possible. It would also be desirable to deal with applications as openly as possible to allow a maximum of discussion. Such openness could be facilitated by providing temporary patent cover to the discoverer while testing continues.

International cooperation and an international policy are also of fundamental importance since the results of any national policy of control has effects outside that country. This is for two major reasons. Firstly the residues from persistent pesticides are widely disseminated without regard for national borders, polluting not only other land but also rivers lakes and the sea itself. Secondly national controls over pesticides may affect the costs of exports so that the nations with the most stringent controls may be the least competitive in international markets.

Provision for the labelling of pesticides seems adequate though labelling as such is of only limited value and reportedly studies in the U.S. confirmed that most pesticide users did not read them (Rodgers, 1970). That is perhaps epitomized in the report of a turkey breeder in the U.S. who spread heptachlor epoxide on his turkey range to control chiggers in spite of the warning that it could cause harm to livestock. 'Hell' replied the grower when challenged 'I ain't raising livestock. I'm raising turkeys' (Rodgers, 1970 at 608).

To conclude it will be seen that most of the problems for the law in controlling pesticides arise from the fact that they are a product of a technological society while the common law at least, is not. Recognizing this fact both excuses the inability of common law to cater for the new circumstances and demonstrates the need to pay regard to the new qualities of new problems. If the restriction must be greater this arises from the greater and more insidious possibilities of harm from something potentially of considerable benefit if used with control and discretion.

REFERENCES

Anon. (1971). 'Social Trends', Central Statistical Office, Her Majesty's Stationery Office.

Anon. (1972). 'Farming Facts and the New Common Market', Barclays Bank.

Dasgupta, A. K. and Pearce, D. W. (1972). 'Cost-Benefit Analysis,' Macmillan, London.

de V. Graaff, J. (1957). 'Theoretical Welfare Economics', Cambridge University Press, London and Cambridge.

Graham, F. (1970). 'Since Silent Spring', Hamish Hamilton Ltd., London.

Jolowicz, J. A. (1971). 'Winfield and Jolowicz on Tort,' 9th edition, Sweet and Maxwell, London.

Kefauver, F. (1966). 'In a Few Hands', Penguin, London.

Kneese, A. V. and Bower, B. T. (1968). 'Managing Water Quality: Economics, Technology, Institutions', The Johns Hopkins Press, Baltimore.

Langham, M. R., Headley, J. C. and Edwards, W. F. (1972). Agricultural pesticides: productivity and externalities. In 'Environmental Quality Analysis', (A. V. Kneese and B. T. Bower, eds), Ch. 5. Johns Hopkins Press, Baltimore.

McLoughlin, J. (1972). 'The Law Relating to Pollution', Manchester University Press, Manchester.

Ministry of Agriculture, Fisheries and Food (1971). 'Pesticides Safety Precautions Scheme'.

Organisation for Economic Co-operation and Development (1971). 'The Problem of Persistent Chemicals—Implications of Pesticides and other Chemicals in the Environment.'

Preston, M. (1965). 'On the Nature of the Public Sector', The Three Banks Review, No. 67.

Price, B. (1973). The paraquat follies, Your Environment, 4, 2–8.

Rodgers, W. H. (1970). 70 Colum. L. Rev. 567–611.

Sjostrom, H. and Nilsson, R. (1972). 'Thalidomide and the Power of the Drug Companies', Penguin, London.

U.S. Dept. of Health Education and Welfare (1969). Secretary's Commission on Pesticides and their Relationship to Environmental Health, Report.

Subject Index